Advancing Maths for AQA

DISCRETE MATHS 2

Victor Bryant

Series editors
Keith Parramore Sam Boardman Graham Eaton
Ted Graham Roger Williamson

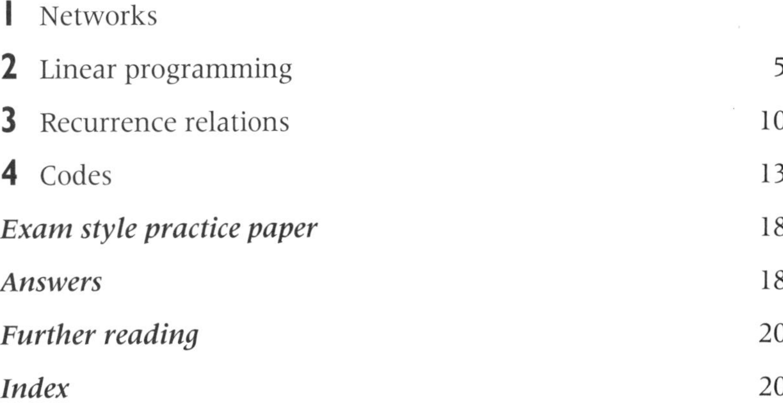

Heinemann Educational Publishers

a division of Heinemann Publishers (Oxford) Ltd,
Halley Court, Jordan Hill, Oxford OX2 8EJ

OXFORD MELBOURNED AUCKLANDD JOHANNESBURG
BLANTYRE GABORONE PORTSMOUTH NH (USA) CHICAGO

First published in 2001

01 02 10 9 8 7 6 5 4 3 2 1

ISBN 0 435 51319 2

Typeset and illustrated by Tech-Set Limited, Gateshead, Tyne & Wear

Printed and bound by Scotprint in the UK

Acknowledgements

The publishers and authors acknowledge the work of the writers, David Burghes, John Deft, Nigel Green, Nigel Price, Ann Ault and Peter Gwilliam of the *AEB Mathematics for ASA A-Level Series*, from which some exercises and examples have been taken.

The publishers and authors also acknowledge the work of Keith Parramore and Joan Stephens in *Decision Mathematics 1* from which some exercises and examples have been taken.

The publishers' and authors' thanks are due to the AEB for permission to reproduce questions from past examination papers.

The answers have been provided by the authors and are not the responsibility of the examining board.

About this book

This book is one in a series of textbooks designed to provide you with exceptional preparation for AQA's new Advanced GCE Specification B. The series authors are all senior members of the examining team and have prepared the textbooks specifically to support you in studying this course.

Finding your way around

The following are there to help you find your way around when you are studying and revising:

- **edge marks** (shown on the front page) – these help you to get to the right chapter quickly;
- **contents list** – this identifies the individual sections dealing with key syllabus concepts so that you can go straight to the areas that you are looking for;
- **index** – a number in bold type indicates where to find the main entry for that topic.

Key points

Key points are not only summarised at the end of each chapter but are also boxed and highlighted within the text like this:

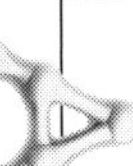

The **travelling salesperson problem** can then be stated simply as:

Given a network which is Hamiltonian, find the **shortest** Hamiltonian cycle.

Exercises and exam questions

Worked examples and carefully graded questions familiarise you with the specification and bring you up to exam standard. Each book contains:

- Worked examples and Worked exam questions to show you how to tackle typical questions; Examiner's tips will also provide guidance;
- Graded exercises, gradually increasing in difficulty up to exam-level questions, which are marked by an [A];
- Test-yourself sections for each chapter so that you can check your understanding of the key aspects of that chapter and identify any sections that you should review;
- Answers to the questions are included at the end of the book.

CHAPTER 1
Networks

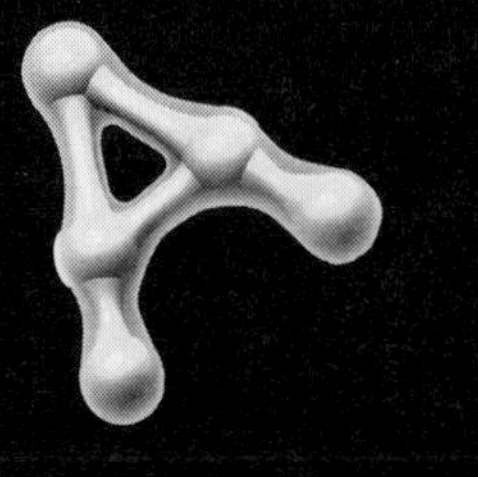

Learning objectives

After reading this chapter, you should be able to:

- understand the travelling salesperson problem and solve it for simple networks
- find upper and lower bounds for the problem
- understand the Chinese postperson problem and solve it for simple networks
- interpret a general algorithm for solving the problem
- understand network flows, sources, sinks and cuts
- interpret the minimum flow/maximum cut theorem
- find a maximum flow in a network, if necessary by using flow augmentation
- interpret the solutions of all these problems in real-life situations.

1.1 Introduction

In this course we shall be extending some of the ideas met in the first Discrete Mathematics course (D1) and introducing some new ideas. In particular in this chapter we shall be looking at some more applications of **networks**.

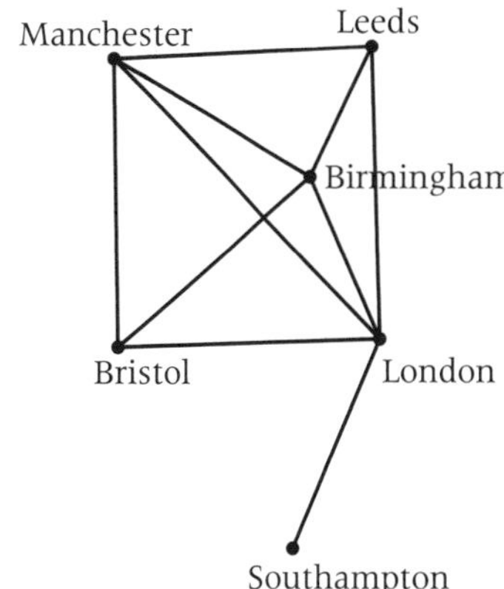

Recall that a **graph** consists of some **vertices** and **edges**, where each edge joins one vertex to another. An example of a graph is shown in the diagram: it illustrates some cities and shows whether they have a direct motorway link between them.

A **directed graph** (or **digraph**) is a graph in which each edge has a direction, indicated by an arrow. The directed graph illustrated is taken from a flow chart explaining pension entitlements: the detailed instructions at each vertex have been left out, so that you can get an idea of the structure of this graph.

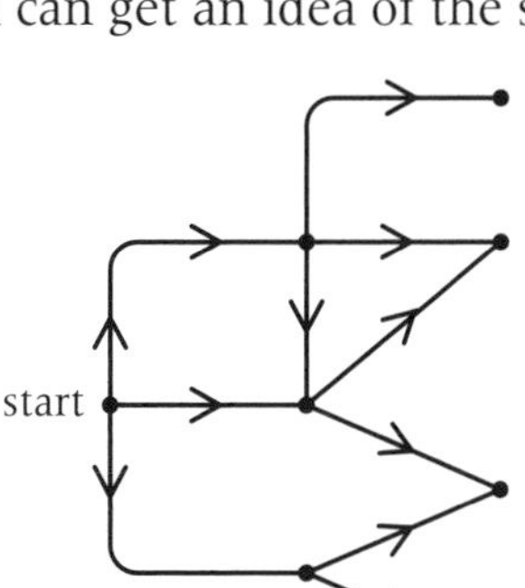

In both a graph and a directed graph we can give each edge (or 'arc') a **weight** which is a number associated with it: the weights are written next to the appropriate edges. The graph together with these weights is called a **network**. In practice the 'weights' can actually represent lengths or costs or time taken, etc. The undirected network illustrated shows the distances of principal routes between some cities, and the directed network shows the times taken for various related tasks when using **critical paths analysis** (discussed in D1).

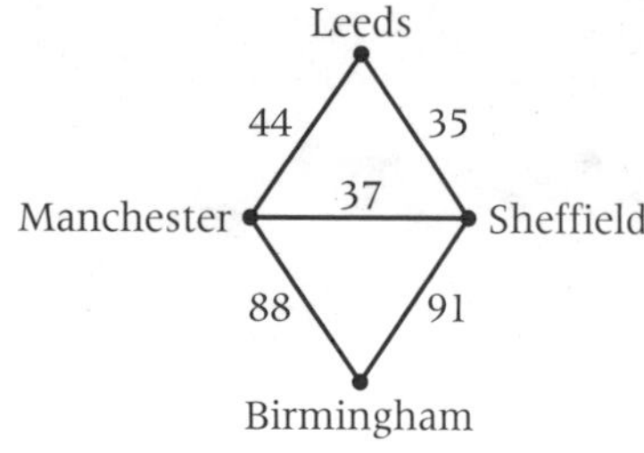

In D1 we learned that a graph is **Hamiltonian** if it has a **cycle** (or a 'round tour') visiting each vertex just once before returning to its starting point. Given a network you could not only ask if it is Hamiltonian but also work out the 'length' of each of the Hamiltonian cycles and look for the shortest one. This is the basis of the **travelling salesperson problem** which we deal with in Section 1.2.

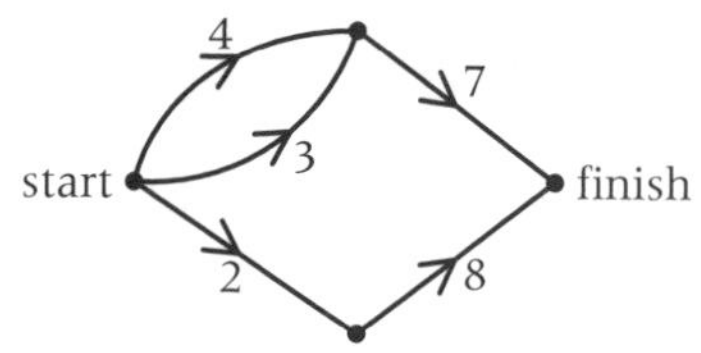

In the earlier course it was established that a graph is **Eulerian** if there is a **trail** (or natural route) through the graph using each edge exactly once before returning to the starting point. This can happen in a connected graph if, and only if, all the vertices have even **degree**. If you considered the same problem in a network, the total length of the **Eulerian trail** would simply be the sum of all the lengths of the edges. But what if the network has some odd degrees and you still want to find a natural route using each edge at least once but in the most economical way possible? This is the basis of the **Chinese postperson problem** considered in Section 1.3.

We have already looked at directed networks when considering critical path analysis. Another use of them is to represent networks of pipes or wires and one such is shown, where the numbers represent the maximum capacity of each edge. In Section 1.4 we shall consider the general problem of trying to find the biggest total flow possible from the **source** to the **sink** in such **networks**.

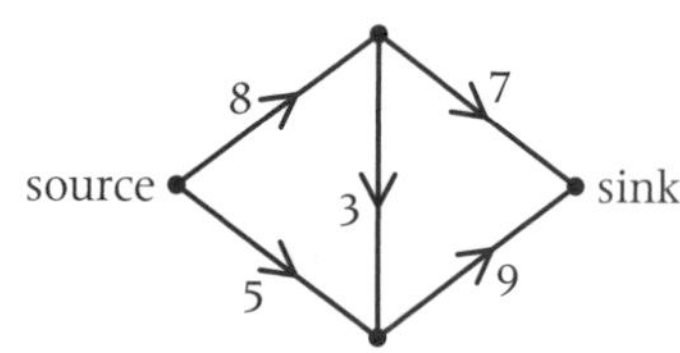

1.2 The travelling salesperson problem

This classic problem concerns a salesperson who wants to visit each of a number of towns before returning to base. For obvious reasons the salesperson wants to do this with the shortest possible route. In practice the salesperson has the flexibility to revisit a town *en route* if that makes a more efficient journey. Also in some situations a round route might be impossible. However we ignore such refinements here.

Worked example 1.1

A salesperson based in Harlow in Essex has to visit each of five other towns before returning to base. If the distances in miles of all suitable routes are as illustrated, in what order should the salesperson make the visits so that the total travelling distance is minimum?

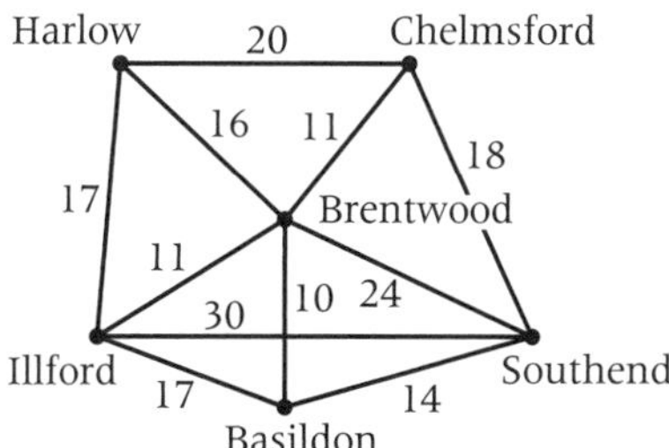

Solution

A little inspection shows us that the outer ring is a fairly economical way of visiting all the towns except Brentwood. All that remains to decide is how to detour to include Brentwood. If travelling clockwise around the outer ring a detour

Basildon – Brentwood – Ilford

will only add 4 miles to the round route (replacing 17 by $10 + 11$). Hence the shortest route visiting each town is:

Harlow – Chelmsford – Southend – Basildon – Brentwood – Ilford – Harlow

which has a total of 90 miles.

In that example the towns were represented by vertices, the routes between them by edges and the lengths of those routes by the weights of the edges, thus producing a **network**. In that example the network had a **Hamiltonian cycle** (i.e. a closed path visiting each vertex once) and indeed the shortest route was such a cycle.

We shall represent each problem as a network in this way, we shall assume in general that the network has a Hamiltonian cycle, and we shall assume that the salesperson's route must be such a cycle.

The **travelling salesperson problem** can then be stated simply as:

> Given a network which is Hamiltonian, find the **shortest** Hamiltonian cycle.

Worked exam question 1.1

A business executive based in London has to visit Paris, Brussels and Frankfurt before returning to London. If the journey times in hours are as shown in the diagram below, work out the total length of every possible Hamiltonian cycle and thus find the route that takes the shortest time.

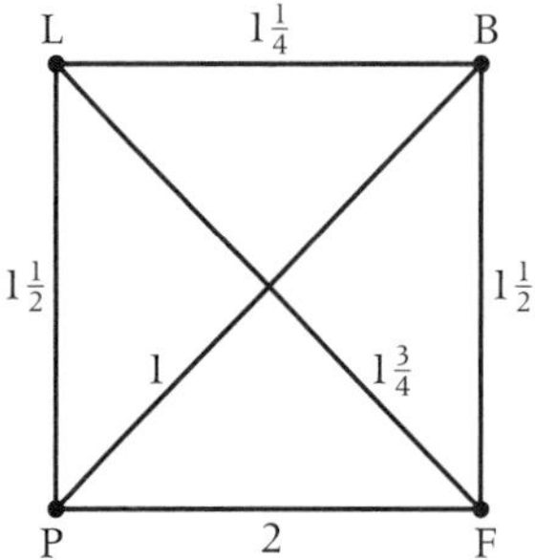

Solution

There are three cities apart from London, and so $3 \times 2 \times 1 = 6$ possible orders. The six journeys with their total lengths are as follows:

$$\begin{array}{ll} \mathrm{L-P-B-F-L} = 5\tfrac{3}{4} \text{ hours} & \mathrm{L-F-B-P-L} = 5\tfrac{3}{4} \text{ hours} \\ \mathrm{L-P-F-B-L} = 6\tfrac{1}{4} \text{ hours} & \mathrm{L-B-F-P-L} = 6\tfrac{1}{4} \text{ hours} \\ \mathrm{L-B-P-F-L} = 6 \text{ hours} & \mathrm{L-F-P-B-L} = 6 \text{ hours} \end{array}$$

It is clear from this that the shortest route is

London – Paris – Brussels – Frankfurt – London

or the same in reverse.

Using a computer

In that example you simply found all the Hamiltonian cycles, but with more vertices this soon becomes impractical. The next step might be to use a computer. Although no simple algorithm exists, a computer program could check all possible orders of the vertices, see if they form a cycle and, if so, to find its total length.

Now it is clear that if a computer can be used to check every possible route and find the shortest, that route will be the solution to the salesperson's problem. That might appear to be an end to the matter, but in fact it is not. For six towns there are only 120 different routes to try, and that is quite manageable even on a desktop computer, but as the number of towns increases the number of possible routes increases factorially. Thus for 10 towns there are 362 880 possible routes, for 15 there are nearly 100 billion, and for 20 there are more than 10^{17}. Even the fastest computers would take many years, if not many centuries, to check all the possible routes around 20 towns, making the full search method of little use in practice.

Upper and lower bounds

Although there is no general algorithm for the solution of the travelling salesman problem, it is possible to find upper and lower bounds for the minimum distance required. This can sometimes be very useful, because if you know that the shortest route is between (say) 47 miles and 55 miles long, and you can find a route of length 47 miles, you know that your answer is actually a solution. Alternatively, from a business point of view, if the best route you can find by trial-and-error is 48 miles long, you might well decide that the expense of looking for a shorter route was just not worthwhile.

Finding an upper bound is easy: simply work out the length of any Hamiltonian cycle. Since this cycle gives a possible solution, the best solution must be no longer than this length. If the graph is not too different from an ordinary map drawn to scale, it is usually possible by a sensible choice of route to find an upper bound quite close to the minimum length.

When considering the travelling salesperson problem it will often be the case that you are told the distances between **every** pair of towns. In other words the given network will often be **complete**. In such cases there is an algorithm for finding a reasonably efficient Hamiltonian cycle (but **not** always the shortest). It is called the **nearest neighbour algorithm** and is another **greedy** algorithm, where you simply do the obvious thing at each stage.

To find a Hamiltonian cycle of a given complete network:

1 Choose the starting vertex.

2 Choose the shortest edge which goes from the current vertex to an unused vertex. Travel along that edge. If you have now visited all the vertices go to step 3, if not repeat step 2.

3 Complete a Hamiltonian cycle by taking the edge back to the starting vertex.

Worked example 1.2

Apply the nearest neighbour algorithm to the network shown. Has the algorithm found a shortest Hamiltonian cycle?

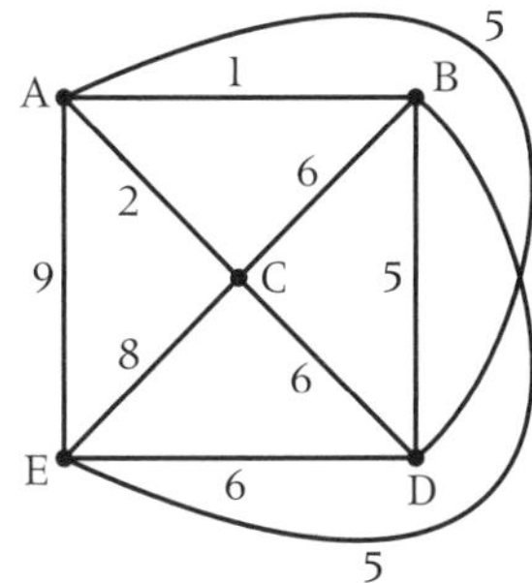

Solution

1 You have a free choice of starting vertex: let us start at A.

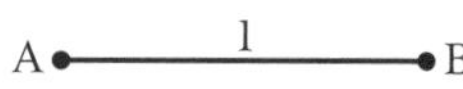

2 The shortest edge from A is AB of length 1. Move along that edge to B. There are still unused vertices, so repeat step 2.

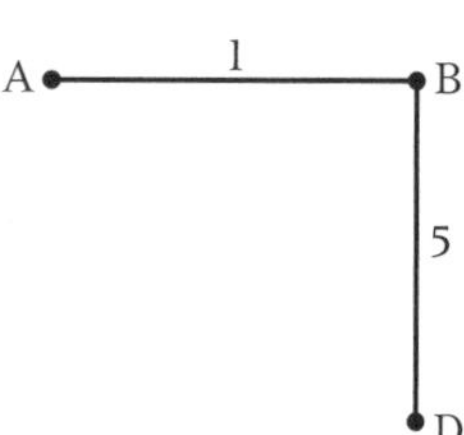

2 The shortest edge from B to an unused vertex is (for example) BD of length 5. Move along that edge to D. There are still unused vertices, so repeat step 2.

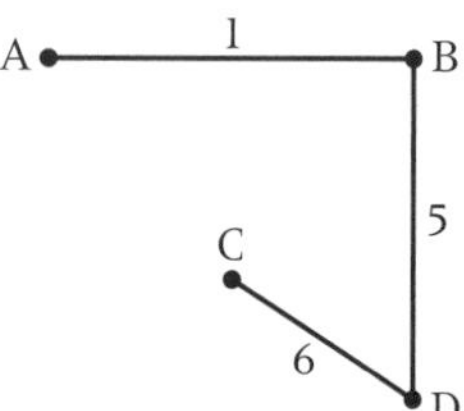

2 The shortest edge from D to an unused vertex is (for example) DC of length 6 (the edge DA of length 5 is not suitable because it leads back to a used vertex). Move along the edge DC to C. There are still unused vertices, so repeat step 2.

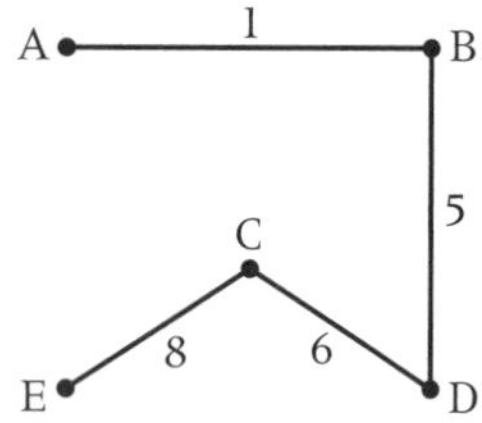

2 The only edge from C to an unused vertex is CE of length 8. Move along that edge E. We have now used all the vertices so go to step 3.

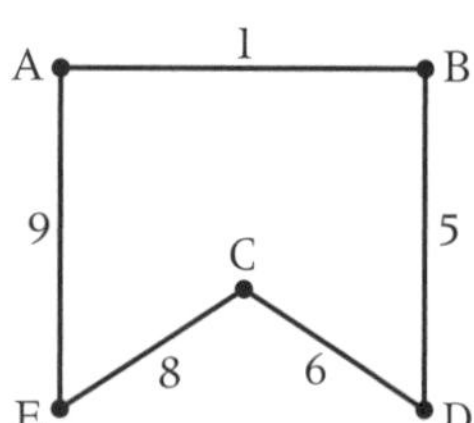

3 Complete the Hamiltonian cycle by using the edge EA back to the starting vertex.

Overall that algorithm has given us a Hamiltonian cycle ABDCEA of length 29. It is **not** the shortest Hamiltonian cycle because, for example, ABEDCA is shorter, being of length 20.

Provided that you only apply the nearest neighbour algorithm to complete networks, it **will** always give you a Hamiltonian cycle. However, as that example shows, it **will not** always give you the shortest. But having constructed one Hamiltonian cycle using the algorithm that does at least give you an **upper bound** for the travelling salesperson problem.

Worked exam question 1.2

A visitor to the County Show wants to start from the main gate, visit each of eight exhibitions, and return to the main gate by the shortest possible route. The distances in metres between the exhibitions are given in the table below.

	Gate	A	B	C	D	E	F	G	H
Gate	–	200	350	400	500	350	150	200	350
A	200	–	200	300	400	450	300	250	200
B	350	200	–	100	250	450	500	300	100
C	400	300	100	–	150	350	500	300	100
D	500	400	250	150	–	250	450	300	200
E	350	450	450	350	250	–	250	200	350
F	150	300	500	500	450	250	–	200	400
G	200	250	300	300	300	200	200	–	200
H	350	200	100	100	200	350	400	200	–

Use the nearest neighbour algorithm to give an upper bound for the distance the visitor has to walk.

Solution

You do not have to draw the network to apply the algorithm – in fact it is just as easy direct from the table:

- Starting at the gate the shortest route is to F, taking 150 metres.
- From F the shortest route to an unused point is to G taking 200.
- From G the shortest route to an unused point is to E or to H, each taking 200: we choose to go to H.
- From H the shortest route to an unused point is to B or to C, each taking 100: we choose to go to C.
- From C the shortest route to an unused point is to B, taking 100.
- From B the shortest route to an unused point is to A, taking 200.
- From A the shortest route to an unused point is to D, taking 400.
- From D the shortest route to an unused point is to E, taking 250.
- We have now used/visited all the points so we must return to the gate, taking a further 350 metres.

Hence the nearest neighbour algorithm has constructed the Hamiltonian cycle

Gate – F – G – H – C – B – A – D – E – Gate

of total length

$$150 + 200 + 200 + 100 + 100 + 200 + 400 + 250 + 350 = 1950.$$

Therefore it is possible to visit all the exhibitions and return to the gate by walking 1950 metres or less. Thus 1950 is an upper bound for this 'travelling salesperson problem'.

(There was a choice of routes when using the algorithm above and an alternative route which could have been chosen is:

Gate – F – G – E – D – C – B – H – A – Gate

giving a Hamiltonian cycle of length

$$150 + 200 + 200 + 250 + 150 + 100 + 100 + 200 + 200 = 1550$$

which is in fact the shortest possible.)

You can probably see why the nearest neighbour algorithm is not infallible: although it often starts off very well, by the time we reach the end of the cycle there is no choice left and we might be forced to use a very long edge. But at least the algorithm gives one possible route for the salesperson, and an upper bound which we know need not be exceeded. Furthermore, given the cycle determined by the algorithm, it is often possible to spot obvious improvements.

Lower bounds

Now we attempt to find a **lower bound** for the travelling salesperson problem. For this recall the idea of a **minimum connector**. Given a network which is connected (i.e. in one piece) it might be possible to remove some edges while still leaving all the vertices there and still leaving the graph connected. When no further edges can be removed without disconnecting the network we are left with a **spanning tree**. You can calculate the total lengths of the edges in a spanning tree, and a spanning tree of least total length is a **minimum connector** of the original network.

In the earlier course we learned how to construct a minimum connector by applying **Prim's algorithm** (to a network or to a table) or **Kruskal's algorithm** (to a network).

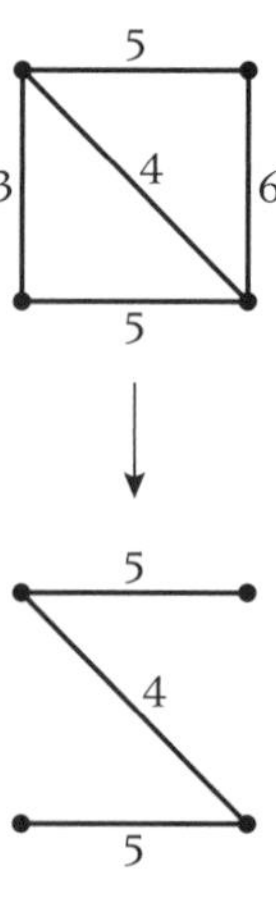

Spanning tree

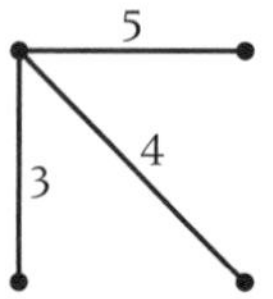

Minimum connector

Worked example 1.3

Consider the network **N** illustrated:

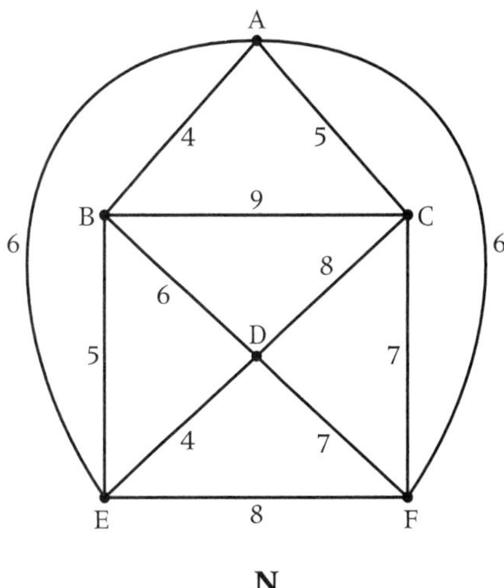

1 Use Prim's algorithm, starting at the vertex A, to find a minimum connector of the network **N**.

2 Consider a new network **N*** obtained from **N** by deleting the vertex A and all the edges which end there. Use Prim's algorithm, starting at the vertex B, to find a minimum connector of the network **N***.

3 In the network **N**, what are the two shortest edges from the vertex A? Show that these two edges together with the minimum connector of **N*** found in **2** form a shortest Hamiltonian cycle of **N**.

Solution

1 Prim's algorithm adds on a new vertex each time by the shortest available edge. Starting at vertex A in **N** that gives us:

- Shortest edge from A to a new vertex is AB of length 4.
- Shortest edge from A, B to a new vertex is (for example) BE of length 5.
- Shortest edge from A, B, E to a new vertex is ED of length 4. At this stage we have illustrated the tree on the right.

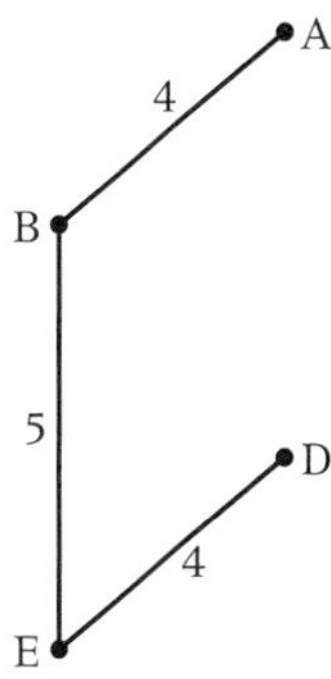

- Continuing, the shortest edge from A, B, E, D to a new vertex is (for example) AC of length 5.
- Shortest edge from A, B, E, D, C to a new vertex is AF of length 6.

We have now used all the vertices and so a minimum connector of **N** is:

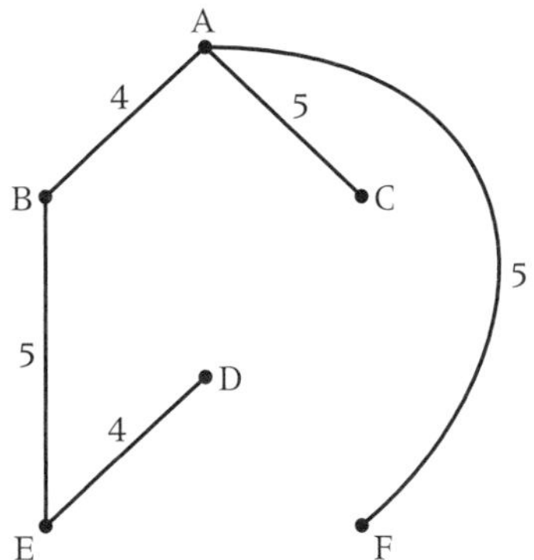

2 A similar process applied to the reduced network **N*** gives:

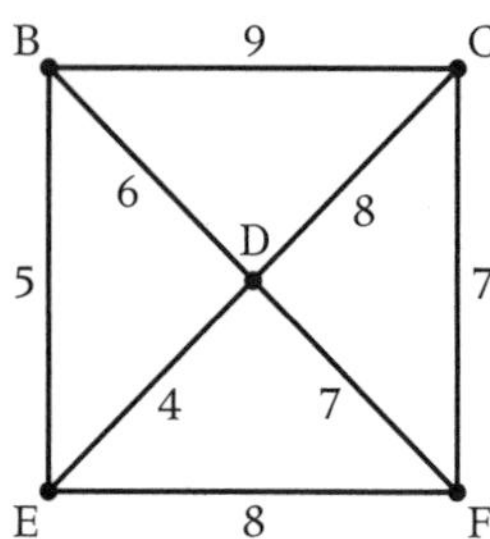

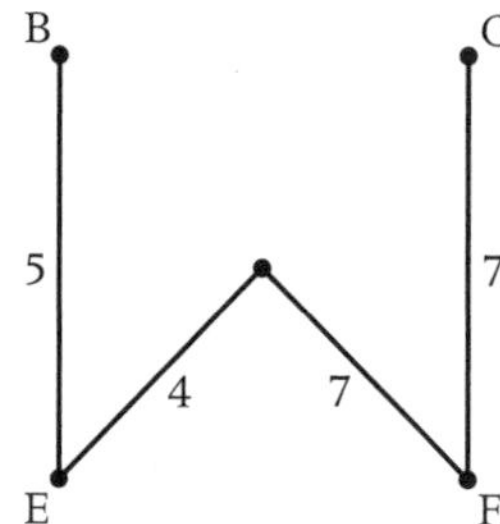

minimum connector, length 23

3 The two shortest edges from A are AB and AC of lengths 4 and 5. By a very lucky coincidence those two edges and the minimum connector of **N*** found in **2** fit together to give a Hamiltonian cycle of **N** of length 32:

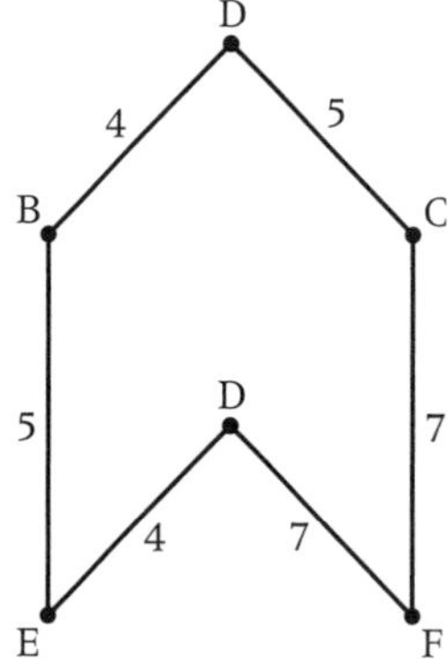

This must be a shortest Hamiltonian cycle because there is no way of connecting up all the vertices B–F (in any way) with total length less than 23, and then there is no way of connecting up to A and back with less than a further 4 + 5.

The process in that worked example in the network **N** was to:

- delete a vertex, A say, to form a network **N***
- find a minimum connector of the reduced network **N***
- find the two shortest edges from A
- add the length of the minimum connector of **N*** to the lengths of the two shortest edges from A.

In that example the process led to a shortest Hamiltonian cycle of the original network, but that was a very lucky fluke. It relied on the fact that the minimum connector of **N*** was a very simple tree of the form

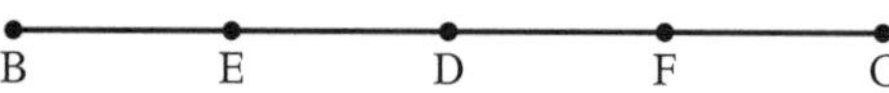

(rather than having 'branches' as trees generally do) and it relied on the fact that the two shortest edges from A were to the two ends of that tree.

Although in general this process will not lead to a Hamiltonian cycle of **N**, it will give us a lower bound for the travelling salesperson problem.

Given a network **N** and any vertex A:

1 Delete the vertex A (and the edges which end there) to form the reduced network **N***.

2 Find a minimum connector of **N*** (e.g. by Prim's algorithm) and let its length be L.

3 Find the lengths of the two shortest edges from A and let their lengths be x and y.

4 Then $L + x + y$ is a lower bound for the travelling salesperson problem; i.e. any Hamiltonian cycle of **N** will have total length

$$\geqslant L + x + y$$

Why does this work? Take any Hamiltonian cycle of a network **N** and break it down into a path in **N*** and two edges from A, as shown:

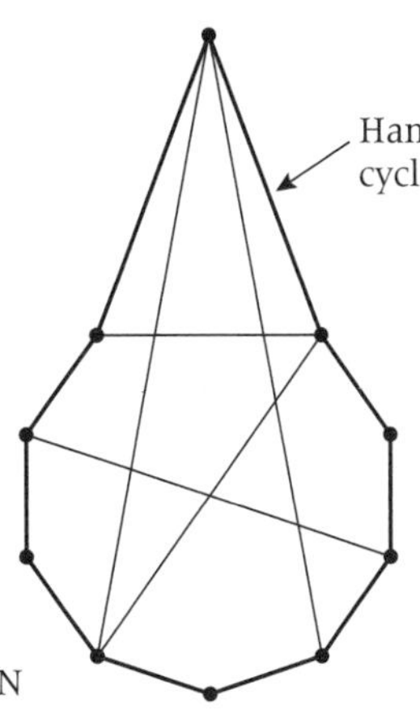

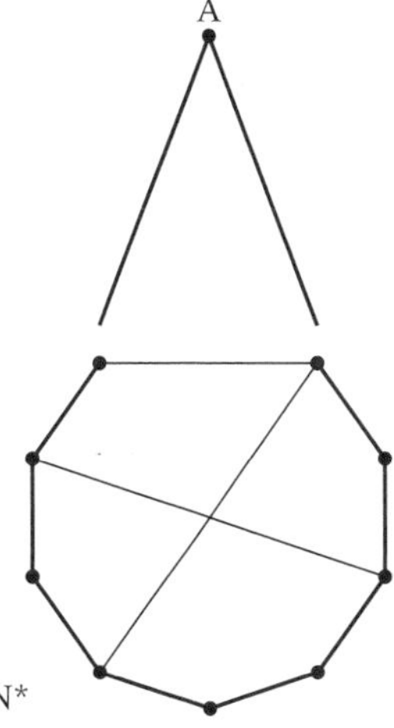

Then the part in **N*** does connect **N*** and so its length is at least L, that of the minimum connector. Also the two edges from A must have length at least $x + y$: so the total length of the Hamiltonian cycle is at least $L + x + y$. (Only very rarely will it equal this.)

Worked exam question 1.3

For the complete network illustrated:

1 Start at Q and use the nearest neighbour algorithm to find a Hamiltonian cycle.

2 Find a minimum connector of the network with vertex P deleted.

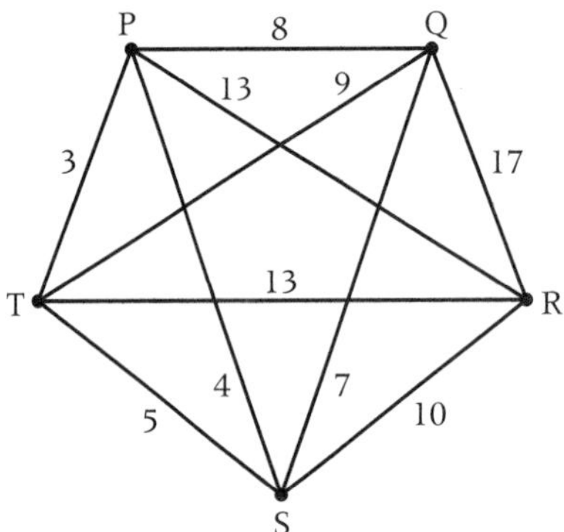

3 We wish to find the length h of the shortest Hamiltonian cycle of the above network. Without actually finding the cycle, show that:

$$29 \leqslant h \leqslant 44.$$

4 Find the length of the Hamiltonian cycle PQRSTP and confirm that it lies between the bounds found in **3**.

Solution

1 Starting at Q the nearest neighbour algorithm gives the Hamiltonian cycle QSPTRQ of length:

$$7 + 4 + 3 + 13 + 17 = 44.$$

2 A minimum connector of the network with P deleted is:

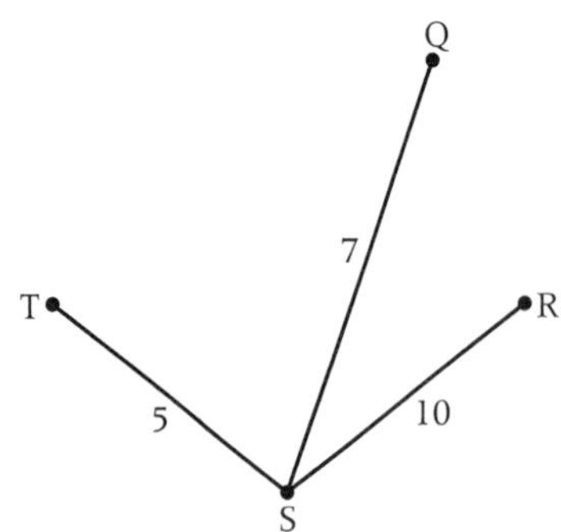

with total length $5 + 7 + 10 = 22$.

3 The two shortest edges from P have lengths 3 and 4. Hence the shortest Hamiltonian cycle must have length $\leqslant 44$ (from **1**) and $\geqslant 22 + 3 + 4$ (from **2**). Therefore:

$$29 \leqslant h \leqslant 44$$

as required.

4 The Hamiltonian cycle PQRSTP has total length:

$$8 + 17 + 10 + 5 + 3 = 43$$

which is between the bounds of 22 and 44.

An extension to incomplete networks

Until now only the classical travelling salesperson problem has been considered; i.e. we have assumed that we are looking for a Hamiltonian cycle in a network and that we are given the distance between any pair of vertices of that network. Sometimes in practical problems only routes between certain towns are possible and the salesperson has to visit some towns more than once. Rather than cover this much more general problem very fully we shall simply illustrate how to convert such a problem to the classical case.

For example, consider the network below representing six towns and the roads between them (with distances given in miles). A salesperson starts at A and wishes to visit each town at least once before returning to A:

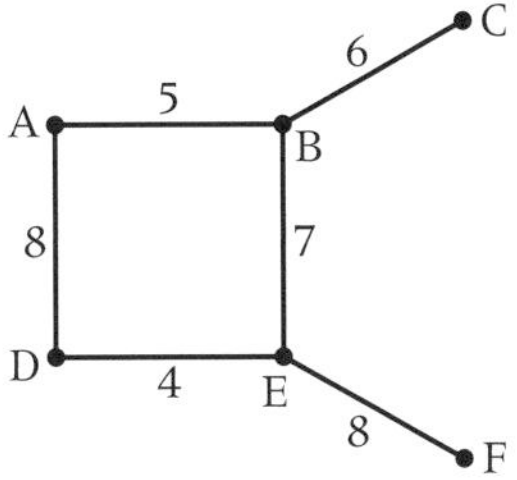

Obviously there is no Hamiltonian cycle in this network and so some vertices will have to be revisited. In fact we are looking for a closed walk in the network (and preferably one which is as short as possible).

To adapt this example to the classical one where every distance is known, we have to fill in all the remaining edges and distances. For example, how far is it from A to E? The shortest route is, for example, ABE of length 12 and so we can add the edge AE with a length of 12. Similarly, the shortest distance from C to F is 6 + 7 + 8 = 21. Repeating this for each unjoined pair of vertices in the original network gives

AC (ABC) 11
AE (ADE or ABE) 12
AF (ADEF or ABEF) 20
BD (BED) 11
BF (BEF) 15
CD (CBED) 17
CE (CBE) 13
CF (CBEF) 21
DF (DEF) 12

The following complete network now incorporates all these distances:

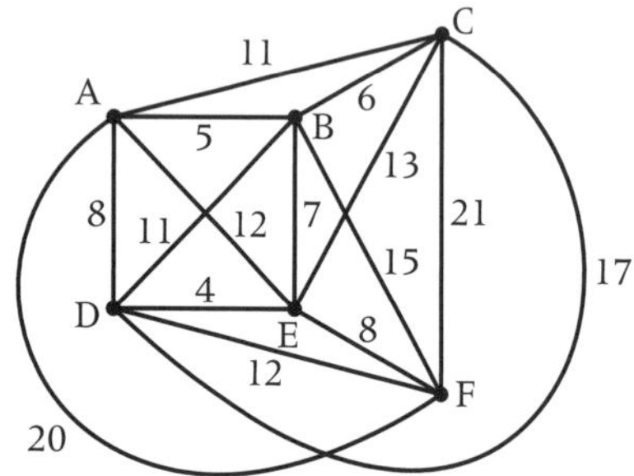

We can now apply our various techniques to the classical problem of finding economical Hamiltonian cycles in this network. For example, the nearest neighbour algorithm starting at A gives the Hamiltonian cycle ABCEDFA of length 5 + 6 + 13 + 4 + 12 + 20 = 60.

We must now interpret this result in the original network. For example the step CE of length 13 is achieved by going via B and so CE must be replaced by CBE. Similarly, DF must be replaced by DEF and FA must be replaced by FEDA (or FEBA). Hence the corresponding walk in the original network is

ABCBEDEFEDA,

(which still has length 60).

However, if you follow that walk in the network you will see that it has some redundancy and it can be reduced to the walk

ABCBEFEDA

of length 52 (which was an obvious route anyway).

In this way we can extend our techniques to more general travelling salesperson problems, but we must take great care in interpreting the results.

EXERCISE 1A

1 Find a minimum-length Hamiltonian cycle in the network shown in the diagram opposite.

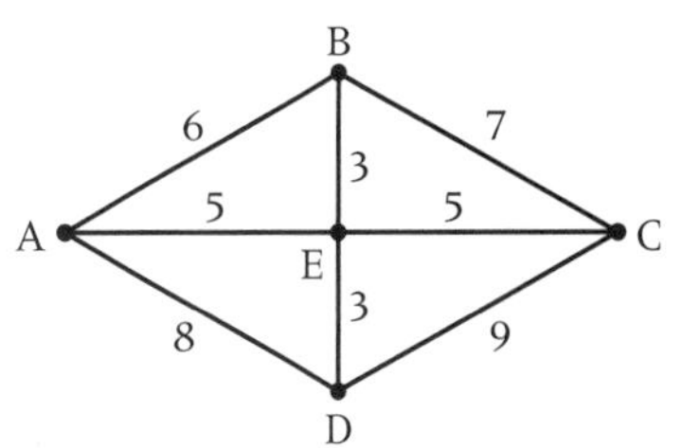

2 The Director of the Scottish Tourist Board, based in Edinburgh, plans a tour of inspection around each of her District Offices, finishing back at her own base. The distances in miles between the offices are shown in the diagram.

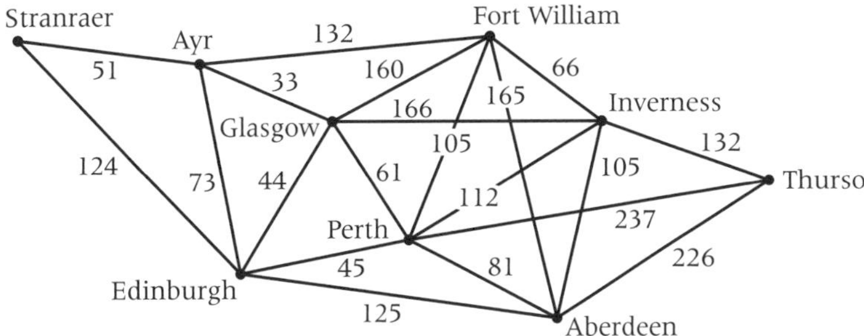

By deleting Stranraer and finding a minimum connector of the remaining network, show that any tour of inspection must take at least 681 miles.
Give one example of a tour and find its length. [A]

3 A milling machine can produce four different types of component as long as its settings are changed for each type. The times in minutes required to change settings are shown in the table.

On a particular day, some of each component have to be produced. The machine must start and finish at 'Off'.

From/To	**A**	**B**	**C**	**D**	**Off**
A	–	5	7	4	8
B	5	–	6	7	6
C	7	6	–	5	9
D	4	7	5	–	7
Off	8	6	9	7	–

(a) Use the nearest neighbour algorithm to find a suitable order in which the components should be made.

(b) Show that the order found in **(a)** does minimise the time wasted in changing settings. [A]

4 Let **N** be the network shown:

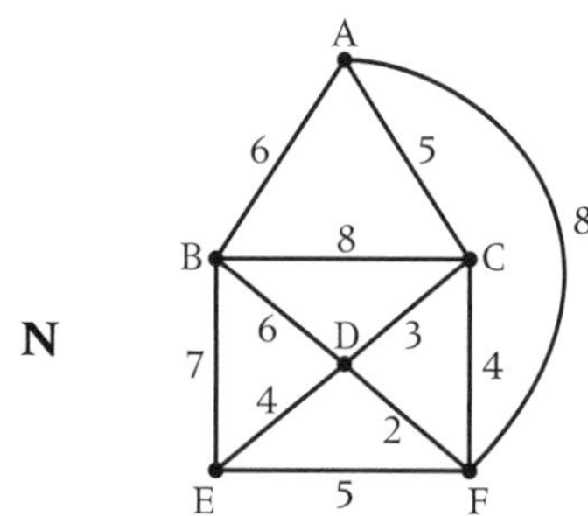

For any vertex V let **N**(V) be the network **N** with vertex V deleted.

(a) For each of the vertices A-F find

Length of minimum connector of **N**(V) + Lengths of two shortest edges ending at V

(b) Deduce that any Hamiltonian cycle of N has length $\geqslant 26$. [A]

5 Below is shown the distance, in miles, between some cities A to H:

	A	**B**	**C**	**D**	**E**	**F**	**G**	**H**
A	–	47	84	382	120	172	299	144
B	47	–	121	402	155	193	319	165
C	84	121	–	456	200	246	373	218
D	382	402	456	–	413	220	255	289
E	120	155	200	413	–	204	286	131
F	172	193	246	220	204	–	144	70
G	299	319	373	255	286	144	–	160
H	144	165	218	289	131	70	160	–

Use the nearest neighbour algorithm to find a tour which visits each city and ends where it started.
Is your tour the shortest possible? [A]

6 [Investigation] It is often claimed that, for any network:

> Length of shortest Hamiltonian cycle $\leqslant 2 \times$ (Length of a minimum connector)

The 'proof' is that by travelling twice along each edge of a minimum connector you can visit each vertex and end back where you started. Give some examples where the 'theorem' is false.

7 A lorry driver has to deliver milk every day to village shops. He starts and finishes at A and and must visit villages B, C, D, E and F. The distances between them are shown in the table:

	A	B	C	D	E	F
A	–	11	13	8	15	13
B	11	–	10	16	5	6
C	13	10	–	17	8	8
D	8	16	17	–	17	16
E	15	5	8	17	–	4
F	13	6	8	16	4	–

(a) Obtain an upper bound for the distance the lorry must travel.

(b) Obtain a lower bound for the distance travelled.

(c) Using the best upper bound and lower bound you can obtain, write down an inequality for L, the minimum distance travelled.

(d) Write down the shortest possible route.

8 A computer engineer lives in town A and needs to visit each of the towns B, C, D and E to service various installations. He must return to town A and visit each town once. The distances in miles between the towns are shown in the table.

	A	B	C	D	E
A	–	17	10	9	12
B	17	–	8	14	5
C	10	8	–	7	11
D	9	14	7	–	11
E	12	5	11	11	–

(a) Use Prim's algorithm to find the length of a minimum spanning tree that connects the five towns.

(b) Find a route for the engineer of less than twice the length of the spanning tree found in **(a)**.

(c) Obtain lower bounds to the distance travelled by the computer engineer by:

(i) deleting A, **(ii)** deleting B, **(iii)** deleting C,

(iv) deleting D, **(v)** deleting E.

(d) From your previous answers obtain a minimum tour of length 41.

1.3 The Chinese postperson problem

Recall that a Hamiltonian cycle is one visiting every **vertex** of a graph just once. On the other hand an **Eulerian trail** is one visiting every **edge** once. The idea of Hamiltonian cycles/vertex-tours led to the travelling salesperson problem and now the idea of an Eulerian trail/edge-tour leads to the **Chinese postperson problem**.

We need to recall the terms for the various sorts of tours in a graph or network; **walks**, **trails** and **paths**. In each case they are natural ways of getting around a graph or network and they consist of sequences of vertices where each is joined to the next by an edge:

- In a **walk** you can use vertices and edges as often as you like. For example, P, A, B, P, A, Q is a walk from P to Q in the network illustrated (it has total length $6 + 3 + 5 + 6 + 7 = 27$).

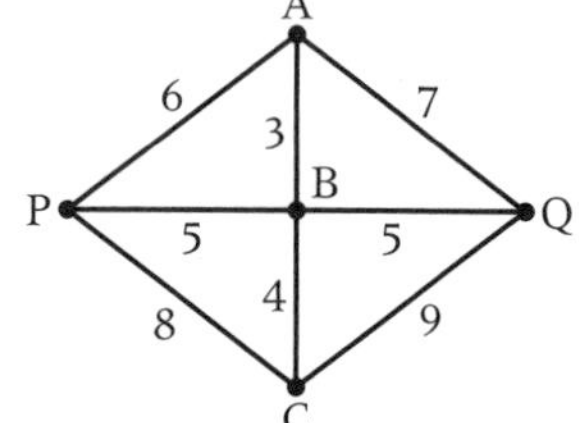

- In a **trail** you can use vertices as often as you like but you must not repeat an edge. So the above example of a walk (which uses edge PA twice) is not a trail. An example of a trail from P to Q in the network illustrated is P, A, B, P, C, Q (with length 31).
- In a **path** you must not repeat vertices (or edges) so P, A, B, C, Q is an example of a path of length 22 from P to Q in the network illustrated.
- In each case if the walk/trail/path ends where it started, then it is called **closed**.

Now an **Eulerian trail** of a graph or network is a trail using each edge and, because it is a trail, it uses each edge **exactly once**. Graphs or networks which have a closed Eulerian trail are called **Eulerian**. One such network is illustrated: one of its closed Eulerian trails is:

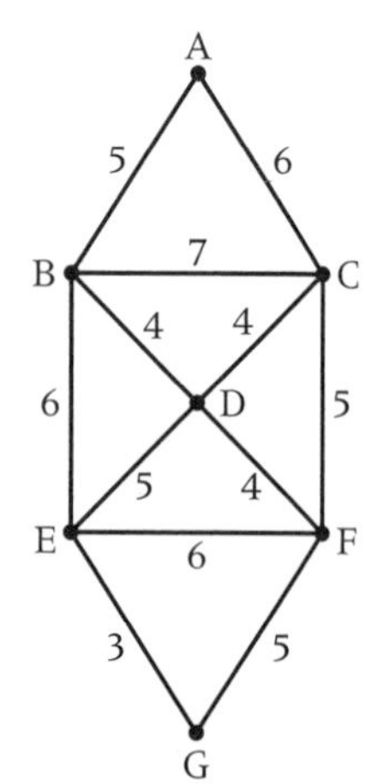

A, C, F, G, E, F, D, E, B, C, D, B, A.

Its length is 60, which is just the total of the lengths of the edges of the network.

Note that the vertex degrees of the illustrated Eulerian network are:

A : 2   B : 4   C : 4   D : 4   E : 4   F : 4   G : 2

In the earlier course we discovered that a connected graph or network is Eulerian if and only if all its vertices have even degree.

Now consider the **Chinese postperson problem**. It derives its name not from the postperson's nationality but from the fact that it was first seriously studied by the Chinese mathematician

Mei-ko Kwan in the 1960s. It concerns a postperson who wants to walk along every road in an estate, and end back at the starting point, walking the minimum distance possible. (So, whereas the travelling salesperson wants to visit every town, the postperson wants to cover every road.) The same problem would be encountered by someone who wanted to check the quality of the road surface throughout an estate, and for this reason the problem is also known as the **route inspection problem**.

Posing the problem in a network, we cannot restrict attention to looking for closed Eulerian trails – they only exist in the rare cases when all the vertices have even degree. In all other cases the postperson is bound to repeat at least one edge (i.e. to go along a road twice). So the problem becomes as follows.

Chinese postperson problem (or the route inspection problem):

Given a network, find its shortest closed walk which uses all the edges.

In the cases of Eulerian networks the solution is for the postperson to use any of the Eulerian trails. Then no edges are repeated and the total distance travelled is just the sum of all the lengths of the edges, and this of course is absolutely the best possible. In such cases finding an Eulerian trail is usually straightforward: if necessary, to find an Eulerian trail we can use **Fleury's algorithm** which we met in the earlier course.

The problem becomes interesting when the network has some vertices of odd degree:

Worked example 1.4

Find a shortest closed walk which uses every edge of the network illustrated:

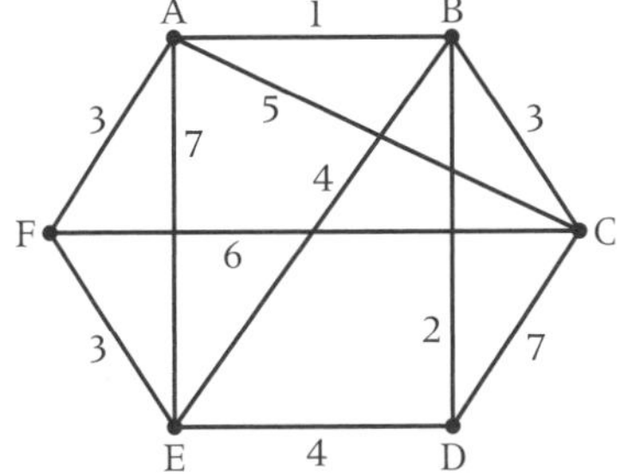

Solution

The total length of the edges of this network is 46. The degrees of the vertices are

A : 4 B : 4 C : 4 D : 3 E : 4 F : 3

There are two vertices of odd degree, D and F. Hence the network does not have a closed Eulerian trail. However, as we saw in the earlier course, the network is **semi-Eulerian** and it has a trail which uses all the edges once but starting at D and finishing at F. So any closed walk using all the edges is bound to repeat some edges to get back from F to D. The shortest walk from F to D is F, A, B, D of length $3 + 1 + 2 = 6$. So our shortest walk is bound to cover all the edges of the network and to repeat the edges FA, AB and BD. We can illustrate this by drawing repeated edges twice:

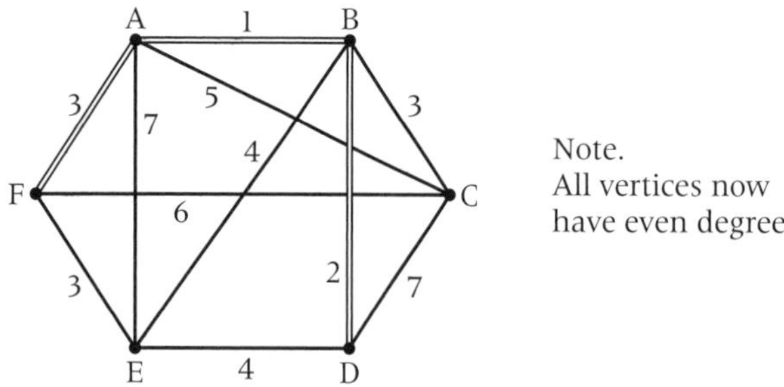

Note.
All vertices now have even degree

In this revised network notice that every vertex has even degree and a little thought shows that it **is** the one of shortest possible total length. Its length is actually 52, being the total length of the edges of the original network (46) plus the total length of the repeated edges (6).

To actually find a closed walk of length 52 using all the marked edges in the revised network is equivalent to finding an Eulerian trail of it. One such (using Fleury's algorithm if necessary) is

ABCAFEAFCDBEDBA.

That example is typical of the cases where there are two vertices of odd degree. But what if there are more? We have seen that, in any graph or network, there is always an even number of vertices of odd degree. So the next case to consider is when there are four vertices of odd degree.

Worked example 1.5

Find a shortest closed walk which uses every edge of the network illustrated:

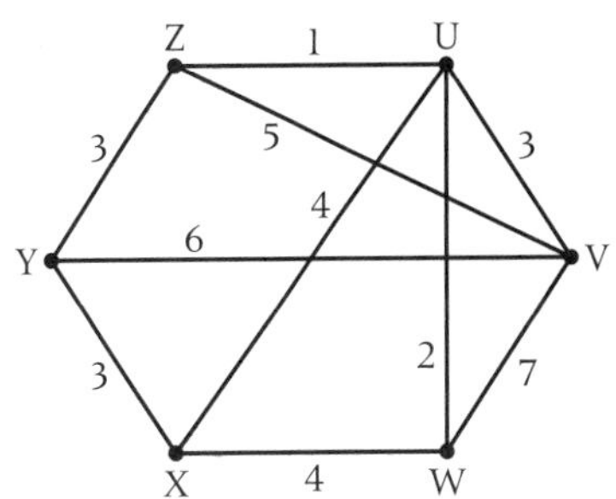

Solution

The total length of the edges of the network is 38.
The degrees of the vertices are

U : 4 V : 4 W : 3 X : 3 Y : 3 Z : 3

Hence the four vertices W, X, Y and Z have odd degree. In order to add repeated edges and get a revised network which is Eulerian we could add a walk from W to X and a walk from Y to Z. In both cases the shortest walk is by a single edge (WX of length 4 and YZ of length 3) and so we would get the revised network

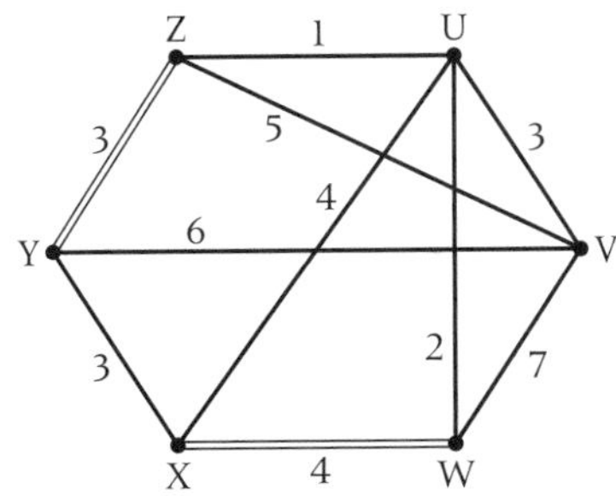

Our method guarantees that this revised network is Eulerian and so there is a closed trail using all its edges. This will give a closed walk using all the edges of the original network. Its length is:

original edges + repeated edges = 38 + 7 = 45.

However, that is not the end of the story. To make the four vertices W, X, Y and Z even we could have joined W to Y and X to Z (or indeed W to Z and X to Y). Each of these possibilities is called a **pairing** and to be sure that we find the shortest route we must consider all pairings:

Pairing	Shortest routes	Lengths of repeated edges
WX/YZ	WX and YZ	4 + 3 = 7
WY/XZ	WUZY and XUZ	2 + 1 + 3 + 4 + 1 = 11
WZ/XY	WUZ and XY	2 + 1 + 3 = 6

So the shortest pairing is WZ/XY with repeated edges as shown:

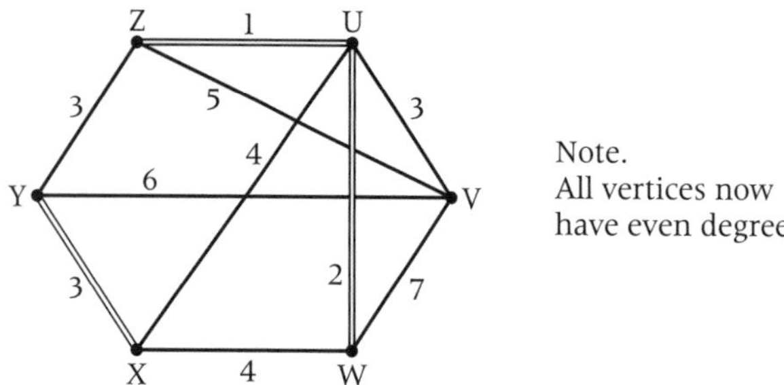

Note.
All vertices now have even degree

Any Eulerian trail in this revised network will give the required shortest walk in the original network. One such is

UVWUZVYXWUXYZU

It is a closed walk in the original network, it uses each edge at least once, and its length of 44 (= 38 + 6) cannot be improved.

An algorithm

The method used in that example can be generalised to the following algorithm. Unlike the travelling salesperson problem, where we could only in general obtain bounds for the answer, this algorithm always leads to the best possible solution. The **route inspection/Chinese postperson algorithm** is as follows:

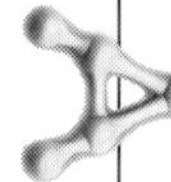

Given a network, to find a shortest closed walk which uses all the edges:

1 List all the vertices of odd degree.

2 List all possible ways of pairing off the vertices of odd degree.

3 For each pairing:

- **(a)** take each pair of vertices
- **(b)** find the shortest path between them and note its length
- **(c)** add up the answers in **(b)**.

4 Choose the pairing which gives the lowest total in **3(c)**. Then the required shortest walk is obtained by repeating just those edges used in obtaining that lowest total.

This is straightforward in practice, as we have seen. If you draw as multiple edges those which have to be repeated, then the revised network is Eulerian and a closed Eulerian trail of it gives the required shortest walk in the original network.

Worked exam question 1.4

The table shows the lengths in miles of the existing rail-track between five Canadian towns A, B, C, D, E. The Canada Rail Company wishes to inspect all the track whilst travelling the shortest possible distance.

	A	B	C	D	E
A	–	120	60	–	45
B	120	–	50	110	–
C	60	50	–	50	–
D	–	110	50	–	40
E	45	–	–	40	–

1 Draw a network representing this information.

2 Use an appropriate algorithm to find a shortest rail-inspection route. What is its length?

Solution

1 The network is

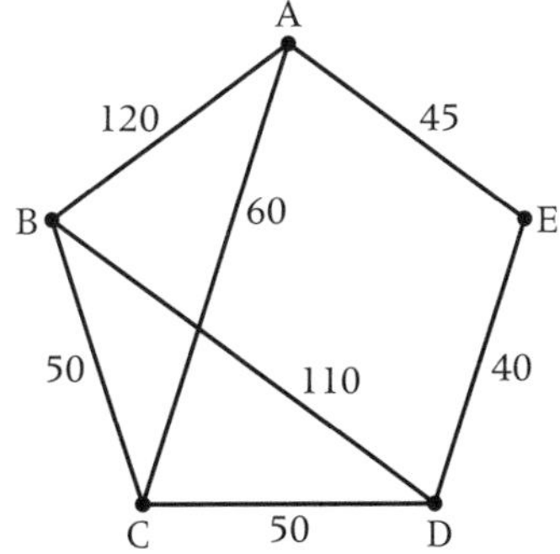

2 The network has total length 475 miles.

To find the required shortest route we shall follow the steps of the route inspection algorithm.

(a) The degrees of the vertices are

A : 3 B : 3 C : 3 D : 3 E : 2

and so those of odd degree are A, B, C, D.

(b) The possible pairings are AB/CD or AC/BD or AD/BC.

(c) For each pairing, the lengths of shortest paths joining them are as shown:

Pairing	Shortest routes	Lengths of repeated edges
AB/CD	ACB and CD	$60 + 50 + 50 = 160$
AC/BD	AC and BCD	$60 + 50 + 50 = 160$
AD/BC	AED and BC	$45 + 40 + 50 = 135$

(d) The pairing giving the lowest total is AD/BC with 135. The revised network showing the repeated edges is

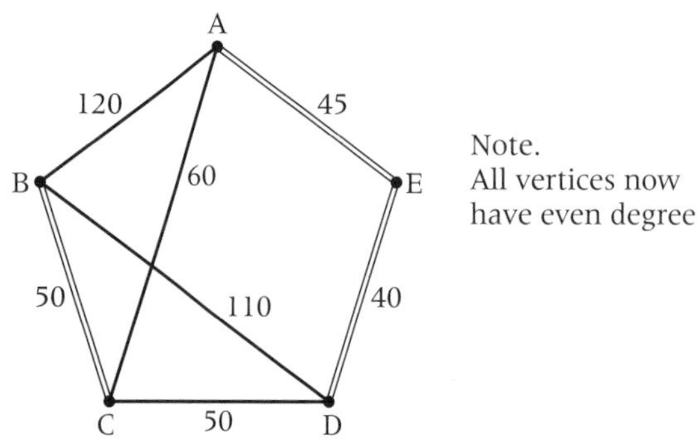

An example of a shortest inspection route (which is an Eulerian trail in this revised network) is

ABCDEACBDEA

and it has total length $475 + 135 = 610$ miles.

EXERCISE 1B

1 Find a solution to the Chinese postperson problem on each of the networks shown:

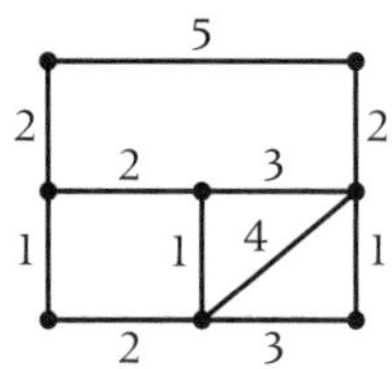

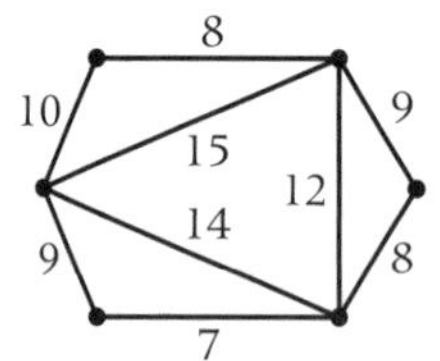

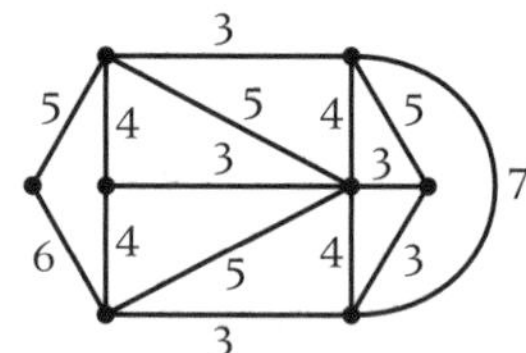

2 The table shows lengths of roads (where they exist) between five towns A, B, C, D, E:

	A	B	C	D	E
A	–	27	40	30	20
B	27	–	28	45	–
C	40	28	–	–	–
D	30	45	–	–	22
E	20	–	–	22	–

Represent this as a network and hence find the shortest distance needed to travel along each of the roads at least once and end back where you started. [A]

3

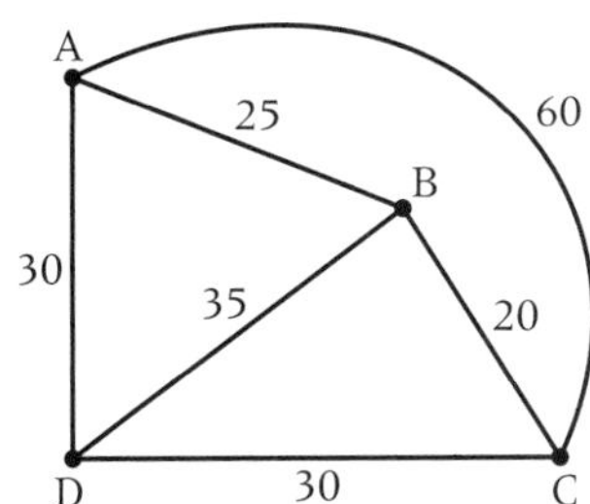

The diagram shows the layout of footpaths in a garden. The lengths of the paths are given in metres. The paths are all to be swept. Starting at A and finishing at A find a route of minimum length. Give the length of this route. [A]

4 After a night of heavy snow, the County Council sends out its snow ploughs to clear the main roads shown (with their lengths in miles) in the diagram below.

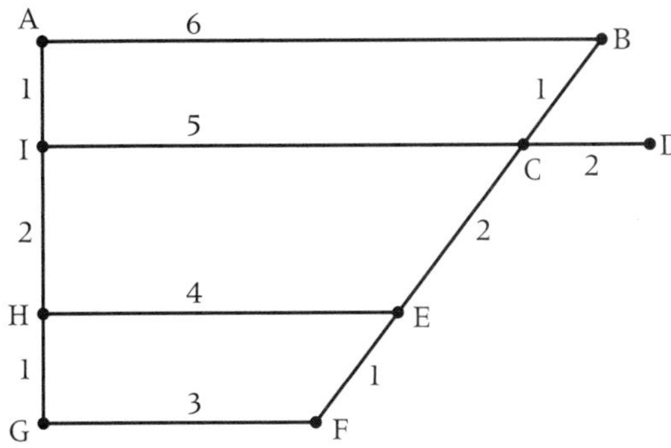

The ploughs must drive at least once along each of the roads to clear it, but should obviously take the shortest route starting and finishing at the depot D. Which way should it go? [A]

5 A church member has to deliver notices to the houses along each of the roads shown in the diagram below. The distances shown are in metres.

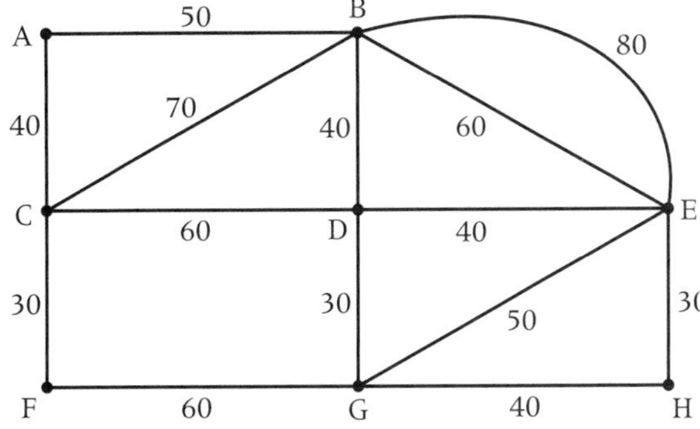

If her own house is at H, what route should she follow in order to make her total walking distance as short as possible? [A]

6 The table below gives fares for direct bus journeys between towns P, Q, R, S, T, U and V, in a tourist area. Blanks indicate no direct service.

Fares in pence

	P	Q	R	S	T	U	V
P		67		45			80
Q	67		63	71		170	
R		63			59		
S	45	71			40		54
T			59	40		58	62
U		170			58		70
V	80			54	62	70	

Find one of the cheapest ways for a tourist to use every route. [A]

7 A skier can travel across a section of mountain country by using a system of drag lifts. She can then ski to the bottom of another lift, or, in some cases, back to the bottom of the same lift. The time in minutes to ski from the top of a lift to the bottom of a lift, where a route exists, is given in the following table:

From

		A	B	C	D	E	F	G	H
	A	6	8	8	10				
	B	10			5				
	C	8							7
To	**D**	11	5		5		15		
	E		12			4			
	F				17	5		4	
	G						6		7

(a) Represent this information in a directed network.

(b) The skier wishes to ski all the runs. By using a 'directed' version of an Eulerian trail with additional repeated edges, find a quickest tour.

8 A clothing company is to produce a logo incorporating the letters NX. A diagram of the logo is shown below. Vertices have been labelled ABCDEFG for convenience. The numbers indicate distances in cm between vertices.

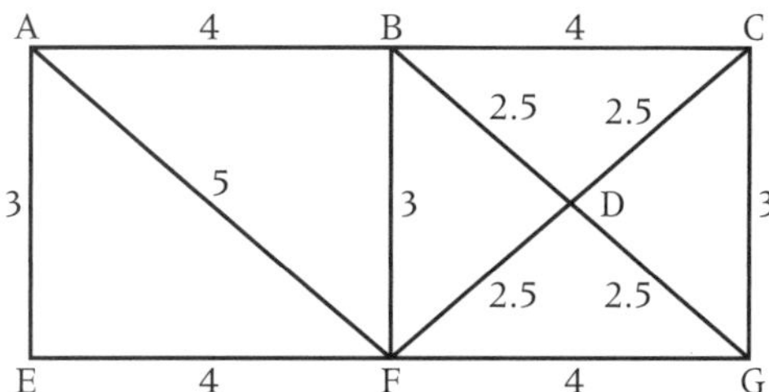

Plans involve the production of large numbers of garments, so it is important to produce the logo with the minimum of stitching. Machinists will start and end stitching at A, with no breaks.

(a) Explain why it will be necessary to sew some edges more than once.

(b) Use an appropriate algorithm to determine the order of stitching which minimises the length to be sewn. Give your minimum length, and a corresponding order in which the edges should be sewn. [A]

1.4 Network flows

There are many situations in life which involve flow rates; some are self-evident, such as traffic flow or the flow of oil in a pipeline; others have the same basic structure but are less obviously flow problems, for example movement of money between financial institutions and activity networks for building projects. In most of the problems you will meet, the objective is to maximise a flow rate, subject to certain constraints. In order to get a feel for these types of problem, try the following activity.

Worked example 1.6

This diagram represents a road network. All vehicles enter at S and leave at T. The numbers represent each road's capacity in vehicles per hour in the direction from S to T. What is the maximum number of vehicles which can enter and leave the network every hour?

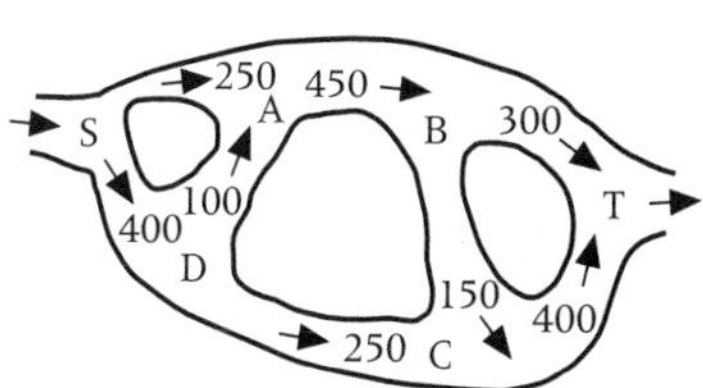

Capacities

Which single section of road could be improved to increase the traffic flow in the network?

Solution

By a bit of trial-and-error we can see that the maximum flow of vehicles from S to T is 600 per hour, achieved by flows along each road as indicated on the right.

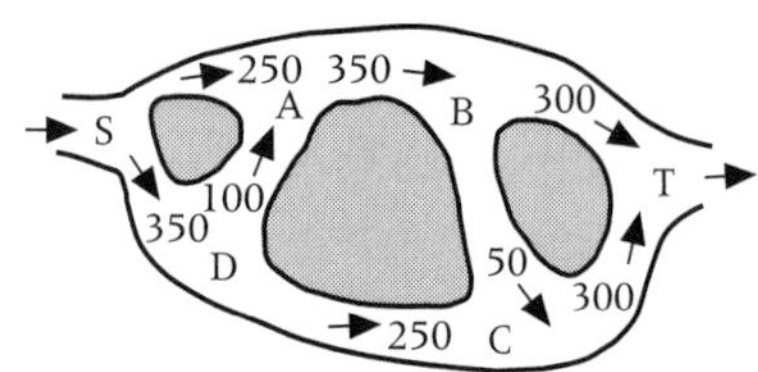

Maximum flow S to T

The improvement of several sections of road can improve this flow. For example, if the stretch SA had its capacity increased to 350 vehicles per hour, then the overall flow from S to T can be increased to 700 per hour: this is the best possible improvement by changing just one road.

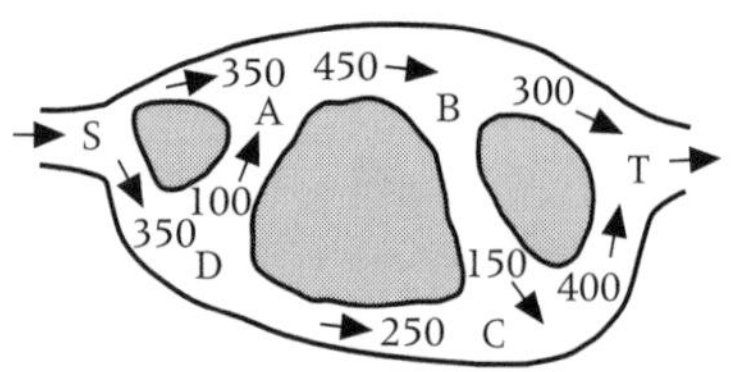

Maximum flow in improved road network

The road network in the previous example can be more easily analysed when drawn as a mathematical directed network, as shown. The arrows on the edges show the flow direction and the numbers show the **capacities** of the edges. The vertex S is called the **source** and the vertex T is called the **sink**. A **flow** from S to T consists of a number on each edge which does not exceed that edge's capacity and such that, at each intermediate vertex, in an obvious sense the **inflow** equals the **outflow**. The second figure shows a flow in the network: it has **value** 400.

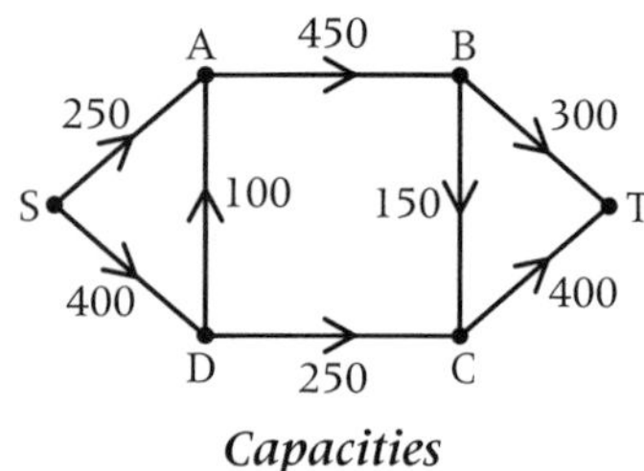

Capacities

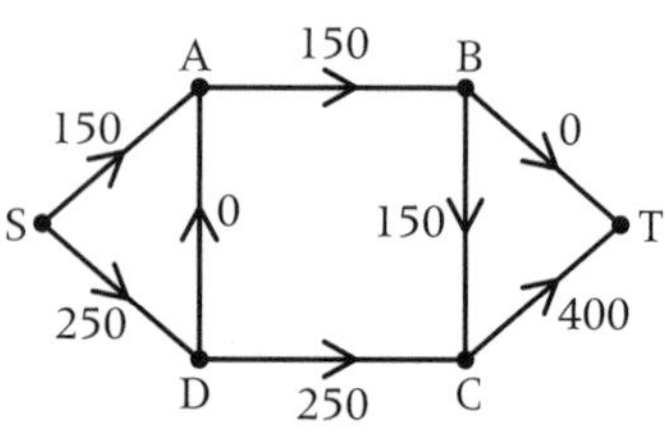

Flow of value 400
(Note: at verticies A, B, C, D inflow = outflow)

The purpose of the exercise was to find a flow from S to T which maximised the total outflow from S (which equals the inflow to T). That total is then referred to as the **maximum flow**. As we saw in the previous solution, this network has a maximum flow of 600 and it can be achieved as shown.

In achieving that maximum flow the edges SA, DA, DC and BT use their full capacities: they are said to be **saturated**.

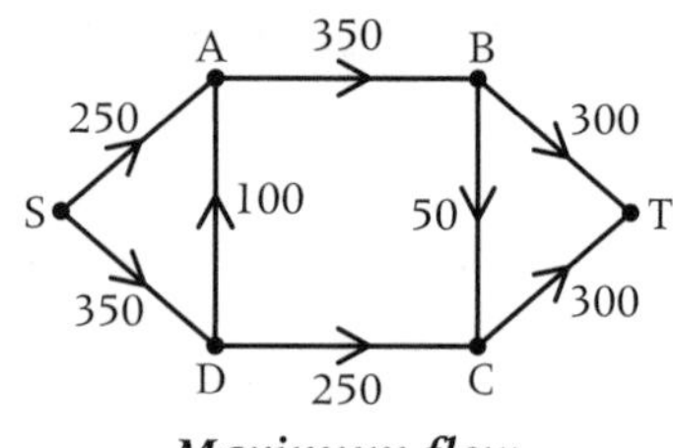

Maximum flow

For a (usually directed) network with a **source**, **sink** and a **capacity** on each edge, a **flow** is a number on each edge not exceeding its capacity which makes each vertex (apart from the source and sink) have the same inflow as outflow.

The **value** of the flow is the total outflow from the source, the problem generally being to maximise this to find a **maximum flow**.

Worked example 1.7

Find the maximum flow from S to T in this network:

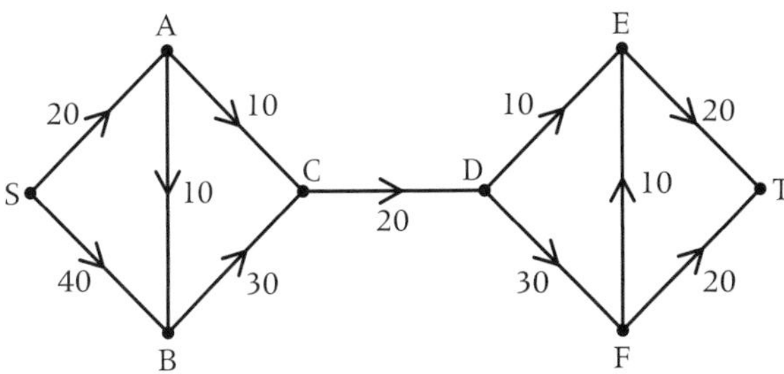

Solution

One obvious property of the given network is the 'bottleneck' from C to D. No matter how high the capacities are elsewhere, you will never exceed a flow of 20 from C to D and hence you will never exceed a flow of 20 overall from S to T. That maximum of 20 can be achieved in several ways, for example:

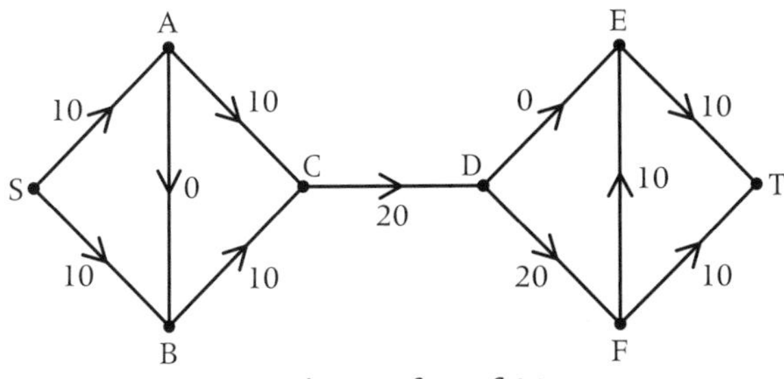

Maximum fow of 20

In any such example the edge CD is bound to be saturated.

Worked example 1.8

Find the maximum flow from S to T in this network:

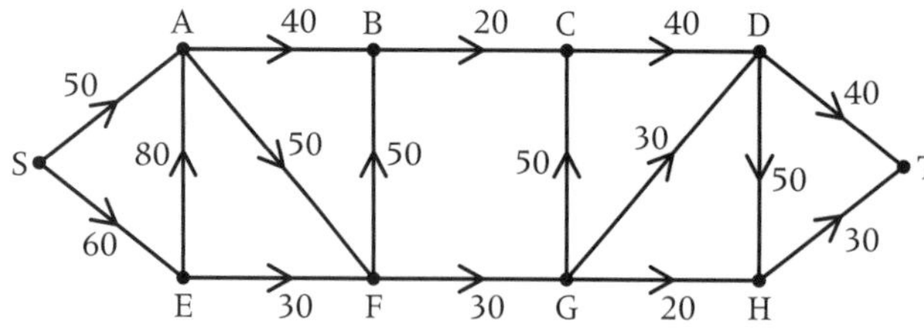

Solution

Although it is a little less obvious, this network also has a 'bottleneck' of sorts caused by the two edges BC and FG. (If this was a road system across a city, these could well be bridges over the river, for example.) No matter how high the other capacities are the flow from S to T cannot exceed the total flow across these two edges. Hence the flow from S to T can never exceed 20 + 30 = 50 and one way of reaching that maximum flow is:

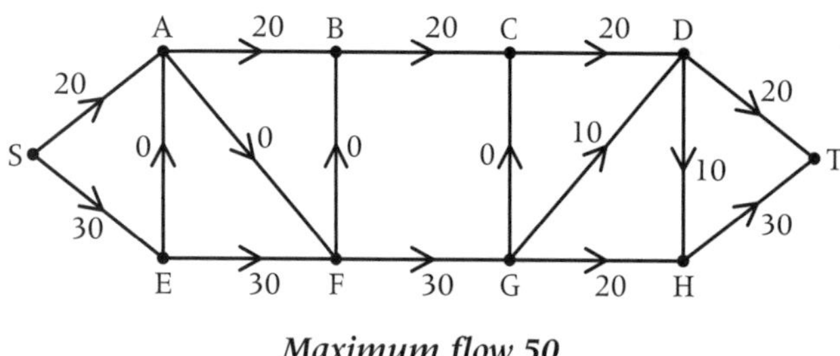

Maximum flow 50

In any such example BC and FG are bound to be saturated.

Cuts

The idea of looking for such 'bottlenecks' leads us to the concept of a **cut**. When trying to find flows from S to T in a network a **cut** is a collection of edges whose removal stops the possibility of any flow from S to T. In other words, if you cut them you would cut off the flow. In Worked example 1.7 the edge CD alone was a cut. (So the set of edges CD, DE would also be a cut but it is conventional not to include unnecessary edges like DE and to simply consider sets of edges which 'only just' cut the network. Alternatively the cut is given by the sets of vertices on each side, namely {S, A, B, C} and {D, E, F, T} in this case.) The **capacity of a cut** is the sum of the capacities of the edges used in the cut. So in Worked example 1.8 the cut BC, FG had capacity 20 + 30 = 50. The cut with the smallest capacity possible is called a **minimum cut** of the network.

A **cut** is a minimal set of edges whose removal would stop any flow from the source to the sink.

The **capacity** of a cut is the sum of the capacities of its edges. A **minimum cut** is a cut of the smallest possible capacity.

Worked exam question 1.5

For the network shown opposite:

1 list all the cuts
2 find the capacity of each cut
3 find the minimum cut and its capacity
4 find the maximum flow and show how it can be achieved.

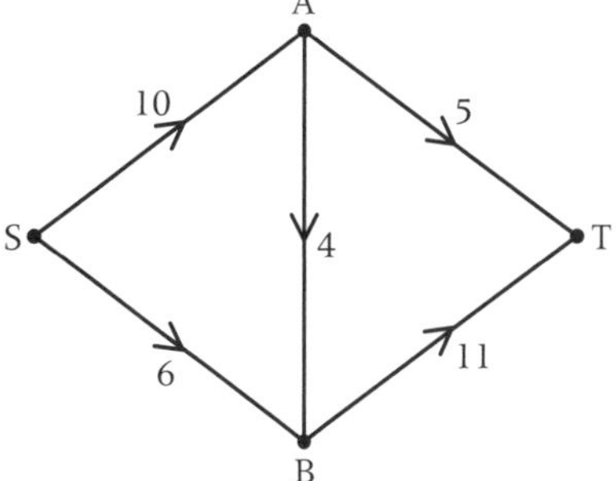

Solution

1 and **2** You can specify a cut by listing its edges or by specifying the two sets of disconnected vertices, but it is easier to illustrate cuts by a line in a picture of the network. The various cuts and their capacities in this case are:

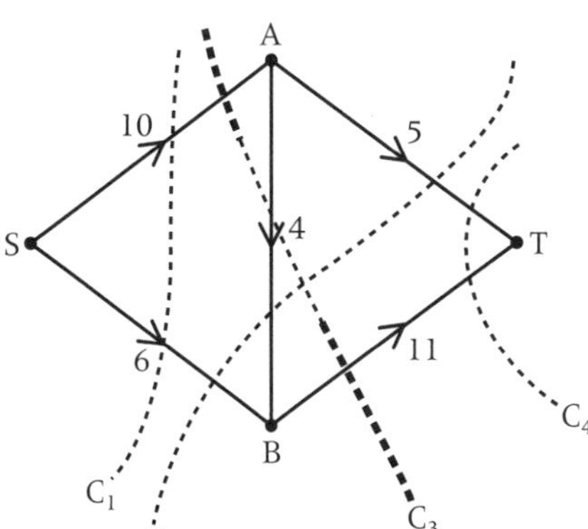

C_1: $10 + 6 = 16$
C_2: $6 + 4 + 5 = 15$
C_3: $10 + 11 = 21$
C_4: $5 + 11 = 16$

(Notice in the case of C_3 that it only includes SA and BT: there is no need to include AB as that is going the **wrong way** across the cut. Check for yourselves that the removal of SA and BT alone would leave a network with no possible flow from S to T.)

3 Hence the minimum cut is C_2 with a capacity of 15.

4 You could just use trial-and-error to find the maximum flow. However, if you bear in mind our work on 'bottlenecks' you might realise that our flow can never exceed the capacity of the minimum cut found in **3**, namely 15. Therefore we might hope for a maximum flow of 15. Certainly no higher is possible because no more than 15 can cross the cut C_2.

You might also suspect that the minimum cut found in **3** is bound to have all its edges saturated in any maximum flow. Therefore to achieve the maximum flow we would saturate the edges of C_2 (SB, AB and AT) and it is then easy to fill in the rest to get the maximum flow of 15 as shown:

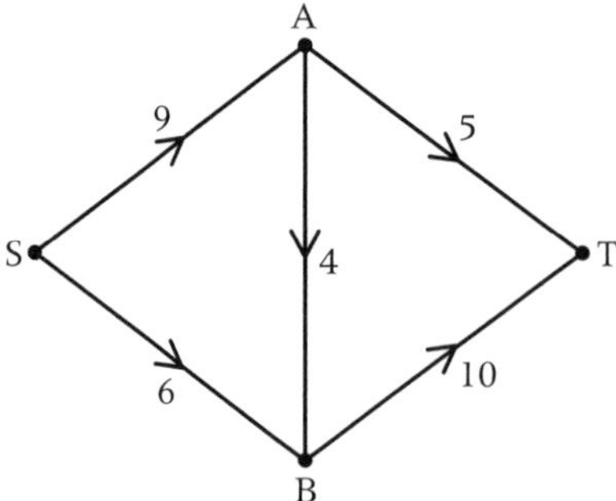

It is clear that if you take any such network, any flow in it, and any cut of it, then that flow has got to go across that cut and so:

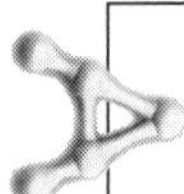

value of the flow $\leqslant$ capacity of the cut

Basically, the value of every flow is less than or equal to the capacity of every cut. If by chance you manage to find a flow whose value equals the capacity of some cut then that flow must be the maximum possible and that cut must the minimum possible.

Worked exam question 1.6

For the network illustrated:

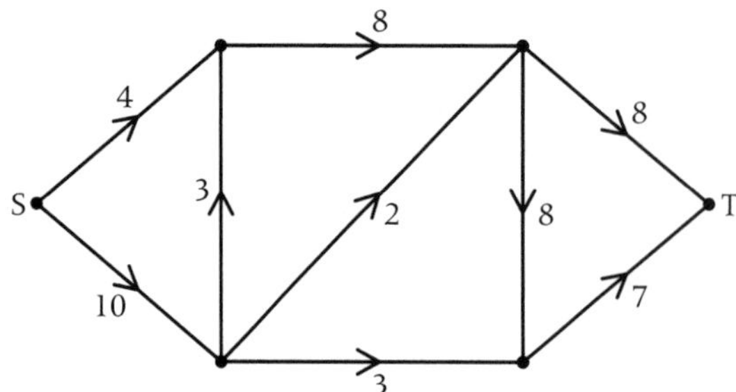

1 Find a minimum cut.

2 Find a flow of value 12.

3 Explain how you can be sure, without calculating any further flows, that your flow in **2** gives a maximum flow.

Solution

1 Searching through lots of cuts can be quite tricky, but here the examiner has tried to be kind by having noticeably lower capacities on the relevant edges. The minimum cut is as shown – it has a capacity of 12:

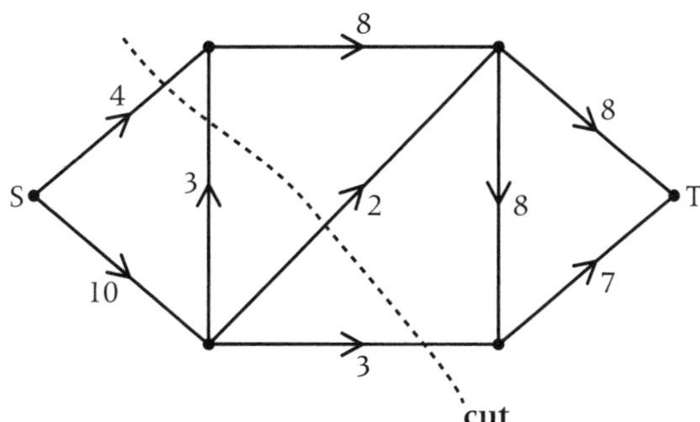

2 To achieve a flow of 12 we shall have to saturate each edge of the cut found in **1**, as shown on the left below:

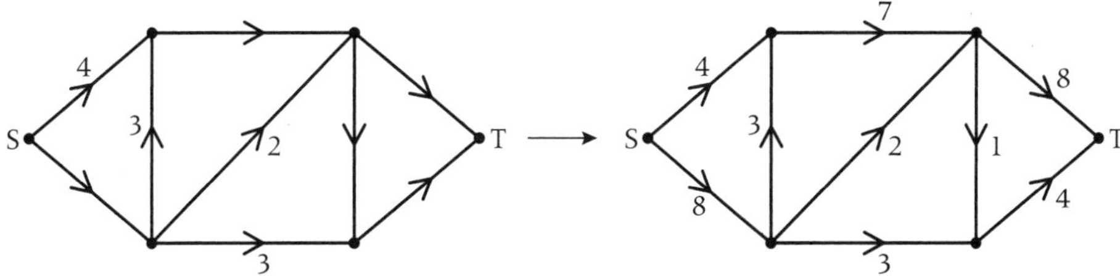

Then it is easy to fill in the flows in the other edges to make inflow = outflow at the intermediate vertices, as shown on the right above. This gives a flow of value 12 as required.

3 Any flow will have to cross that cut of capacity 12 and so there is no way that a flow can exceed 12. Hence the flow of value 12 found in **2** must be a maximum flow.

In all our examples not only has it been the case that:

every flow $\leqslant$ every cut

but also there has always been a value where the two come together; i.e. a flow whose value actually coincides with the capacity of a cut. Because of the above inequality it follows that this flow is bound to be a maximum flow and the cut is bound to be a minimum cut. It is a major theorem that in any network the two are **bound** to come together somewhere; in other words it is always the case that:

The max flow–min cut theorem

maximum flow = minimum cut

Furthermore, for any maximum flow all the edges of the minimum cut will be saturated.

Finding maximum flows by flow augmentation

Our technique so far to find a maximum flow has been to compare cuts and flows and use a little logic, and for small networks that is usually quite sufficient. However, in more complex networks the usual technique for building up to a maximum flow is by starting with any flow and **augmenting** it.

Worked example 1.9

The figure on the left shows the capacities in a network and the figure on the right shows a flow of value 24.

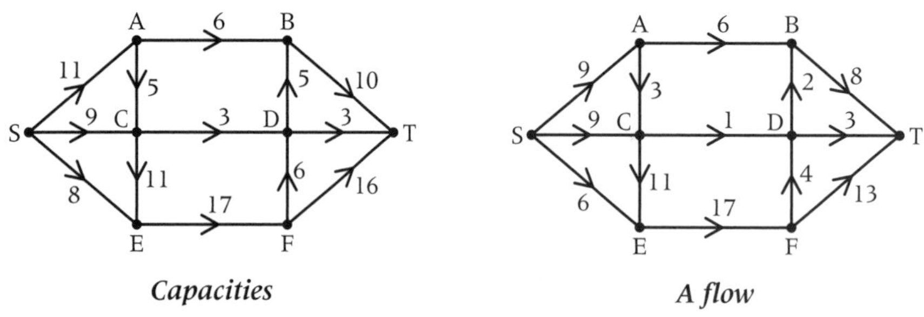

Capacities *A flow*

Show how to increase the flow to a maximum flow of 26.

Solution

If we redraw the flow and mark each edge with its remaining **potential flow** (i.e. capacity–current flow) we get:

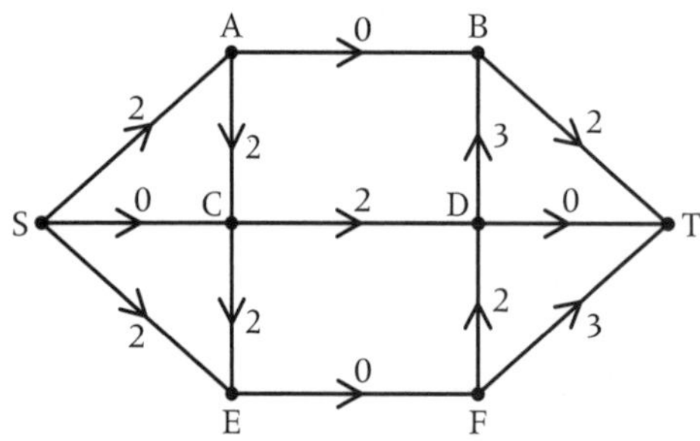

The edges with 0s on them are the saturated edges: can you see a path from S to T which only uses unsaturated edges? The edges of the path SACDBT all go in the right direction and are unsaturated. In fact each of them has a potential flow of at least 2. So you can add a flow of 2 along that path to change the overall flow to:

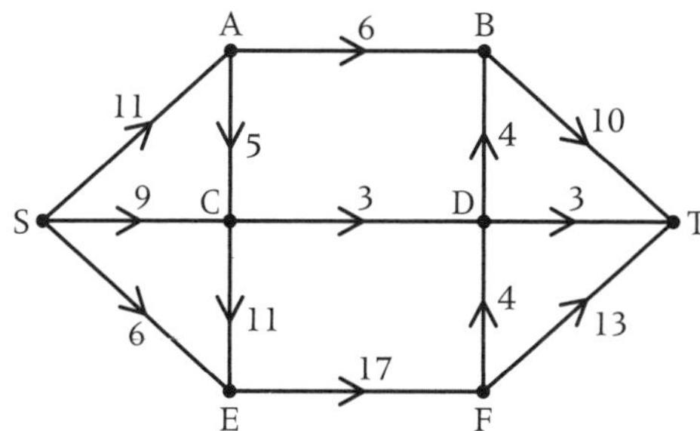

That gives a flow of 26 and, as the cut AB, CD, EF is saturated, the flow of 26 is a maximum.

In that example the path SACDBT is called a **flow augmenting path**. Given the network on the left below and the flow shown on the right, can you see any obvious flow augmenting path?

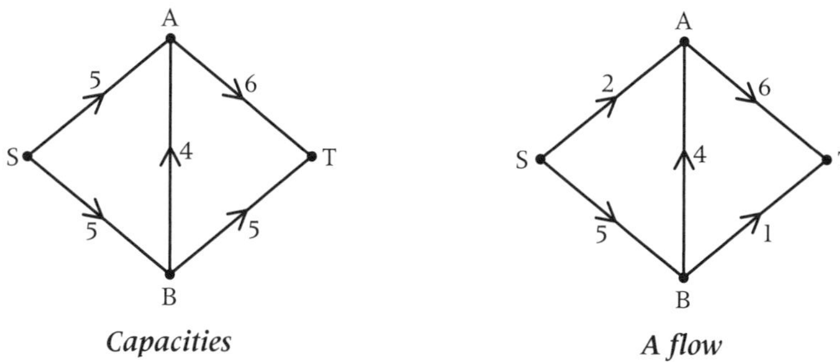

Capacities *A flow*

This time it is not so obvious and we shall return to the problem in a moment. To apply the process of flow augmentation some special labelling is necessary. Given a flow in a network, if we wish to use a flow augmenting process we shall replace the original labelling on each edge by the two following items:

> the current flow, with a backward arrow – this is called the **potential backflow**;
>
> the spare capacity, with a forward arrow – this is called the **potential flow**.

e.g. a flow of 6 in an edge of capacity 9 would be shown as:

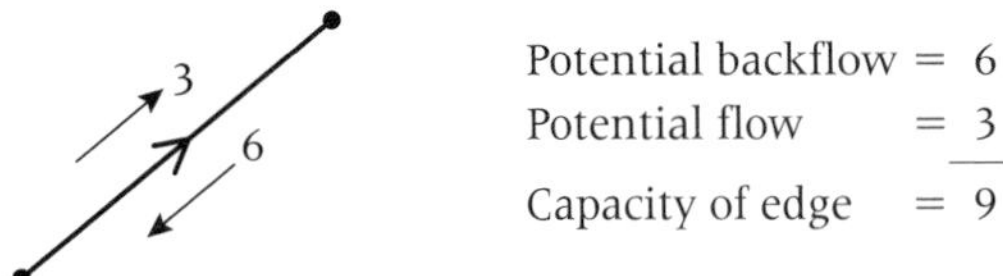

For example, let us return to the network and flow given above:

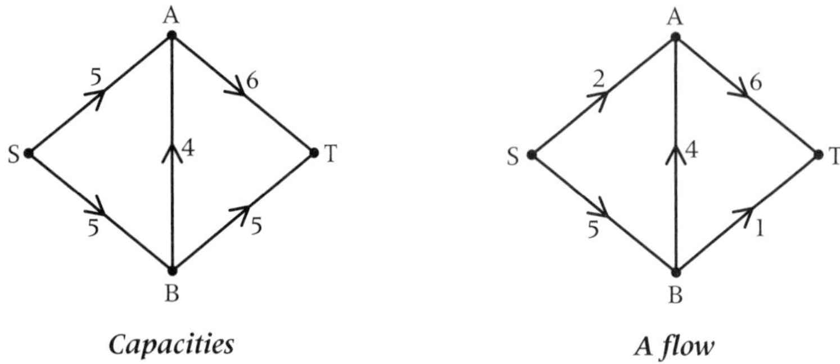

Capacities ***A flow***

With our new labelling these two pictures can be amalgamated into one:

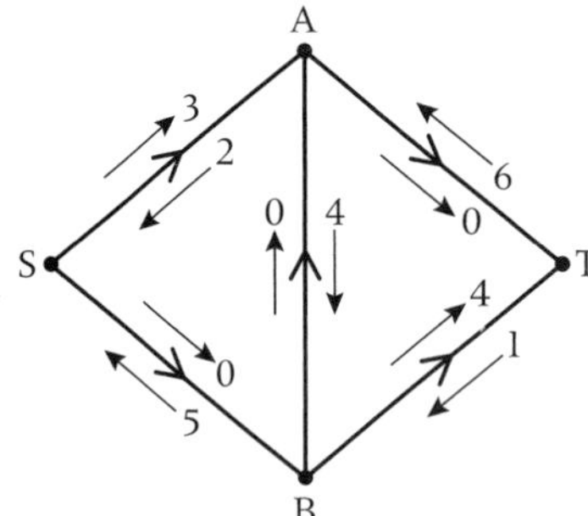

Now to use a flow-augmenting path you can go from S to T following positive numbers along any of the new arrows. For example you can add 3 along the path SABT – there are arrows of 3 or more in the right direction on each of those edges. That augmentation would change the arrows along the route by ±3 in the following way:

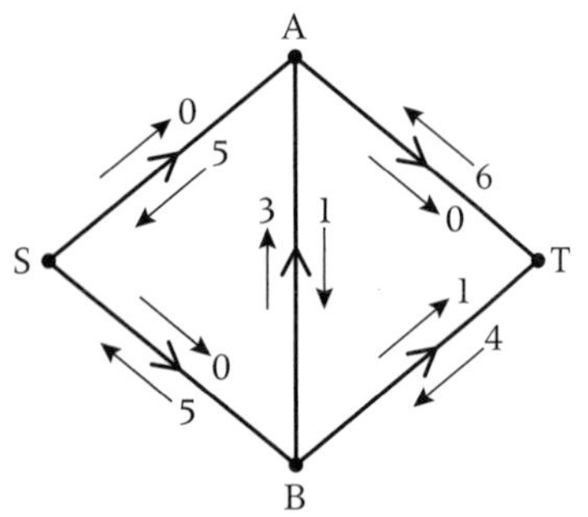

Along the edges used in their original direction: potential flow decreased by 3 potential backflow increased by 3

Along the edge used against their original direction: potential backflow decreased by 3 potential flow increased by 3

What we have actually done is to increase the value of the flow by increasing the flow by 3 along SA and BT and paradoxically by **decreasing** the flow along BA by 3. That flow-augmenting process would be very hard to spot without our new labelling. Now in that last picture there is no further path of positive numbers on arrows from S to T and so we have reached the maximum flow. Changing the labelling back to its traditional form gives:

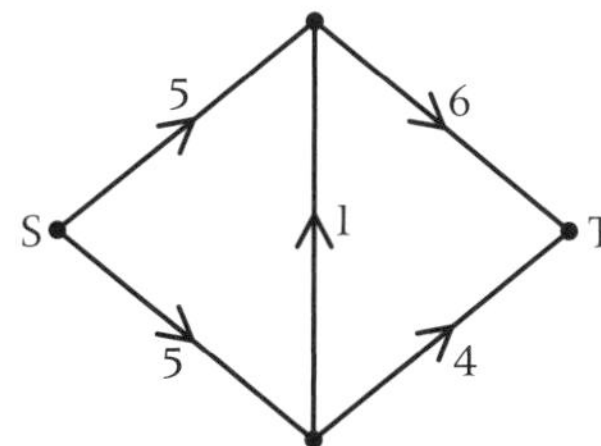

Maximum flow of 10

Flow-augmenting paths can be used to find systematically the maximum flow, starting if necessary from zero flow. To do this each edge must be labelled with its **potential backflow** and its **potential flow**. Then a flow-augmenting path is a path of arrows with positive numbers from source to sink.

We shall now work through one long example of building up to a maximum flow by flow augmentation.

Worked example 1.10

Use a flow augmenting process to find a maximum flow in the network illustrated.

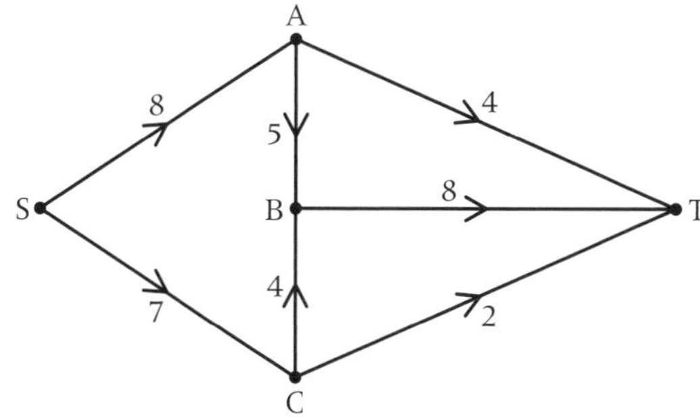

Solution

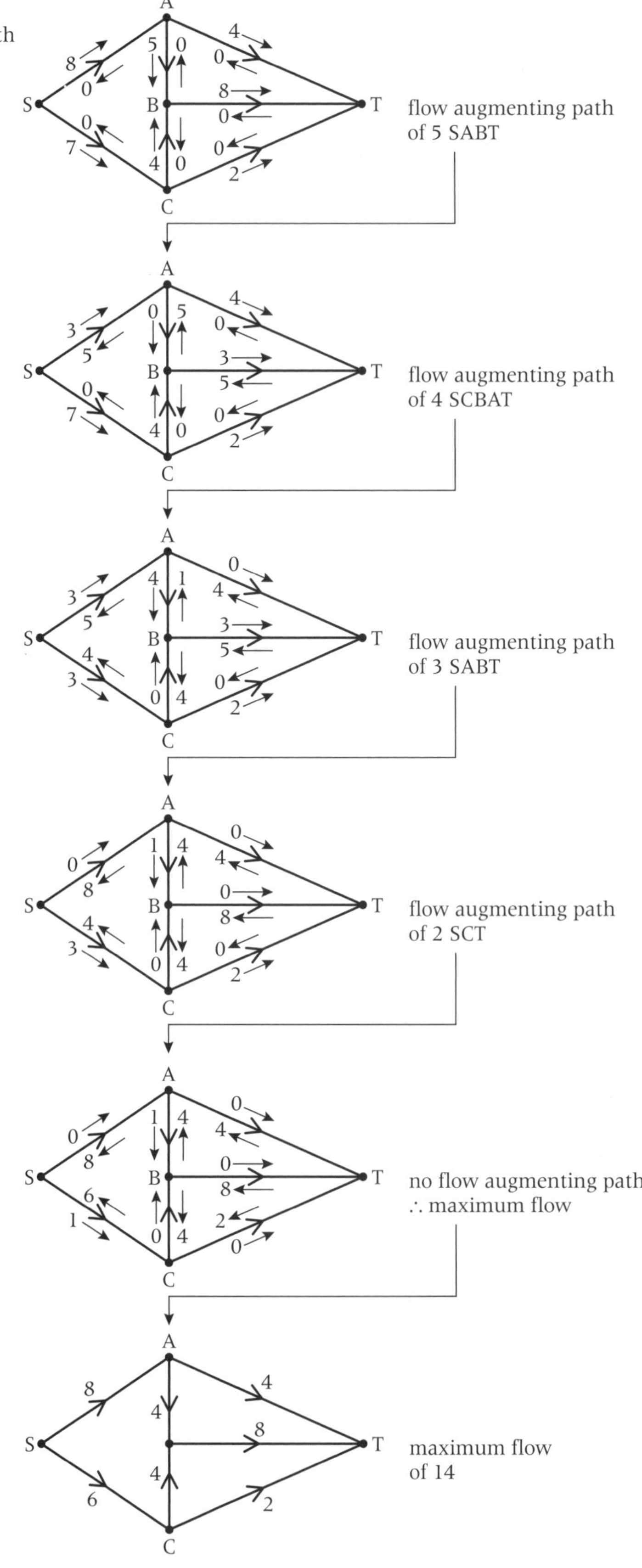
Start with
0 flow
A
S
B
T
C
flow augmenting path
of 5 SABT
flow augmenting path
of 4 SCBAT
flow augmenting path
of 3 SABT
flow augmenting path
of 2 SCT
no flow augmenting path
∴ maximum flow
maximum flow
of 14

Some extensions

Sometimes you may wish to find the maximum flow in an undirected network; in other words the capacities are known but the flows can be in either direction along each edge. All the theories of flows and cuts extend easily to this situation. When using a flow-augmenting process in an undirected network you have to adjust the potential flow and backflow labelling accordingly. For example, given a flow of 6 in an undirected edge of capacity 10, the flow can be increased by up to 4 or decreased by up to **16** (to give a flow of 10 in the opposite direction).

This section started with an example of traffic entering and leaving a network of roads. In that example there was just one entry-point (the source) and one exit-point (the sink). We conclude this section by commenting that in most practical situations there is more than one source and more than one sink. However, our theory easily extends to such cases by the introduction of dummy **super sources** and **super sinks**. Our final example should make it clear how these work and how our theory extends to undirected networks.

Worked exam question 1.7

The network opposite represents the road system in an ancient walled city. Traffic can only enter or leave the city at the westerly points W_1 and W_2 and the easterly points E_1, E_2 and E_3. The number on each road represents the maximum total number of cars per hour which can use that road. What is the maximum number of cars which in one hour could enter the city at a westerly point and leave it an easterly point?

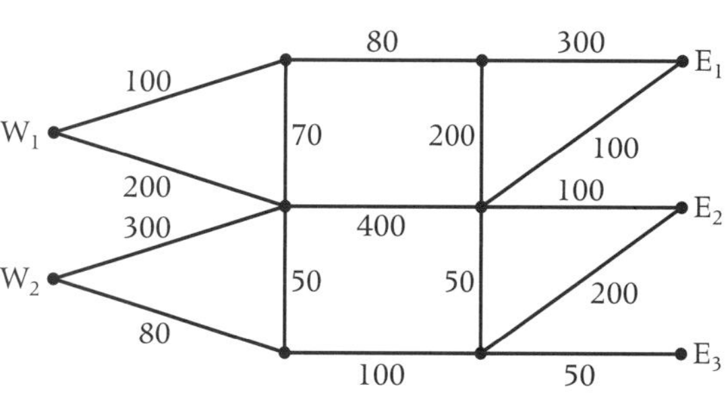

Solution

The maximum total per hour that can enter at W_1 is 300 (100 + 200) and so we add a dummy edge from a new source S to W_1 of capacity 300. Repeating this for W_2 and doing a corresponding thing from each E_i to a new sink T gives:

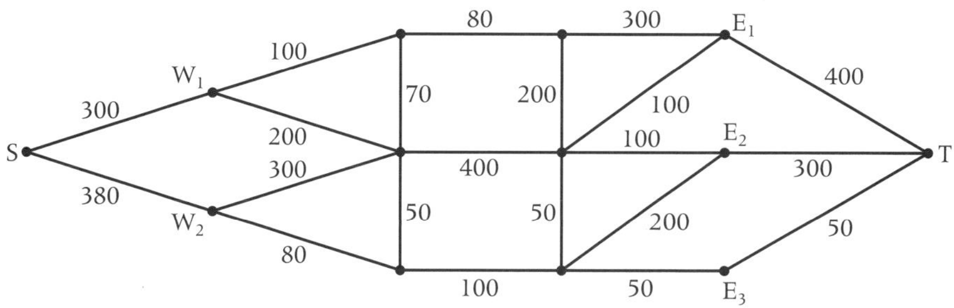

It is clear that a flow from west to east in the original network is exactly equivalent to a flow from S to T in this new network. The new point S is called a **super source** and the new point T is called a **super sink**.

Now to find the maximum flow in this new network we can either use the theory of cuts or a flow-augmenting process. In this case it is not hard to spot the cut of capacity 580 (= 80 + 400 + 100) formed by the three west-east roads across the middle. Then saturating each of those edges (from west to east) enables us to build up easily to a maximum flow of 580, for example as illustrated:

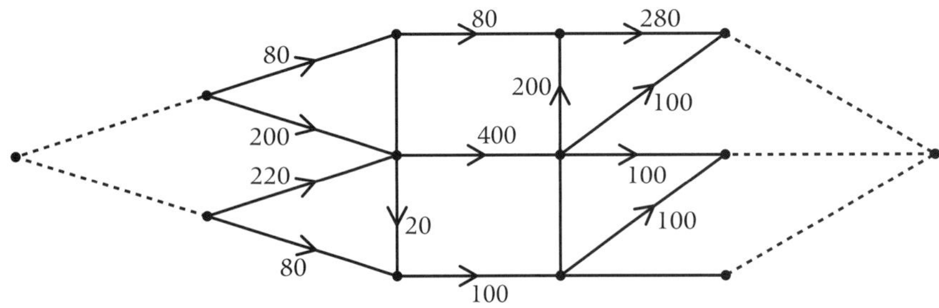

EXERCISE 1C

1 Find a minimum cut and maximum flow for each of these networks:

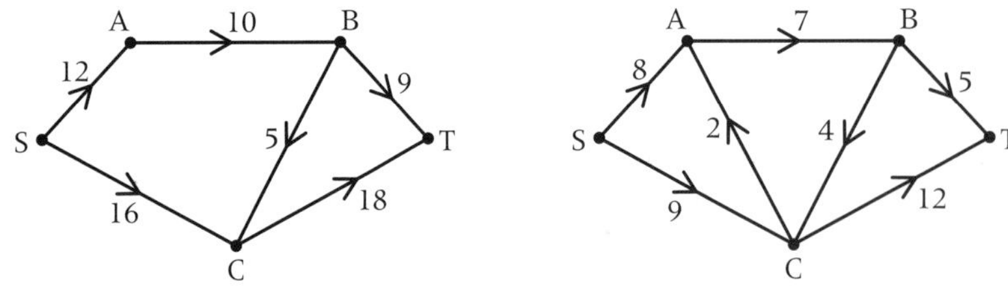

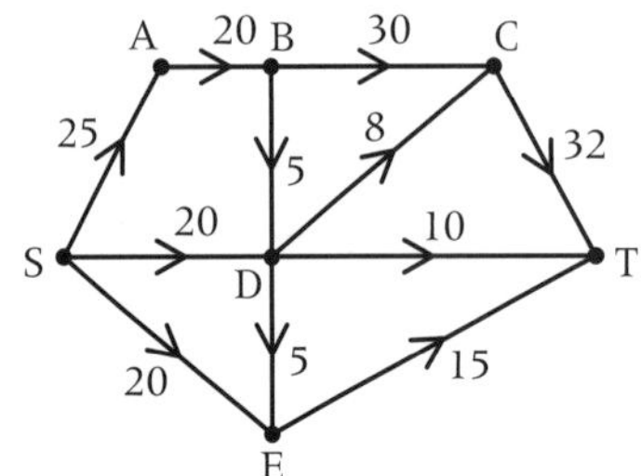

2 A directed network has edges with maximum capacities as shown in this table.

From \ To	A	B	C	D	E	T
S	40	40	–	–	–	–
A	–	–	–	15	20	–
B	–	–	45	–	–	–
C	–	–	–	–	–	50
D	–	10	15	–	–	15
E	–	–	–	–	–	25

The letters refer to vertices of the network, where S and T are the source and sink respectively.

Draw a diagram of the network.

Find a maximum flow for the network, labelling each edge with its actual flow. [A]

3 Use a flow-augmenting process to find maximum flows in the following networks:

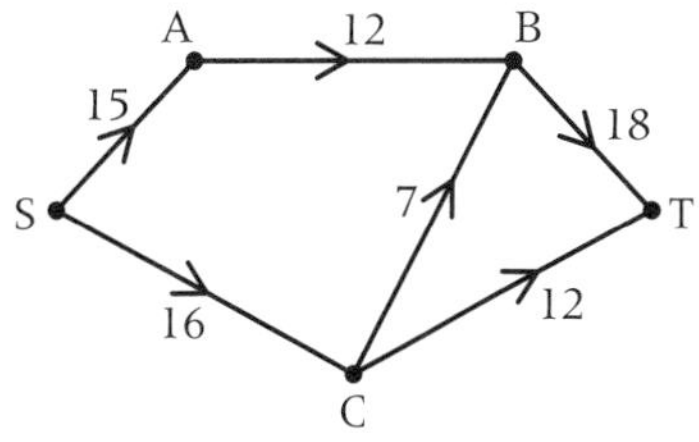

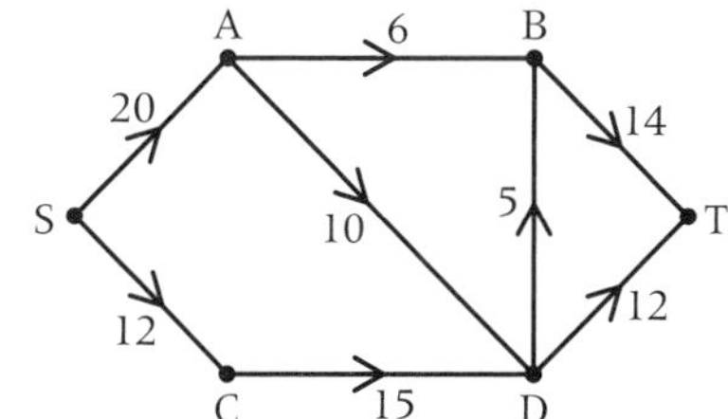

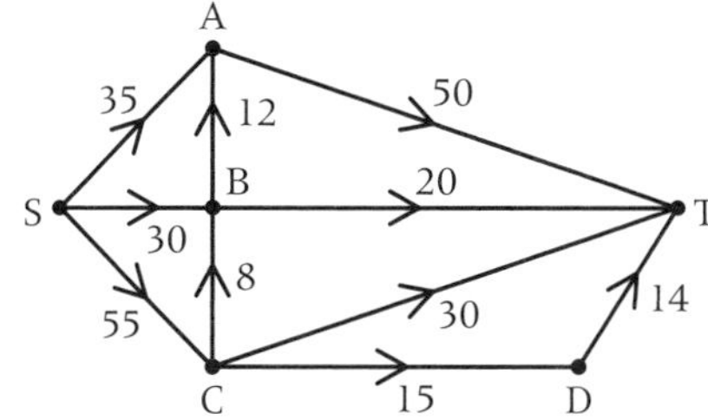

4 There are a number of road routes from town A to town B as shown in the diagram opposite. The numbers show the maximum flow rate of vehicles in hundreds per hour. Find the maximum flow rate of vehicles from A to B. Suggest a single road section which could be widened to improve its flow rate. How does this affect traffic flow on other sections, if the network operates to its new capacity?

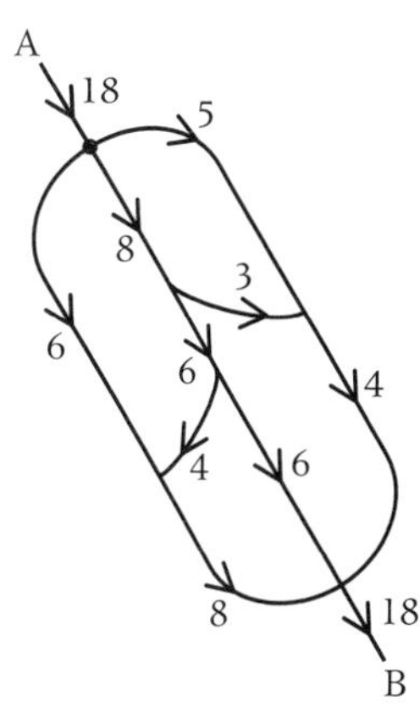

[A]

5 The diagram shows a directed flow network with two numbers on each edge, the capacity of the edge and, circled, the flow currently passing through the edge.

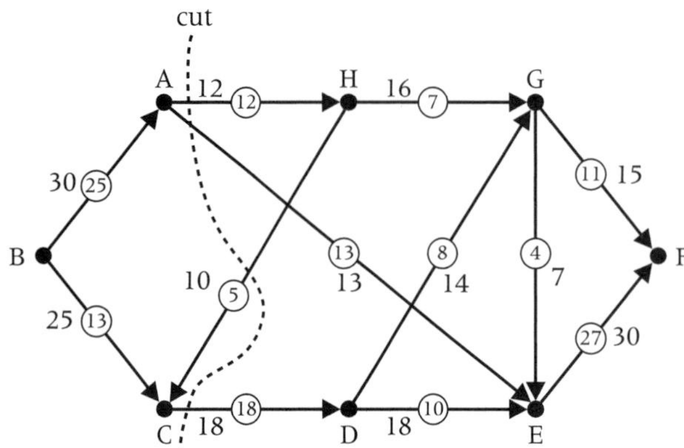

(a) Identify the source and the sink.

(b) What is meant by a *cut*? What is the capacity of the cut indicated?

(c) Find and indicate one flow augmenting path, and use it to augment the flow as far as is possible.

(d) Is the flow now maximal? If not use flow augmentation to find the maximal flow. Draw a diagram showing your maximal flow.

(e) Explain how you can tell whether the flow in part **(d)** is maximal. [A]

6 The matrix represents the capacities of roads (in thousands of cars per hour) in a road network connecting seven towns.

	A	B	C	D	E	F	G
A	–	2	2	–	–	1	–
B	2	–	–	5	1	–	–
C	2	–	–	1	–	3	–
D	–	5	1	–	–	1	1
E	–	1	–	–	–	–	1
F	1	–	3	1	–	–	1
G	–	–	–	1	1	1	–

road capacities

(a) Draw the road network.

(b) Find the maximum hourly flow of cars from B to F, showing how this may be achieved. Prove that this is a maximum. [A]

7 A travel agent is asked by a youth organisation to try to organise coach transportation between London and Manchester for a musical extravaganza. He obtains from the coach operator the daily maximum capacity of coaches between various appropriate cities (in terms of hundreds of people). These are shown in the table.

From \ To	London	Leicester	Nottingham	Birmingham	Oxford	Manchester
London	–	–	–	30	15	–
Leicester	–	–	8	–	–	5
Nottingham	–	–	–	–	–	25
Birmingham	–	10	4	–	–	20
Oxford	–	–	10	15	–	–

(a) Draw a network showing the capacities.

(b) Find the maximum number of people that can be transported by coach from London to Manchester in a day.

(c) On a given day there is a strike at Nottingham coach station so that no coaches may use it.
Find the maximum number of people that can be transported from London to Manchester on that day. [A]

8 A manufacturing company has two factories, F_1 and F_2, and wishes to transport its products to three warehouses, W_1, W_2 and W_3. The capacities of the various possible routes are shown in the diagram.

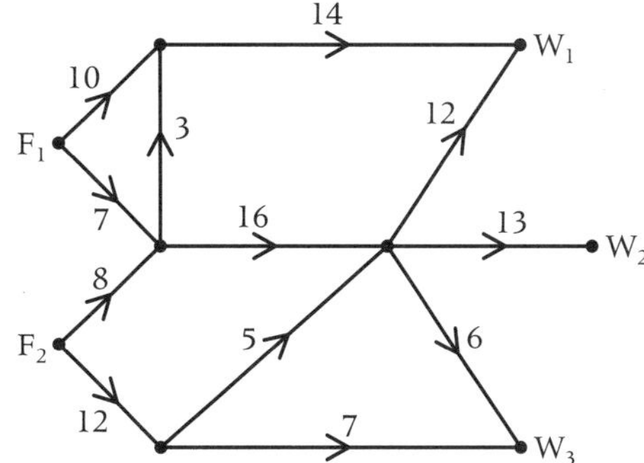

(a) By adding a source, S, and a sink, T, find the maximum number of products that can be transported.

(b) Interpret your flow pattern giving
(i) the number of products leaving F_1 and F_2
(ii) the number of products reaching W_1, W_2 and W_3. [A]

MIXED EXERCISES

1 Find a minimum cut and maximum flow for each of these networks:

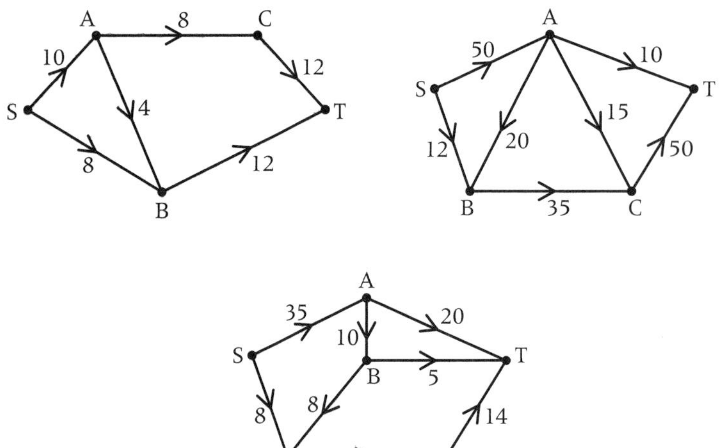

2 Use flow augmentation to find maximum flows from S to T in the following networks:

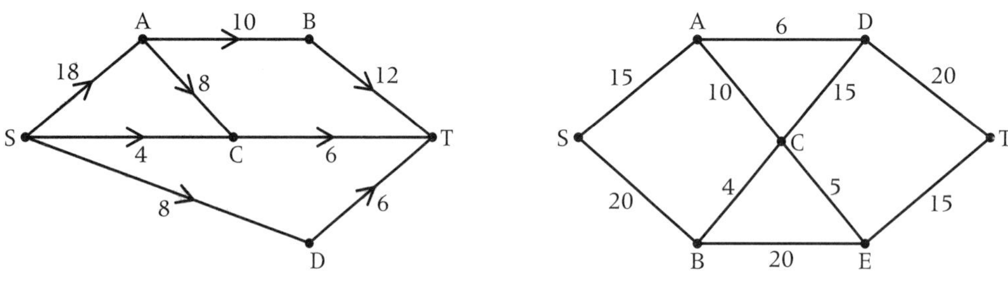

3 Following a storm, all the roads in a village have to be checked for fallen trees. The streets link five locations, A, B, C, D and E. The lengths of the streets, in metres, are given in the table.

	A	B	C	D	E
A	–	20	60	–	45
B	20	–	50	70	–
C	60	50	–	50	–
D	–	70	50	–	40
E	45	–	–	40	–

Find the minimum length route starting and finishing at A. Give the length of this route. [A]

4 In the algorithm for the Chinese postperson problem you have to consider all possible pairings of the vertices of odd degree.

(a) Why is there an even number of odd vertices?

(b) With four odd vertices there are three possible pairings (AB/CD, AC/BD, AD/BC). How many pairings are there of six vertices? How many for eight?

(c) Can you spot the pattern for the number of pairings of $2n$ vertices? [The full solution will be dealt with in Chapter 3 on recurrence relations – see Exercise 3B, Question 4.]

5 The diagram shows a housing estate with the length in metres of each road. The postman's round must begin and end at A, and must take him along each section of road at least once. What is the minimum distance he must walk?

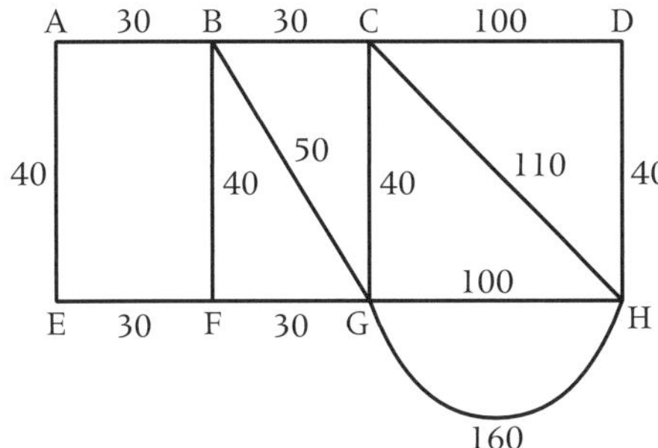

6 By creating a super source and a super sink find a maximum flow for this network which shows maximum capacities.

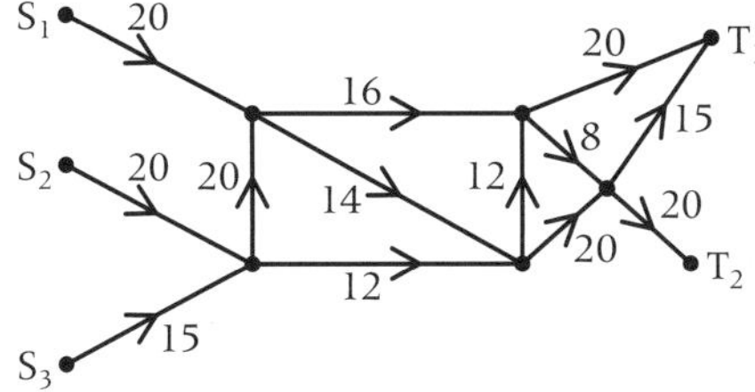

7 A railway track inspector wishes to inspect all the tracks shown in the diagram opposite, starting and finishing at the base B (distances shown in km).

Explain why this cannot be done without going over some sections of track more than once, and find the shortest route the inspector can take.

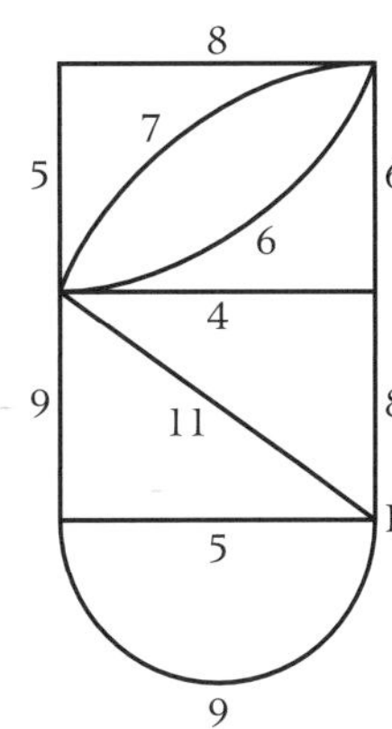

8 A sales rep based in Bristol has to visit shops in each of seven other towns before returning to her base. The distances in miles between the towns are as shown in the diagram below.

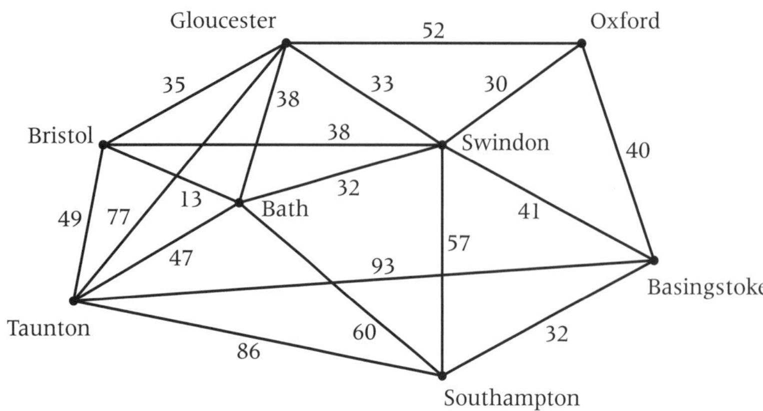

(a) Find one Hamiltonian cycle in the network, and calculate its length.

(b) Find a minimum connector of the network with Bristol deleted.

(c) State upper and lower bounds for the distance the rep will have to travel. [A]

9 Find a maximum traffic flow on this grid-type road system from X to Y, in which maximum flow rates are given in hundred of vehicles per hour.

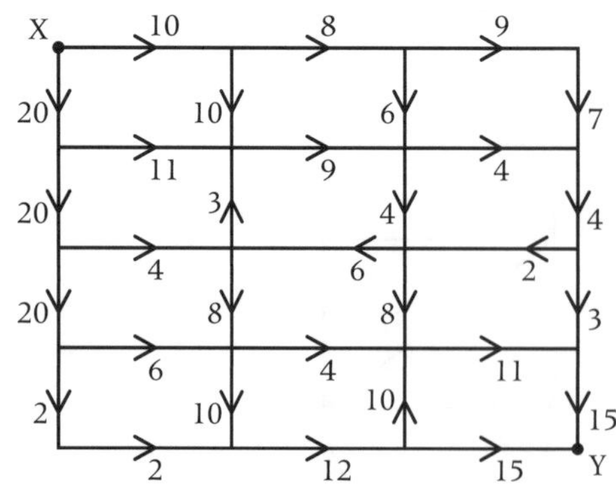

10 A delivery van based at A is required to deliver goods in towns B, C, D, E shown in the diagram. The numbers on the edges are the distances in miles.

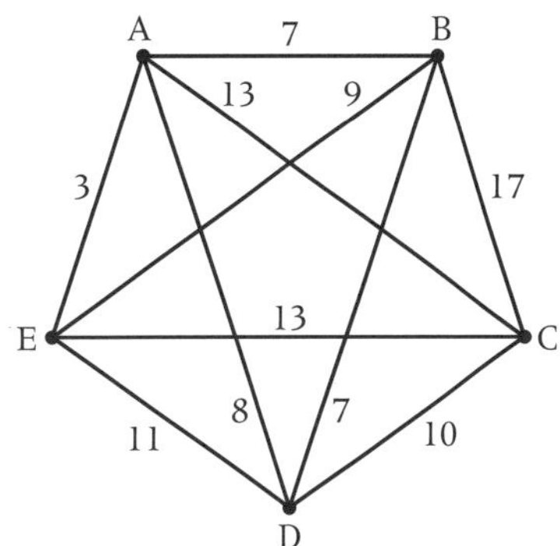

(a) Use the nearest neighbour algorithm to find one possible route for the delivery van.

(b) Find a minimum connector of the network with A excluded.

(c) Use **(a)** and **(b)** to find upper and lower bounds for the distance the delivery van will have to travel.

[A]

11

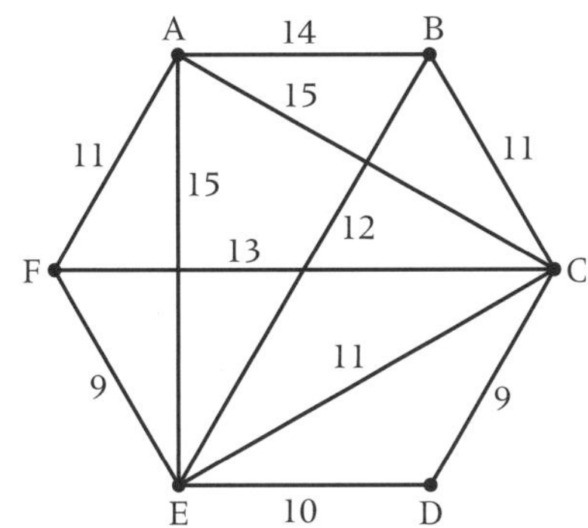

(a) Find a minimum connector of this network with A deleted. Hence find a lower bound for the length of the shortest Hamiltonian cycle in the original network.

(b) By looking at your minimum connector's structure, find a shorter Hamiltonian cycle in the given network.

12 The table shows the daily maximum capacity of coaches between various cities (in hundreds of people).

Draw a network to show the capacities of the routes from London through to Newcastle. A festival is taking place in Newcastle. Find the maximum number of people who can travel by coach from London for the festival. Investigate what happens when there is a strike at Liverpool coach station.

From \ To	London	Birmingham	Manchester	Leeds	Liverpool	Newcastle
London	–	40	–	20	–	–
Birmingham	–	–	10	15	12	–
Manchester	–	–	–	12	–	15
Leeds	–	–	–	–	–	30
Liverpool	–	–	7	–	–	8

[A]

13 Consider the following network, where each arc is labelled with its capacity.

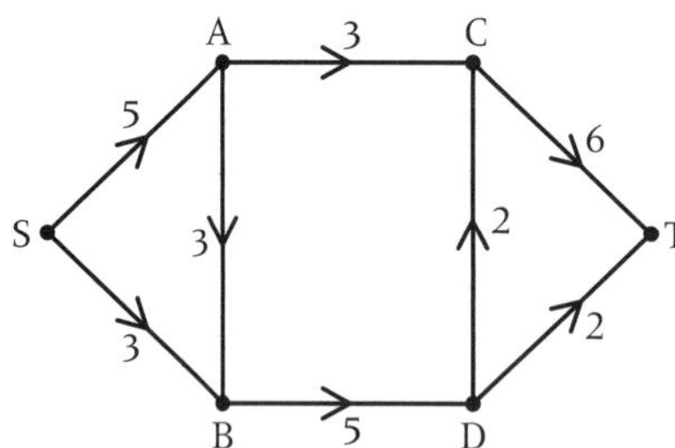

(a) Find a flow of value 7, and draw a diagram showing the flow in each arc.

(b) Find a cut of capacity 7.

(c) What is the value of a maximum flow?

(In part **(c)**, you should give a brief reason for your answer.) [A]

14 Verify that the max flow – min cut theorem holds for the following network:

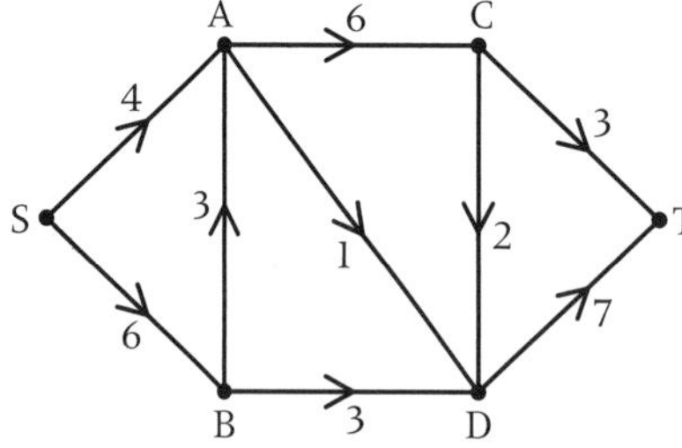

15 The diagram opposite shows a gas distribution network consisting of three supply points, A, B and C, three intermediate pumping stations, P, Q and R, two delivery points, X and Y, and connecting pipes. The figures on the arcs are measures of the amounts of gas which may be passed through each pipe per day. The figures by A, B and C are measures of the daily availability of gas at the supply points.

(a) Copy the network, introducing a single source with links to A, B and C, the capacities on the links showing the supply availabilities.

(b) Introduce a single sink linked to X and Y. Give appropriate capacities to the links.

(c) Find the maximal daily flow through your network, making a list of the flows through each pipe.

(d) Find a suitable cut to prove that your flow in part **(c)** is maximal.

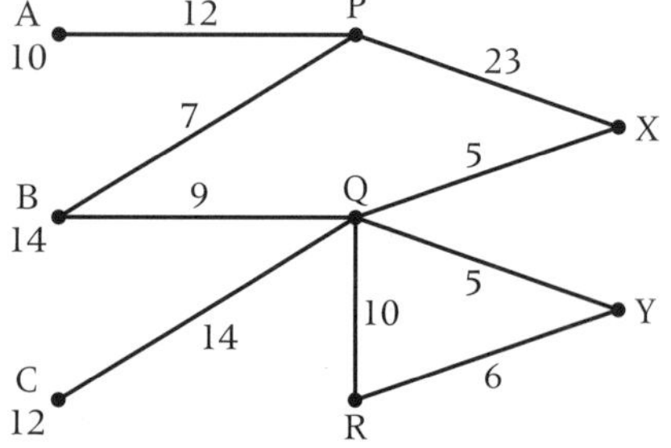

(e) Interpret the flows in the new links, from the source and to the sink.

(f) A new pipeline is constructed with capacity 6 units per day, connecting P and Q.
Use a new labelling procedure to augment the flow, and thus find the new maximal flow. [A]

16 (a) In the following basic network, find a flow of value k from S to T, and cut with capacity k, for the same value of k.

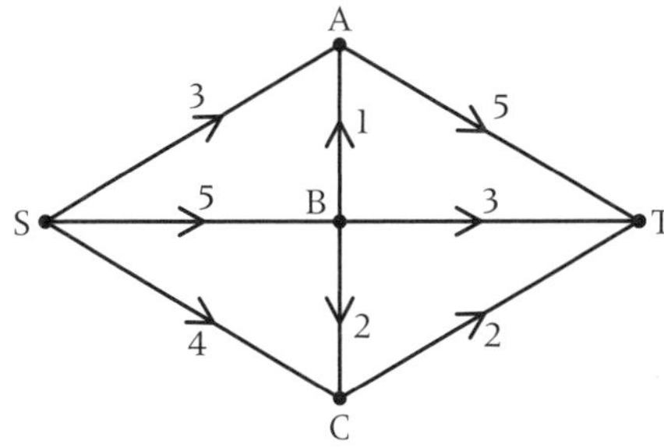

(b) Is the flow in part **(a)** a maximum flow?
(Give a reason for your answer.) [A]

17 The map shows a number of roads in a housing estate. Road intersections are labelled with capital letters and the distances in metres between intersections are shown. The total length of all the roads in the estate is 2300 m.

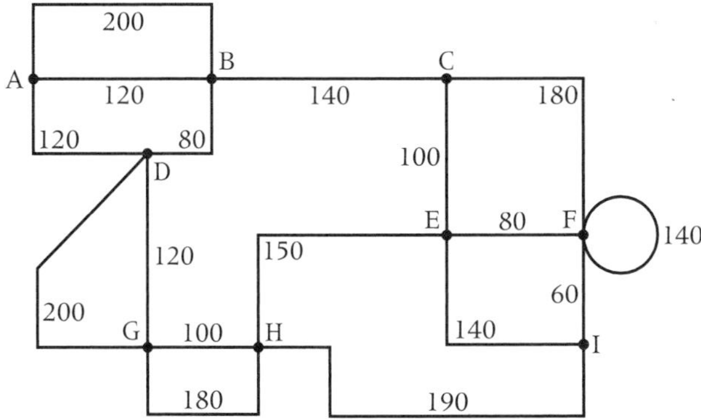

(a) A newspaper deliverer has to walk along each road at least once, starting and ending at A. By investigating all possible pairings of odd intersections, find the minimum distance which the newspaper deliverer has to walk.
(You should show the distance computations which lead to you choosing a particular pairing of odd intersections.)

For each intersection other than A, give the number of times that the newspaper deliverer must pass through that intersection whilst following the shortest route.

(b) The newspaper deliverer only calls at a proportion of houses. The postwoman has to call at most houses, and since the roads are too wide to cross continually back and forth, she finds it necessary to walk along each road twice, once along each side. She requires a route to achieve this in the minimum distance. Describe how to produce a network to model this problem. Without drawing such a network, say why it will be traversable and calculate the minimum length of road along which the postwoman will have to walk.

(c) The streetcleaner needs to drive his vehicle along both sides of each road. He has to drive on the correct side of the road at all times. He too would like a shortest route. Explain how the streetcleaner's problem differs from the postwoman's, and say how the network would have to be modified to model this. [A]

18 The network below shows the maximum rates of flow (in vehicles per hour) between towns S, A, B, C, D and T in the direction from S to T.

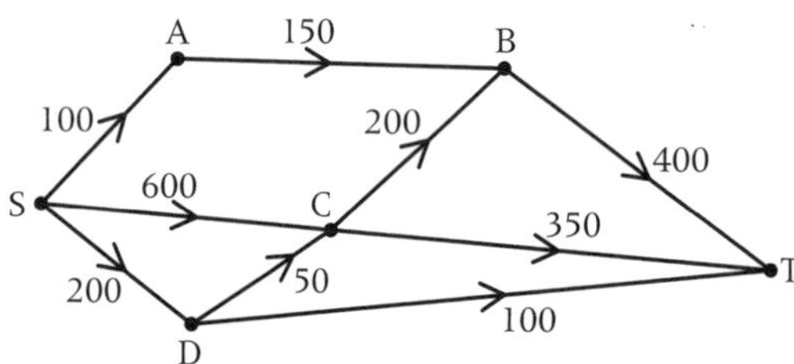

(a) By choosing a minimum cut, or otherwise, find the maximum traffic flow from S to T. Give the actual rates of flow in each of the edges BT, CT and DT when this maximum flow occurs.

(b) When a maximum flow occurs from S to T, how many of those vehicles per hour pass through C?

(c) It is decided to reduce the traffic flow through C (in the direction from S to T) to a maximum of 480 vehicles per hour. In order to maintain the same maximum flow from S to T the capacity of a single edge is to be increased. Which edge should be chosen, and by how much must its capacity be increased? [A]

19 The distances between the greens and the clubhouse at a nine-hole golf course are as follows: each is linked by a footpath of the given lengths.

	CH	**1**	**2**	**3**	**4**	**5**	**6**	**7**	**8**	**9**
1	250	–	350	50	200	350	550	400	200	300
2	600	350	–	300	600	200	200	150	350	600
3	400	50	300	–	300	150	500	300	100	400
4	100	200	600	300	–	400	750	550	350	100
5	500	350	200	150	400	–	350	250	50	500
6	800	550	200	500	750	350	–	150	400	850
7	600	400	150	300	550	250	150	–	250	600
8	350	200	350	100	350	50	400	250	–	350
9	50	300	600	400	100	500	850	600	350	–

The groundsman wants to visit each green once and return to the clubhouse.

(a) Use the nearest neighbour algorithm to find one possible route for the groundsman.

(b) Consider the nine greens (without the clubhouse). What is the minimum length of footpath that will connect them together?

(c) Use **(a)** and **(b)** to deduce bounds for the distance the groundsman will have to cover. [A]

20 The distances between an oil terminal (T) and eight oil-wells (A–H) are as follows:

	T	**A**	**B**	**C**	**D**	**E**	**F**	**G**	**H**
T	–	120	150	140	120	100	260	70	180
A	120	–	60	60	90	190	210	160	40
B	150	60	–	20	80	180	170	160	50
C	140	60	20	–	40	160	150	140	60
D	120	90	80	40	-	130	70	110	120
E	100	190	180	160	130	–	140	30	220
F	260	210	170	150	70	140	–	150	170
G	70	160	160	140	110	30	150	–	200
H	180	40	50	60	120	220	170	200	–

A helicopter is going to start at the terminal, visit each oil-well once, and return to the terminal.

(a) Use an appropriate algorithm to find one possible route for the helicopter. then find one other route which is shorter.

(b) By applying Prim's or Kruskal's algorithm to the distances between the oil-wells alone (without the terminal), find a lower bound for the distance the helicopter will have to travel. [A]

Key point summary

1 Given a network, the **travelling salesperson problem** is to find a Hamiltonian cycle of shortest length. There is no known practical algorithm for doing this. *p3*

2 In a complete network the **nearest neighbour algorithm** finds a Hamiltonian cycle which is often quite close to the shortest. But in general its length just gives an **upper bound** for the travelling salesperson problem. *p5*

3 Given a network with one of its vertices V deleted, let L be the length of a minimum connector of the reduced network and let x and y be the lengths of the two shortest edges from V. Then any Hamiltonian cycle of the original network will have length at least $L + x + y$; i.e. this is a **lower bound** for the travelling salesperson problem. *p11*

4 Given a network, the **Chinese postperson problem** (or the **route inspection problem**) is to find a shortest closed walk which uses all the edges. *p19*

5 If a network is Eulerian (i.e. all the vertices have even degree) then any Eulerian trail satisfies the Chinese postperson problem. In all other cases an algorithm has to be applied which pairs the vertices of odd degree. This algorithm always leads to the shortest walk. *p22*

6 Given a network (usually directed) with a **source**, a **sink** and a **capacity** on each edge, a **flow** is a number on each edge which does not exceed its capacity and which makes each vertex apart from the source and sink have the same inflow as outflow (in an obvious sense). The **value** of the flow is the total inflow at the source (which equals the total outflow at the sink). The problem is generally to maximise that value and find a **maximum flow**. *p29*

7 When considering flows in networks a **cut** is a minimal set of edges whose removal would stop any flow from the source to the sink. The **capacity** of a cut is the sum of the capacities of its edges. A **minimum cut** is a cut of smallest capacity. *p31*

8 The value of any flow is less than or equal to the capacity of any cut. Therefore if you find a flow whose value equals the capacity of some cut, then the flow is a maximum flow and the cut is a minimum cut. In fact such common values will always exist, and this is known as the **max flow–min cut theorem**. *p34*

9 One way of systematically finding a maximum flow is to start from the zero flow and build up using **flow-augmenting paths**. For this process each edge has to be labelled with its **potential backflow** (= current flow in that edge, with an arrow going against the edge's direction) and its **potential flow** (= capacity − current flow, with its arrow going in the edge's direction). Then a flow-augmenting path is a path of arrows with positive numbers from source to sink. *p37*

Test yourself — What to review

1 The network illustrated gives distances by direct train services between the towns A–E.

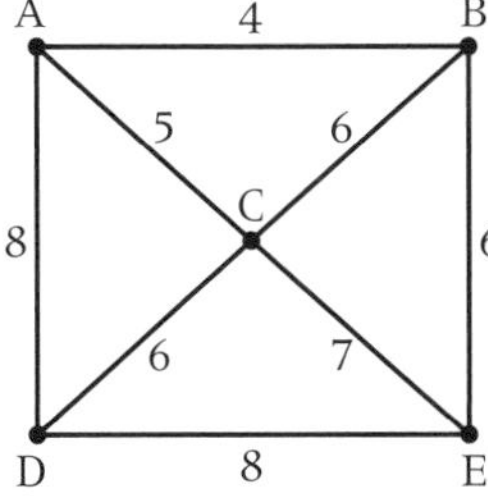

(a) Find a shortest round tour which visits each vertex once. *Section 1.2*

(b) Find a shortest route which uses each stretch of rail at least once and ends back where it started.

Test yourself (continued) | What to review

2 *Section 1.2*

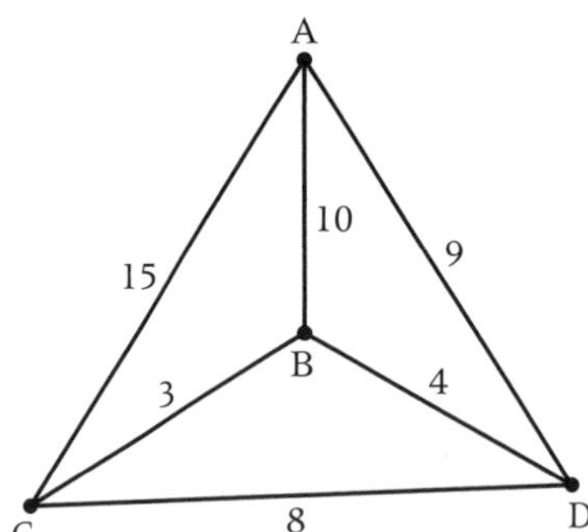

(a) Apply the nearest neighbour algorithm to the network shown above in order to find a Hamiltonian cycle starting at A.

(b) Find a minimum connector of the network with vertex A deleted.

(c) Deduce upper and lower bounds for the length of a shortest Hamiltonian cycle.

---

3 For the network illustrated below, find a maximum flow and a minimum cut: *Section 1.4*

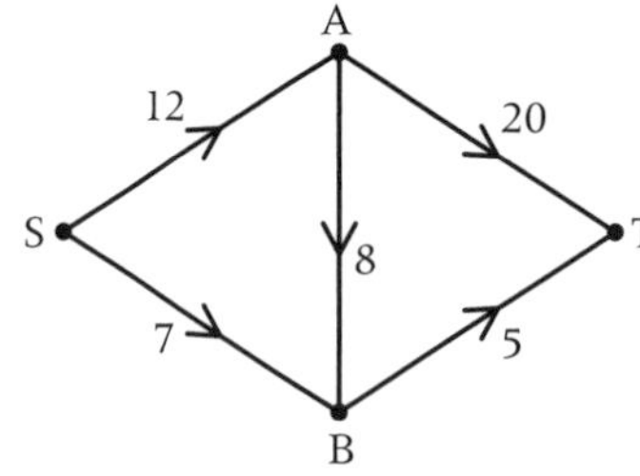

---

4 Find a maximum flow for the network in question **3** by the alternative method of flow-augmenting paths. *Section 1.4*

Test yourself ANSWERS

1 (a) ACDEBA, **(b)** repeat AB, DE; e.g. ABEDABCEDCA.

2 (a) ADBCA **(b)** BC and BD, **(c)** 31 and 26.

3

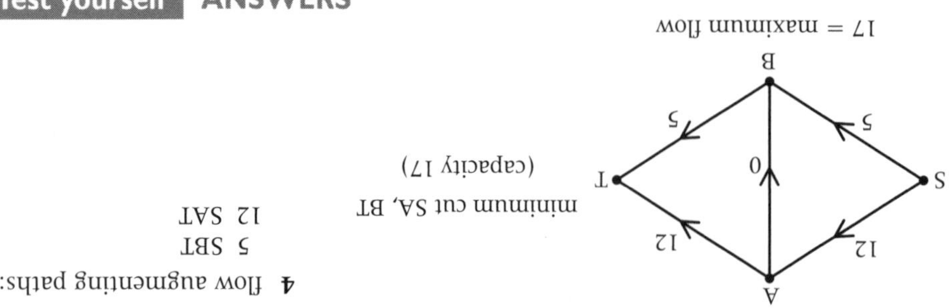

CHAPTER 2

Linear programming

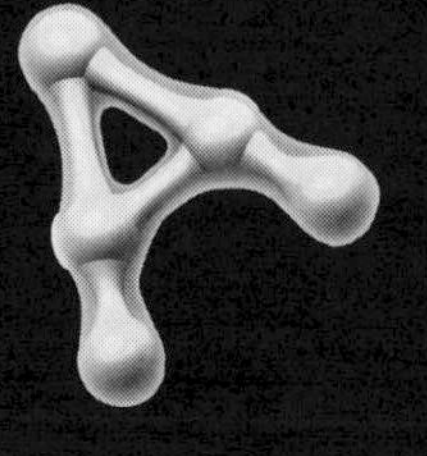

2

Learning objectives

After reading this chapter, you should be able to:

- convert real problems into a linear programming format
- introduce slack variables
- represent a standard linear programming problem in a simplex tableau
- carry out iterations of the simplex method
- understand the geometrical interpretation of the method
- solve some simple linear programming problems by the simplex method.

2.1 Introduction

You are already familiar with linear programming problems from the course D1. In that course we took many real-life problems and

- formulated them as a mathematical model which involved maximising (or minimising) an **objective function** subject to some inequalities
- represented those inequalities as a **feasible region** in the plane
- found the **optimal point**; i.e. the vertex of the feasible region at which the objective function was maximised (or minimised)
- found the **optimal value** of the objective function, i.e. its maximum (or minimum) on the feasible region.

So why are we doing it again? Firstly, since the method used an (x, y)-plane it was restricted to problems involving two variables. The method would extend to three variables, using a three-dimensional model rather than a two-dimensional picture, but it is not very practical. Furthermore, problems of four or more variables would be impossible by our earlier geometrical method.

The second disadvantage of our geometrical approach is that it cannot be solved mechanically; i.e. it is not easy to adapt the method to be suitable for solution by a computer program.

The purpose of this chapter is to introduce an algebraic (rather than geometric) way of solving linear programming problems: it is known as the **simplex method** and it was first developed in 1947 by *George Dantzig*.

At first the process will seem rather complicated but its key advantages are:

- the method has an algorithm to follow in the form of a list of mechanical instructions
- it works for any number of variables
- it can easily be computerised.

Indeed its principal use is for solving large-scale problems by means of a computer: the technical manipulations needed are not very user-friendly, but do not let them put you off a rewarding and useful piece of mathematics.

2.2 Formulating the problem

We have already formulated linear programming problems in the earlier course. We include two straightforward worked examples here to remind ourselves of the process and to give us some problems to solve by our new methods.

Worked example 2.1

In order to prepare a thesis a student wants to borrow some books from a specialist library.

The books can be paperback or hardback.

The library allows her up to 24 books altogether, at most 10 of which can be hardback.

The paperbacks weigh 500 grams each, the hardbacks weigh 2 kilograms each and she can only carry up to 21 kilos.

The library charges £1 for each paperback and £2 for each hardback.

Formulate a linear programming problem to find the maximum income that the library will make.

Solution

(a) Unknowns

Define

x = number of paperbacks borrowed

y = number of hardbacks borrowed.

(b) Constraints

Total number of books: $x + y \leqslant 24$

Number of hardbacks: $y \leqslant 10$

Weight: $500x + 2000y \leqslant 21\,000$ (or $x + 4y \leqslant 42$)

(c) Objective function

Maximise the profit: $P = x + 2y$

So, in summary, the linear programming problem is to:

Maximise	$P = x + 2y$
subject to	$x + y \leqslant 24$
	$y \leqslant 10$
	$x + 4y \leqslant 42$
	$x \geqslant 0$
	$y \geqslant 0$

We shall actually solve this problem algebraically later in the chapter.

Worked exam question 2.1

Thornchox make three types of boxes of chocolates – plain, milk and continental. Each type goes through the same four processes during production. The factory's daily capacity (in thousands) for each process is:

Preparing ingredients:	9 plain or 6 milk or 4 continental
Making centres:	6 plain or 9 milk or 2 continental
Covering with chocolate:	3 plain or 4 milk or 18 continental
Packing and dispatch:	9 plain or 8 milk or 12 continental

and it can mix types in each process. The profits on each 1000 boxes are £250, £200 and £150, respectively, and the factory wishes to maximise its profit.

Formulate this as a linear programming problem.

Solution

(a) Unknowns

Define:

x = number (thousands) of boxes of plain chocolates made daily

y = number (thousands) of boxes of milk chocolates made daily

z = number (thousands) of boxes of continentals made daily

(b) Constraints

For example, in the first process the factory has a capacity (in thousands) of 9 plain or 6 milk or 4 continental. So if, say, there were 36 units of time available in the day, then each plain would take 4, each milk would take 6, each continental would take 9 and the constraint would be

$$4x + 6y + 9z \leqslant 36$$

The choice of 36 was arbitrary – we would end up with the same inequality whatever unit of time we took. In this way the constraints arising from the capacities in the four processes are:

Preparing ingredients:	$4x + 6y + 9z \leqslant 36$
Making centres:	$3x + 2y + 9z \leqslant 18$
Covering with chocolate:	$12x + 9y + 2z \leqslant 36$
Packing and dispatch:	$8x + 9y + 6z \leqslant 72$

(c) Objective function

Maximise the profit: $P = 250x + 200y + 150z$

So, in summary, the linear programming problem is to

Maximise	$P = 250x + 200y + 150z$
subject to	$4x + 6y + 9z \leqslant 36$
	$3x + 2y + 9z \leqslant 18$
	$12x + 9y + 2z \leqslant 36$
	$8x + 9y + 6z \leqslant 72$
	$x \geqslant 0$
	$y \geqslant 0$
	$z \geqslant 0$

Linear programming problems sometimes arise in surprising places. For example, in the previous chapter we considered network flows. It turns out that maximising a flow through a network is in fact a linear programming problem.

Worked exam question 2.2

Consider the network illustrated, where the numbers denote the capacities of the arcs and the x_is denote the flow in those arcs:

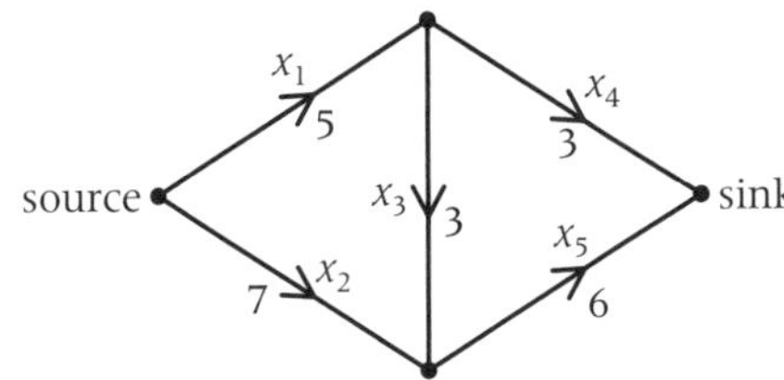

1 What is the purpose of the following linear programming problem?

Maximise	$F = x_1 + x_2$	
subject to	$x_1 \leqslant 5$	$x_1 \geqslant 0$
	$x_2 \leqslant 7$	$x_2 \geqslant 0$
	$x_3 \leqslant 3$	$x_3 \geqslant 0$
	$x_4 \leqslant 3$	$x_4 \geqslant 0$
	$x_5 \leqslant 6$	$x_5 \geqslant 0$
	$x_1 - x_3 - x_4 = 0$	
	$x_2 + x_3 - x_5 = 0$	

2 Interpret the ten inequalities and the final two equations.

3 Give an alternative objective function.

Solution

1 The objective function $F = x_1 + x_2$ is measuring the total flow out of the source, so the purpose is to maximise the overall flow through the network.

2 The two inequalities associated with each x_i make sure that the flow is not negative and that it does not exceed the capacity of its arc.

The first equation is equivalent to $x_1 = x_3 + x_4$ and ensures that the flow in to the upper vertex equals the flow out: similarly $x_5 = x_2 + x_3$ ensures that the flows balance at the lower vertex. So the two equations together make sure that the x_is do form a flow through the network.

3 The flow out of the source equals the flow in to the sink, so we could equivalently maximise $F = x_4 + x_5$.

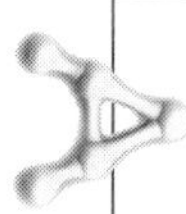

In general, a real-life linear programming problem can be expressed in terms of maximising (or minimising) an objective function, subject to some **linear inequalities**.

EXERCISE 2A

1 A factory is to install two types of machine, Type A and Type B.

(a) Type A machines require 1 operator each, Type B require 2 operators each and there are 40 operators available.

(b) Type A machines take up 3 m^2 of space each, Type B take up 4 m^2 of space each and there is 100 m^2 of space available.

(c) Type A machines make £75 profit a week and Type B machines make £120 profit a week and the factory wishes to maximise its profit.

Formulate this as a linear programming problem.

2 A gardener is planting a flower bed with two types of plants, annuals and perennials.

Each annual costs £1, needs 4000 cm^2 of space and 2 litres of water a day.

Each perennial costs £2, needs 1000 cm^2 of space and a litre of water a day.

The gardener has £24 to spend, the flower bed has an area of 4.4 m^2, and there is a restriction of 24 litres of water a day in total.

Formulate a linear programming problem to decide how many plants of each type should be used in order to maximise the total number of plants.

3 Inklein make four types of undergarments – Wonderwear, Xtra, Y-fronts and Zip-gear. Each type goes through the same three processes during production and the factory's daily maximum throughput (in hundreds) for each process is:

2

Process	Capacity						
1	21 W	or	28 X	or	42 Y	or	84 Z
2	24 W	or	30 X	or	24 Y	or	20 Z
3	24 W	or	28 X	or	21 Y	or	42 Z

and it can mix types proportionately in each process. The profits on 100 of each item are £40, £35, £32 and £30, respectively. Formulate a linear programming problem to maximise Inklein's daily profits. [A]

4 We wish to maximise the flow in the network illustrated, where the numbers represent the capacities of the arcs:

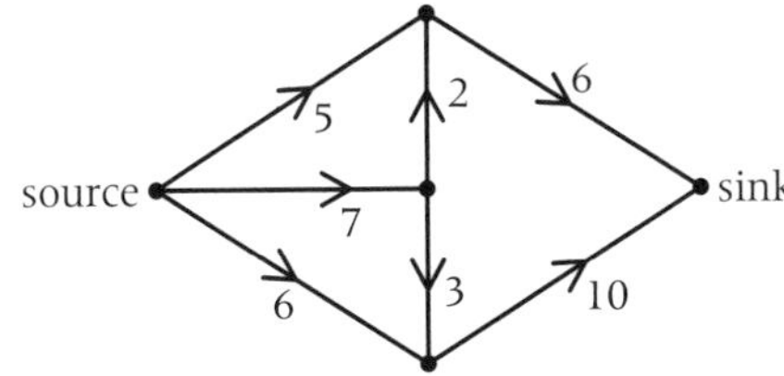

By assigning seven variables to the flows in the arcs, express the problem in a linear programming format. [A]

2.3 Slack variables and linear equations

The next step towards an algebraic solution of our linear programming problems is to transfer each non-trivial inequality into an **equation** using a **slack variable.** For example, if we have the inequality:

$$x + 2y \leqslant 10$$

then we can let the 'excess' (or **slack**) of 10 over $x + 2y$ be denoted by the **slack variable** s, i.e.

$$s = 10 - (x + 2y) = 10 - x - 2y$$

Then

$\boxed{x + 2y \leqslant 10}$ is equivalent to $\boxed{x + 2y + s = 10 \text{ and } s \geqslant 0}$

Using slack variables, each non-trivial inequality will become an equation together with a non-negativity condition, which in general is easier to handle.

In this course you will not be asked to solve large sets of linear equations for yourselves, but if you follow the next worked example you will see how it is possible to manipulate equations. Then, when we study the **simplex method** in the next section, the calculations involved will not seem so strange.

Worked example 2.2

Given the linear programming problem

Maximise	$P = x + y$
subject to	$x + 2y \leqslant 10$
	$3x + 2y \leqslant 18$
	$x \geqslant 0$
	$y \geqslant 0$

1 Introduce slack variables s and t and rewrite the problem as two equations together with $x \geqslant 0$, $y \geqslant 0$, $s \geqslant 0$, $t \geqslant 0$.

2 Manipulate your equations to express x and y in terms of s and t.

3 Express $P = x + y$ in terms of s and t and deduce that P has a maximum value of 7.

4 For what values of x and y does that maximum occur?

Solution

1 We introduce s as the slack variable of $x + 2y \leqslant 10$ (i.e. $s = 10 - (x + 2y)$) and t as the slack variable of $3x + 2y \leqslant 18$ (i.e. $t = 18 - (3x + 2y)$). Then:

$x + 2y \leqslant 10$ is equivalent to $x + 2y + s = 10$ and $s \geqslant 0$

and

$3x + 2y \leqslant 10$ is equivalent to $3x + 2y + t = 10$ and $t \geqslant 0$

so overall the problem is transformed to:

Maximise	$P = x + y$
subject to	$x + 2y + s = 10$
	$3x + 2y + t = 18$
	$x \geqslant 0, y \geqslant 0, s \geqslant 0, t \geqslant 0$

2 Ignoring, for the moment, the non-negativity conditions, we consider the equations

$$\begin{aligned} x + 2y + s \qquad &= 10 \\ 3x + 2y \qquad + t &= 18 \end{aligned}$$

(where for clarity we have kept different columns for different variables). Since we only have two equations in four variables we shall not be able to find specific numerical values of x and y, but we can express each of them in terms of s and t:

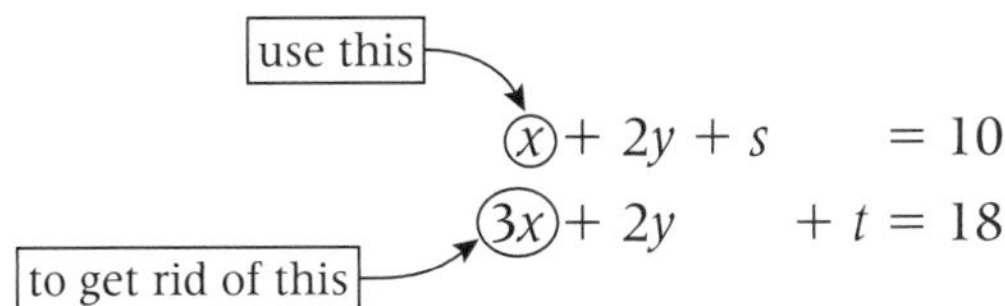

Taking three times the first equation from the second changes the equations to the equivalent ones:

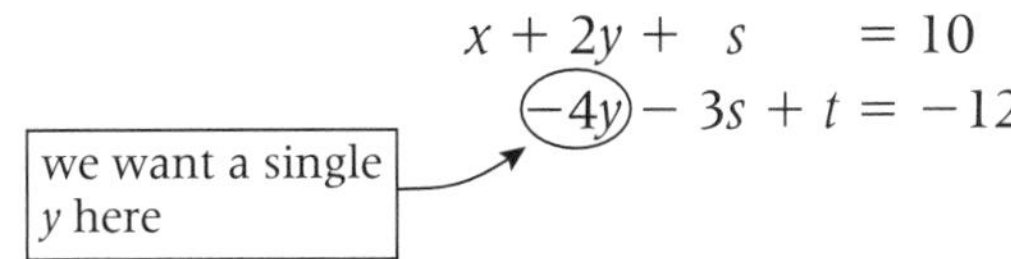

Dividing the second equation by −4 changes the equations to the equivalent ones:

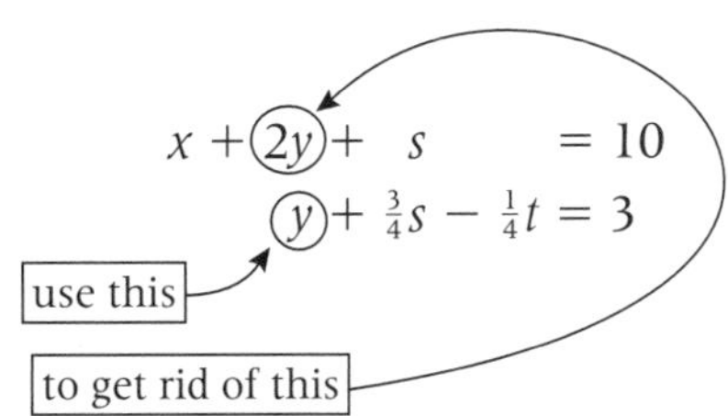

Taking twice the second equation from the first changes the equations to the equivalent ones:

$$\begin{aligned} x \qquad - \tfrac{1}{2}s + \tfrac{1}{2}t &= 4 \\ y + \tfrac{3}{4}s - \tfrac{1}{4}t &= 3 \end{aligned}$$

The crucial thing is that x occurs without y in the first equation and y occurs without x in the second. We can now express x and y in terms of s and t as required:

$$\begin{aligned} x &= 4 + \tfrac{1}{2}s - \tfrac{1}{2}t \\ y &= 3 - \tfrac{3}{4}s + \tfrac{1}{4}t \, (*) \end{aligned}$$

3 It follows from the results (*) above that

$$P = x + y = (4 + \tfrac{1}{2}s - \tfrac{1}{2}t) + (3 - \tfrac{3}{4}s + \tfrac{1}{4}t) = 7 - \tfrac{1}{4}s - \tfrac{1}{4}t$$

Since $s \geqslant 0$ and $t \geqslant 0$ we can see that $P \leqslant 7$. In fact it will equal 7 only when $s = 0$ and $t = 0$.

4 Putting $s = 0$ and $t = 0$ in the equations (*) gives $x = 4$ and $y = 3$. Hence $P = x + y$ has a maximum of 7 which occurs when $x = 4$ and $y = 3$.

If you took the simple linear programming problem from that worked example and solved it graphically you would confirm by our old methods that the maximum occurs at (4, 3). But the advantage of our alternative approach is that it is gradually familiarising you with algebraic manipulations which eventually can be used to solve much more complicated problems.

You will be expected to introduce slack variables for yourselves and to solve simple equations (perhaps with a little guidance).

Worked exam question 2.3

Consider the linear programming problem:

Maximise	$P = 5x + 3y$
subject to	$2x + 3y \leqslant 36$
	$x + y \leqslant 13$
	$2x + y \leqslant 20$
	$x \geqslant 0$
	$y \geqslant 0$

1 Illustrate the feasible region in an (x, y)-plane. State the coordinates of each of its vertices.

2 Introduce slack variables s, t and u and transform the problem to a set of equations together with $x \geqslant 0$, $y \geqslant 0$, $s \geqslant 0$, $t \geqslant 0$ and $u \geqslant 0$.

3 For each vertex of the feasible region in **1** state the values of the three slack variables.

4 Use the fact that

$$P = 5x + 3y = (x + y) + 2(2x + y)$$

to show that $P = 53 - t - 2u$. Is there a point in the feasible region where $t = 0$ and $u = 0$? Deduce that P has a maximum value of 53 and state the values of x and y at which this maximum occurs.

Solution

1 The standard geometrical method from course D1 gives the feasible region as shown:

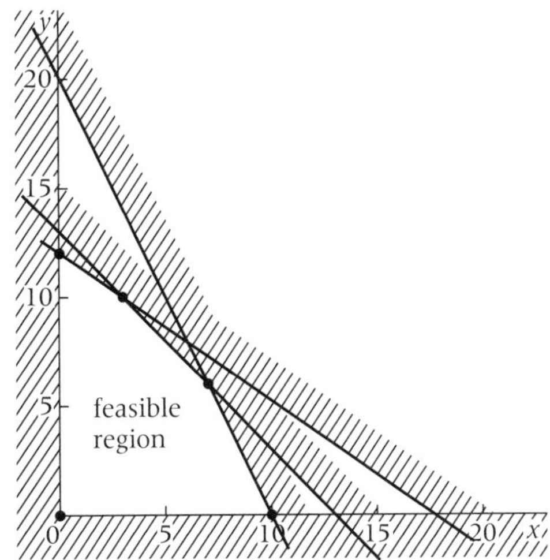

The coordinates of the vertices of the feasible region are found by considering the equations of the lines which meet there. For example, solving the simultaneous equations

$$2x + 3y = 36 \quad \text{and} \quad x + y = 13$$

gives $x = 3$ and $y = 10$. which shows that those two lines meet at $(3, 10)$. The other coordinates are found similarly to give:

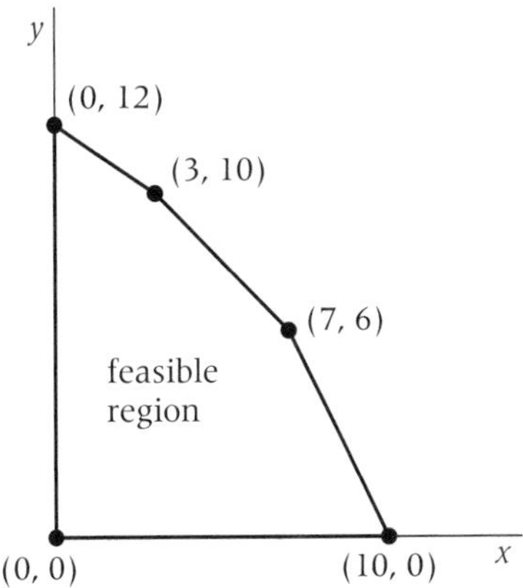

2 We introduce s as the slack variable of $2x + 3y \leqslant 36$ (i.e. $s = 36 - (2x + 3y)$) and t as the slack variable of $x + y \leqslant 13$ (i.e. $t = 13 - (x + y)$) and u as the slack variable of $2x + y \leqslant 20$ (i.e. $u = 20 - (2x + y)$). Then:

$2x + 3y \leqslant 36$ is equivalent to $2x + 3y + s = 36$ and $s \geqslant 0$

and

$x + y \leqslant 13$ is equivalent to $x + y + t = 13$ and $t \geqslant 0$

and

$2x + y \leqslant 20$ is equivalent to $2x + y + u = 20$ and $u \geqslant 0$

So overall the problem is transformed to:

Maximise	$P = 5x + 3y$
subject to	$2x + 3y + s = 36$
	$x + y + t = 13$
	$2x + y + u = 20$
	$x \geqslant 0, y \geqslant 0, s \geqslant 0, t \geqslant 0, u \geqslant 0$

3 Consider, for example, the vertex (3, 10) of the feasible region. Substituting $x = 3$ and $y = 10$ into the equations:

$$2x + 3y + s = 36$$
$$x + y + t = 13$$
$$2x + y + u = 20$$

shows that:

$$s = 36 - 2.3 - 3.10 = 0$$
$$t = 13 - 3 - 10 = 0$$
$$u = 20 - 2.3 - 10 = 4.$$

In a similar way, at the vertex (0, 12) the slack variables take the values:

$$s = 36 - 2.0 - 3.12 = 0$$
$$t = 13 - 0 - 12 = 1$$
$$u = 20 - 2.0 - 12 = 8.$$

The other values can be calculated similarly to give:

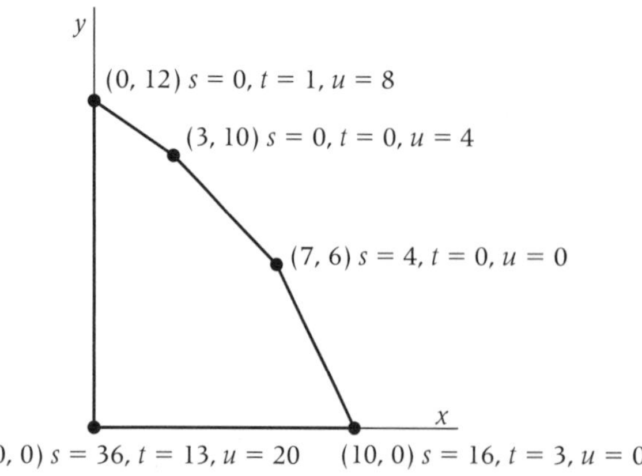

4 Now using the slack variables for $x + y \leqslant 13$ and $2x + y \leqslant 20$ gives:

$$P = 5x + 3y = (x + y) + 2(2x + y) = (13 - t) + 2(20 - u) = 53 - t - 2u$$

as required. Since:

$$P = 53 - t - 2u$$

and $t \geqslant 0$, $u \geqslant 0$ it follows that $P \leqslant 53$ and it will equal 53 only when both $t = 0$ and $u = 0$.

We saw in **3** that at the vertex $(7, 6)$ the slack variables t and u are both 0. Hence P reaches its maximum of 53 when $x = 7$ and $y = 6$.

EXERCISE 2B

1 Introduce slack variables to transform the given linear programming problem into a set of equations with the requirement that all the variables are non-negative:

Maximise	$P = 250x + 200y + 150z$
subject to	$4x + 6y + 9z \leqslant 36$
	$3x + 2y + 9z \leqslant 18$
	$12x + 9y + 2z \leqslant 36$
	$8x + 9y + 6z \leqslant 72$

2 Consider the linear programming problem:

Maximise	$P = 2x + 5y$
subject to	$x + y \leqslant 24$
	$y \leqslant 10$
	$x + 4y \leqslant 42$

(a) Introduce slack variables s, t and u.

(b) **(i)** Find the values of x and y for which $s = t = 0$. Is $u \geqslant 0$ there? What is the value of P there?

(ii) Find the values of x and y for which $s = u = 0$. Is $t \geqslant 0$ there? What is the value of P there?

(iii) Find the values of x and y for which $t = u = 0$. Is $s \geqslant 0$ there? What is the value of P there?

(c) Show that $P = 66 - s - u$ and use your answers to **(b)** to solve the linear programming problem. [A]

3 Given the problem:

Maximise	$P = x + y$
subject to	$2x + y \leqslant 48$
	$x + 2y \leqslant 60$
	$x + 4y \leqslant 116$
	$x \geqslant 0$
	$y \geqslant 0$

(a) Introduce slack variables and transform the problem to a set of equations together with some non-negativity conditions.

(b) Use the fact that

$$P = x + y = \tfrac{1}{3}((2x + y) + (x + 2y))$$

to express P in terms of some of the slack variables.

(c) Use your answer to **(b)** to find the maximum value of P and the values of x and y at which this maximum occurs.

[A]

4 Consider the linear programming problem:

Maximise	$P = 2x + y$
subject to	$x + y + s = 20$
	$x + y + t = 10$
	$x \geqslant 0, y \geqslant 0, s \geqslant 0, t \geqslant 0$

(a) Show that:

$2x + s + t = 30$ and

$2y + s - t = 10.$

(b) Express P in terms of the slack variables.

(c) Solve the linear programming problem. [A]

2.4 The simplex method

The key step in solving linear programming problems will be the **simplex method**. For the moment we shall only apply it to **standard** linear programming problems of the following form:

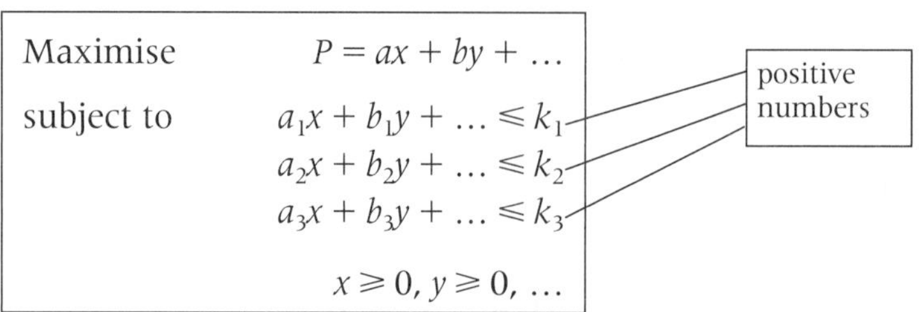

where the 'origin' $x = 0, y = 0, \ldots$ satisfies all the inequalities and where there **is** a point at which P is maximised.

We have already seen how to transform a set of inequalities into a set of equations involving slack variables together with some non-negativity conditions. The next stage is to manipulate those equations in order to find the maximum value of P. However, manipulating equations can be made a little neater by just working with the coefficients (this will be familiar to those of you who know about solving linear equations using matrices). As an example, on the left below we take two equations in x, y, s and t and manipulate them so that we can express x and y in terms of s and t alone. (So our aim will be to get one equation with x in it but not y, and a second equation with y in it but not x.)

Meanwhile, on the right-hand side we shall carry out exactly the same calculations working with the coefficients alone. You will know which variable the coefficients refer to by the headings in the 'tableau'.

Equations	Tableau form
use this → $x + 2y + s \quad = 10$ to get rid of this → $2x + 3y \quad + t = 18$	x y s t | 1 2 1 0 | 10 2 3 0 1 | 18
	take twice the first row from the second row
$x + 2y + s \quad = 10$ we want $+y$ here → $-y - 2s + t = -2$	x y s t | 1 2 1 0 | 10 0 −1 −2 1 | −2
	multiply the second row by −1
$x + 2y + s \quad = 10$ use this → $y + 2s - t = 2$ to get rid of this (the $2y$ above)	x y s t | 1 2 1 0 | 10 0 1 2 −1 | 2
	take twice the second row from the first row
$x \quad - 3s + 2t = 6$ $y + 2s - t = 2$	x y s t | 1 0 −3 2 | 6 0 1 2 −1 | 2

To deal with the equations of a linear programming problem in this way we must put them into the form given on the right above: this is known as the **simplex tableau**.

Worked example 2.3

Given the linear programming problem:

Maximise	$P = x + y$
subject to	$x + 2y \leqslant 12$
	$2x + y \leqslant 12$
	$x + 4y \leqslant 22$
	$x \geqslant 0$
	$y \geqslant 0$

introduce slack variables and construct the simplex tableau of the equations.

Solution

With slack variables s, t and u the problem becomes:

Maximise	$P = x + y$
subject to	$x + 2y + s = 12$
	$2x + y + t = 12$
	$x + 4y + u = 22$
	$x \geqslant 0, y \geqslant 0, s \geqslant 0, t \geqslant 0, u \geqslant 0$

In tableau form the equation defining the objective function and the three slack variable equations become:

P	x	y	s	t	u	
1	−1	−1	0	0	0	0
0	1	2	1	0	0	12
0	2	1	0	1	0	12
0	1	4	0	0	1	22

and this is the **simplex tableau** of the problem. Each line can be read as an equation. For example the last line corresponds to:

$$0P + 1x + 4y + 0s + 0t + 1u = 22$$

which is $x + 4y + u = 22$ as required. The first row of the tableau reads as:

$$1P - 1x - 1y + 0s + 0t + 0u = 0$$

which is $P - x - y = 0$ or $P = x + y$, and so it simply defines the objective function. Notice also the format of the $s/t/u$ part of the simplex tableau: it will always consist of a row of zeros on the top and a square array below it which has nothing but a leading diagonal of 1s:

P	x	y	s	t	u	
1	−1	−1	0	0	0	0
0	1	2	1	0	0	12
0	2	1	0	1	0	12
0	1	4	0	0	1	22

The key algorithm

The **simplex method** for solving linear programming problems will consist of processing the simplex tableau following the steps of an algorithm. It is important to be able to execute the algorithm and then to interpret what is really going on. But before we can fully understand the process and interpret its output, it is crucial to be able to follow the algorithm in a mechanical way.

The steps in the algorithm consist of operations on the rows of a tableau. In some cases you have to divide a whole row by a number, which is straightforward enough, and in other cases add one multiple of a row to another. For example if, in the above tableau, we took four times the third row from the bottom row then the bottom row would become:

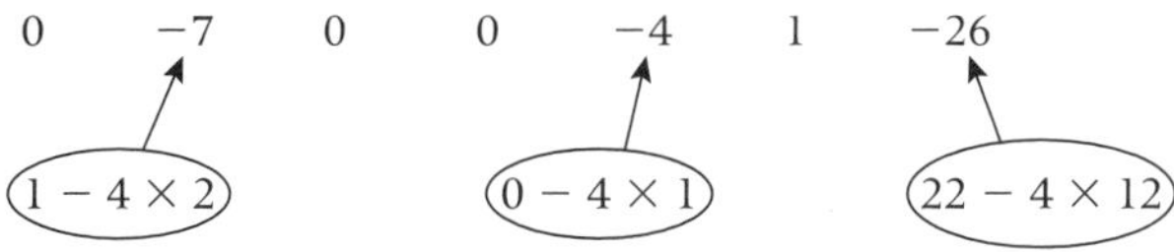

We are now ready to work through the **simplex method**. Below, on the left, you will see the method described in the form of the steps of an algorithm for processing a simplex tableau. On the right you will see the tableau from the above worked example and you can follow the effect of the algorithm on it.

The simplex method

Example

To process a given simplex tableau:

1 Look for any negative number in the first row (there may be a choice). That determines the column which we are going to work on.

P	x	y	s	t	u	
1	−1	−1	0	0	0	0
0	1	2	1	0	0	12
0	2	1	0	1	0	12
0	1	4	0	0	1	22

2 For each positive number in the working column divide it into the number on the extreme right and make a temporary note of all the answers. Find the lowest of those temporary answers (there may be a choice) and ring the corresponding entry in the table. This is the **pivot position**.

For that column the temporary answers are 12/1 (= 12), 12/2 (= 6) and 22/1 (= 22).

P	x	y	s	t	u	
1	−1	−1	0	0	0	0
0	1	2	1	0	0	12
0	2	1	0	1	0	12
0	1	4	0	0	1	22

3 Divide the whole of the pivot's row by the number in the pivot position (thus creating a '1' there).

P	x	y	s	t	u	
1	−1	−1	0	0	0	0
0	1	2	1	0	0	12
0	1	$\frac{1}{2}$	0	$\frac{1}{2}$	0	6
0	1	4	0	0	1	22

4 Add/subtract multiples of the pivot's row to/from other rows so that the only non-zero number left in the pivot's column is the '1' in the pivot position.

P	x	y	s	t	u	
1	0	$-\frac{1}{2}$	0	$\frac{1}{2}$	0	6
0	0	$1\frac{1}{2}$	1	$-\frac{1}{2}$	0	6
0	1	$\frac{1}{2}$	0	$\frac{1}{2}$	0	6
0	0	$3\frac{1}{2}$	0	$-\frac{1}{2}$	1	16

5 You now have completed an **iteration** of the simplex method and produced a new tableau. If there are still negative numbers in the first row, return to step 1 and start again. If not, the process is finished. Then **the number on the right-hand side of the top row is the maximum value which *P* can take**.

One iteration complete – there is still a negative number in the top row, so return to step 1 and start again:

Step 1: choose a negative in the first row

P	x	y	s	t	u	
1	0	$-\frac{1}{2}$	0	$\frac{1}{2}$	0	6
0	0	$1\frac{1}{2}$	1	$-\frac{1}{2}$	0	6
0	1	$\frac{1}{2}$	0	$\frac{1}{2}$	0	6
0	0	$3\frac{1}{2}$	0	$-\frac{1}{2}$	1	16

Step 2: for that column the temporary answers are $6/1\frac{1}{2}$ $(= 4)$, $6/\frac{1}{2}$ $(= 12)$ and $16/3\frac{1}{2}$ $(= 4\frac{1}{7})$. The lowest gives the pivot position

P	x	y	s	t	u	
1	0	$-\frac{1}{2}$	0	$\frac{1}{2}$	0	6
0	0	$1\frac{1}{2}$	1	$-\frac{1}{2}$	0	6
0	1	$\frac{1}{2}$	0	$\frac{1}{2}$	0	6
0	0	$3\frac{1}{2}$	0	$-\frac{1}{2}$	1	16

Step 3: divide that row by $1\frac{1}{2}$

P	x	y	s	t	u	
1	0	$-\frac{1}{2}$	0	$\frac{1}{2}$	0	6
0	0	1	$\frac{2}{3}$	$-\frac{1}{3}$	0	4
0	1	$\frac{1}{2}$	0	$\frac{1}{2}$	0	6
0	0	$3\frac{1}{2}$	0	$-\frac{1}{2}$	1	16

Step 4: add/subtract multiples of that row to/from the others to get 0s above and below the pivot position

P	x	y	s	t	u	
1	0	0	$\frac{1}{3}$	$\frac{1}{3}$	0	8
0	0	1	$\frac{2}{3}$	$-\frac{1}{3}$	0	4
0	1	0	$-\frac{1}{3}$	$\frac{2}{3}$	0	4
0	0	0	$-2\frac{1}{3}$	$-\frac{2}{3}$	1	2

Step 5: second iteration complete – no more negative numbers in the first row so stop. The **8** in the top right is P's maximum.

The simplex method is an algorithm to be applied to the simplex tableau. Each iteration of the method consists of **pivoting** around a point chosen by numerical criteria.

That rather daunting process is not so bad when you get used to it. The great thing about it is that it can be applied to problems with any number of variables. Of course, in large-scale practical problems the actual execution of the algorithm is done by a computer.

You will not be expected to solve complicated problems involving many iterations of the algorithm, but you should be able to solve problems requiring two iterations.

Worked exam question 2.4

The simplex method is to be used to solve the linear programming problem:

Maximise	$P = 30x + 20y$
subject to	$3x + y = 3000$
	$6x + 5y = 12\,000$
	$x \geqslant 0$
	$y \geqslant 0$

1 Introduce slack variables to convert the resource constraints to equations.

2 Perform two iterations of the simplex algorithm and deduce that the maximum possible value of P is 50 000.

Solution

1 With slack variables s and t the problem becomes:

Maximise	$P = 30x + 20y$
subject to	$3x + y + s = 3000$
	$6x + 5y + t = 12\,000$
	$x \geqslant 0, y \geqslant 0, s \geqslant 0, t \geqslant 0$

2 We construct the simplex tableau and follow the steps of the algorithm of the simplex method.

Step 1: choose a negative in the top row:

P	x	y	s	t	
1	−30	−20	0	0	0
0	(3)	1	1	0	3000
0	6	5	0	1	12 000

Step 2: pivot position:

(lowest of the temporary totals 3000/3 (= 1000) and 12 000/6 (= 2000))

Step 3: divide that row by 3:

P	x	y	s	t	
1	−30	−20	0	0	0
0	(1)	$\frac{1}{3}$	$\frac{1}{3}$	0	1000
0	6	5	0	1	12 000

Step 4: add/subtract multiples of that row to get 0s above and below the pivot position.

P	x	y	s	t	
1	0	−10	10	0	30 000
0	(1)	$\frac{1}{3}$	$\frac{1}{3}$	0	1000
0	0	3	−2	1	6000

Step 5: one iteration complete, there's still a negative number in the first row, so go back to step 1.

Step 1: choose a negative in the top row:

P	x	y	s	t	
1	0	−10	10	0	30 000
0	1	$\frac{1}{3}$	$\frac{1}{3}$	0	1000
0	0	(3)	−2	1	6000

Step 2: pivot position:

(lowest of the temporary totals $1000/\frac{1}{3}$ (= 3000) and 6000/3 (= 2000))

Step 3: divide that row by 3:

P	x	y	s	t	
1	0	−10	10	0	30 000
0	1	$\frac{1}{3}$	$\frac{1}{3}$	0	1000
0	0	(1)	$-\frac{2}{3}$	$\frac{1}{3}$	2000

Step 4: add/subtract multiples of that row to get 0s above and below the pivot position

P	x	y	s	t	
1	0	0	$3\frac{1}{3}$	$3\frac{1}{3}$	50 000
0	1	0	$\frac{5}{9}$	$-\frac{1}{9}$	$333\frac{1}{3}$
0	0	(1)	$-\frac{2}{3}$	$\frac{1}{3}$	2000

Step 5: two iterations complete, there are no more negative numbers in the first row, so stop. P's maximum is the number in the top right, namely 50 000 as required.

We have not discussed how to find the point at which the maximum is reached. If, in that last example, you interpret the final tableau as equations again you get

$$P + 3\tfrac{1}{3}s + 3\tfrac{1}{3}t = 50\,000$$
$$x + \tfrac{5}{9}s - \tfrac{1}{9}t = 333\tfrac{1}{3}$$
$$y - \tfrac{2}{3}s + \tfrac{1}{3}t = 2000.$$

In other words

$$P = 50\,000 - 3\tfrac{1}{3}s - 3\tfrac{1}{3}t$$
$$x = 333\tfrac{1}{3} - \tfrac{5}{9}s + \tfrac{1}{9}t$$
$$y = 2000 + \tfrac{2}{3}s - \tfrac{1}{3}t$$

Since $s \geqslant 0$ and $t \geqslant 0$ it follows from the first equation that $P \leqslant 50\,000$. The algorithm tells you that P actually can reach 50 000 and therefore it must happen when $s = 0$ and $t = 0$. Substituting those values of s and t in the other equations tells you that $x = 333\tfrac{1}{3}$ and $y = 2000$. So the maximum is reached for those values of x and y. (**Check:** at that point:

$$P = 30x + 20y = 30.333\tfrac{1}{3} + 20.2000 = 50\,000$$

as claimed.) In the next section we shall see how to interpret each tableau easily.

The **simplex method** works for any number of variables and any number of constraints.

To make you thoroughly familiar with this process, and to demonstrate that it is not restricted to two variables, we have one final complete worked example in which we find not only the maximum but also the point where it occurs.

Worked exam question 2.5

Use the simplex method to solve the linear programming problem:

Maximise	$P = 2x - 3y + z$
subject to	$3x + 6y + z \leqslant 18$
	$4x + 2y + z \leqslant 12$
	$x - y + z \leqslant 9$
	$x \geqslant 0$
	$y \geqslant 0$
	$z \geqslant 0$

Solution

With slack variables s, t and u the problem becomes:

Maximise	$P = 2x - 3y + z$
subject to	$3x + 6y + z + s = 18$
	$4x + 2y + z + t = 12$
	$x - y + z + u = 9$
	$x \geqslant 0, y \geqslant 0, z \geqslant 0, s \geqslant 0, t \geqslant 0, u \geqslant 0$

which is given in tableau form below and then the algorithm is applied to it.

Step 1: choose a negative in the top row:

P	x	y	z	s	t	u	
1	−2	3	−1	0	0	0	0
0	3	6	1	1	0	0	18
0	(4)	2	1	0	1	0	12
0	1	−1	1	0	0	1	9

Step 2: pivot position: (12/4 = 3 is the lowest of 6, 3 and 9)

Step 3: divide that row by 4

P	x	y	z	s	t	u	
1	−2	3	−1	0	0	0	0
0	3	6	1	1	0	0	18
0	(1)	$\frac{1}{2}$	$\frac{1}{4}$	0	$\frac{1}{4}$	0	3
0	1	−1	1	0	0	1	9

Step 4: add/subtract multiples of that row to get 0s above and below the pivot position

P	x	y	z	s	t	u	
1	0	4	$-\frac{1}{2}$	0	$\frac{1}{2}$	0	6
0	0	$4\frac{1}{2}$	$\frac{1}{4}$	1	$-\frac{3}{4}$	0	9
0	(1)	$\frac{1}{2}$	$\frac{1}{4}$	0	$\frac{1}{4}$	0	3
0	0	$-1\frac{1}{2}$	$\frac{3}{4}$	0	$-\frac{1}{4}$	1	6

Step 5: one iteration complete, there's still a negative number in the first row, so go back to step 1.

Step 1: choose a negative in the top row

P	x	y	z	s	t	u	
1	0	4	$-\frac{1}{2}$	0	$\frac{1}{2}$	0	6
0	0	$4\frac{1}{2}$	$\frac{1}{4}$	1	$-\frac{3}{4}$	0	9
0	1	$\frac{1}{2}$	$\frac{1}{4}$	0	$\frac{1}{4}$	0	3
0	0	$-1\frac{1}{2}$	($\frac{3}{4}$)	0	$-\frac{1}{4}$	1	6

Step 2: pivot position
(lowest of the positive temporary totals $9/\frac{1}{4}$, $3/\frac{1}{4}$, $6/\frac{3}{4}$)

Step 3: divide that row by $\frac{3}{4}$:

P	x	y	z	s	t	u	
1	0	4	$-\frac{1}{2}$	0	$\frac{1}{2}$	0	6
0	0	$4\frac{1}{2}$	$\frac{1}{4}$	1	$-\frac{3}{4}$	0	9
0	1	$\frac{1}{2}$	$\frac{1}{4}$	0	$\frac{1}{4}$	0	3
0	0	-2	(1)	0	$-\frac{1}{3}$	$1\frac{1}{3}$	8

Step 4: add/subtract multiples of that row to get 0s above and below the pivot position:

P	x	y	z	s	t	u	
1	0	3	0	0	$\frac{1}{3}$	$\frac{2}{3}$	10
0	0	5	0	1	$-\frac{2}{3}$	$-\frac{1}{3}$	7
0	1	1	0	0	$\frac{1}{3}$	$-\frac{1}{3}$	1
0	0	-2	(1)	0	$-\frac{1}{3}$	$1\frac{1}{3}$	8

Step 5: two iterations complete, there are no more negative numbers in the first row, so stop. P's maximum is the number in the top right, namely 10.

To complete the solution we have to find the values of x, y and z where that maximum of 10 occurs. (We shall have a more mechanical process for this in the next section.) The first line of the final tableau represents the equation

$$P + 3y + \tfrac{1}{3}t + \tfrac{2}{3}u = 10 \quad or \quad P = 10 - 3y - \tfrac{1}{3}t - \tfrac{2}{3}u$$

Since $y \geqslant 0$, $t \geqslant 0$ and $u \geqslant 0$ it follows that $P \leqslant 10$ and that its maximum of 10 is only reached when $y = t = u = 0$.

The other three rows of the final tableau represent the equations:

$$\begin{aligned} 5y + s - \tfrac{2}{3}t - \tfrac{1}{3}u &= 7 \\ x + y + \tfrac{1}{3}t - \tfrac{1}{3}u &= 1 \\ -2y + z - \tfrac{1}{3}t + 1\tfrac{1}{3}u &= 8 \end{aligned}$$

Therefore when P has its maximum (i.e. when $y = t = u = 0$ as above) these equations tell us that:

$$s = 7$$
$$x = 1$$
$$z = 8$$

The values of x and z tell us that P's maximum occurs when $x = 1, y = 0$ (deduced above) and $z = 8$. (**Check**: putting these values into the formula for P does give

$$P = 2x - 3y + z = 2.1 - 3.0 + 8 = 10$$

as required. The remaining result, that $s = 7$, tells us that the first inequality has a 'slack' of 7 when P reaches its maximum at $x = 1, y = 0, z = 8$.) We have thus completely solved the given linear programming problem.

Hopefully, by now you should be able to carry out the iterations of the simplex method for yourselves. However, the process becomes much more interesting when you understand what is going on.

- Why do we follow those particular steps?
- What does each tableau tell us?
- Why does the algorithm work?

We shall answer these questions in the next section.

EXERCISE 2C

Use the simplex method to solve the following linear programming problems:

1

Maximise $P = 30x + 15y$

subject to
$3x + 4y \leqslant 84$
$4x + 3y \leqslant 84$
$x \leqslant 15$
$x \geqslant 0$
$y \geqslant 0$

2

Maximise $P = 2x + 3y$

subject to
$3x + y \leqslant 30$
$x + 2y \leqslant 30$
$x \geqslant 0$
$y \geqslant 0$
[A]

3

Maximise $P = 3x + 6y + 2z$

subject to
$3x + 4y + z \leqslant 20$
$x + 3y + 2z \leqslant 10$
$x \geqslant 0, y \geqslant 0, z \geqslant 0$
[A]

2.5 Why the method works

In this section we shall look at the geometry underlying the simplex method. Then following the algorithm of the simplex method will become more natural. In addition we shall be able to learn much more from the tableau at the end of each iteration.

In order to interpret the tableaux we need to say a little more about their format. Some variables will have a column consisting of a single 1 and nothing else but 0s: these variables are called **basic**. The other variables are **non-basic**. For example:

basic (arrows to P, x, z, t, v)

P	x	y	z	s	t	u	v	
1	0	−1	0	2	0	4	0	32
0	0	3	1	0	0	0	0	16
0	1	7	0	1	0	2	0	12
0	0	−2	0	3	0	1	1	15
0	0	0	0	4	1	2	0	10

So in that example the variables P, x, z, t and v are basic, the rest being non-basic. Put all the non-basic variables equal to 0 and see what the rest tells you:

Put non-basics equal to 0 (so that in effect we can ignore them):

		$y = 0$		$s = 0$		$u = 0$		
P	x	y	z	s	t	u	v	
1	0	−1	0	2	0	4	0	32
0	0	3	1	0	0	0	0	16
0	1	7	0	1	0	2	0	12
0	0	−2	0	3	0	1	1	15
0	0	0	0	4	1	2	0	10

Now interpret the rows as equations. The first row tells us that $P = 32$, the second that $z = 16$, the third that $x = 12$, the fourth that $v = 15$ and the bottom row tells us that $t = 10$. In other words the tableau represents the point

$$x = 12, y = 0, z = 16$$

and at that point

$$P = 32$$

and the slack variables take the values $s = 0, t = 10, u = 0, v = 15$.

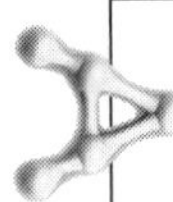

Each tableau represents a vertex of the feasible region. Its details are found by putting all the **non-basic** variables equal to 0 and solving the other equations.

Worked example 2.4

In Worked exam question 2.4 the simplex tableau initially and after each iteration took the form:

P	x	y	s	t	
1	−30	−20	0	0	0
0	3	1	1	0	3000
0	6	5	0	1	12 000

P	x	y	s	t	
1	0	−10	10	0	30 000
0	1	$\frac{1}{3}$	$\frac{1}{3}$	0	1000
0	0	3	−2	1	6000

P	x	y	s	t	
1	0	0	$3\frac{1}{3}$	$3\frac{1}{3}$	50 000
0	1	0	$\frac{5}{9}$	$-\frac{1}{9}$	$333\frac{1}{3}$
0	0	1	$-\frac{2}{3}$	$\frac{1}{3}$	2000

1 Which points do they represent?

2 What is the value of P at those points?

3 What are the values of the slack variables at those points?

Solution

First tableau

Make non-basic variables = 0

	$x = 0$	$y = 0$				
P	x	y	s	t		
1	−30	−20	0	0	0	$\therefore P = 0$
0	3	1	1	0	3000	$\therefore s = 3000$
0	6	5	0	1	12 000	$\therefore t = 12\,000$

So this tableau represents the point $x = 0, y = 0$ (i.e. the origin) where $P = 0$ and the slack variables have the values $s = 3000$ and $t = 12\,000$.

Second tableau

Make non-basic variables = 0

		$y = 0$	$s = 0$			
P	x	y	s	t		
1	0	−10	10	0	30 000	$\therefore P = 30\,000$
0	1	$\frac{1}{3}$	$\frac{1}{3}$	0	1000	$\therefore x = 1000$
0	0	3	−2	1	6000	$\therefore y = 6000$

So this tableau represents the point (1000, 0) (i.e. where $x = 1000$ and $y = 0$). At that point $P = 30\,000$ and the slack variables have the values $s = 0$ and $t = 6000$.

Final tableau

Make non-basic variables = 0

			$s = 0$	$t = 0$		
P	x	y	s	t		
1	0	0	$3\frac{1}{3}$	$3\frac{1}{3}$	50 000	$\therefore P = 50\,000$
0	1	0	$\frac{5}{9}$	$-\frac{1}{9}$	$333\frac{1}{3}$	$\therefore x = 333\frac{1}{3}$
0	0	1	$-\frac{2}{3}$	$\frac{1}{3}$	2000	$\therefore y = 2000$

So this tableau represents the point $(333\frac{1}{3}, 2000)$ (i.e. where $x = 333\frac{1}{3}$ and $y = 2000$). At that point $P = 50\,000$ and the slack variables are both 0. Since there are no negatives in the top row, this is the point at which P reaches its maximum.

The route taken by the simplex method

That worked example showed that the stages of the simplex method took us from (0, 0) to (1000, 0) and then finally to ($333\frac{1}{3}$, 2000) **with *P* increasing at each stage**. Why did the method choose those points? The original problem involved the inequalities shown opposite which give the feasible region

$$3x + y \leqslant 3000$$
$$6x + 5y \leqslant 12\,000$$
$$x \geqslant 0$$
$$y \geqslant 0$$

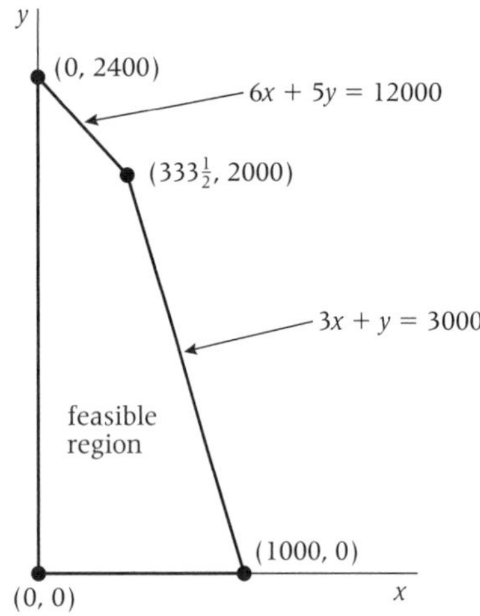

Notice that its vertices are (0, 0), (1000, 0), ($333\frac{1}{3}$, 2000) and (0, 2400). So the simplex method was moving from the origin at the start, to the vertex (1000, 0) and finally to the vertex ($333\frac{1}{3}$, 2000). At each stage it moved along an edge of the feasible region and did it so that *P* would increase.

In the next example the geometric solution on the left and the simplex method on the right are briefly outlined. You will then be able to see once again that the simplex method is taking us around edges of the feasible region from one vertex to the next, but is cleverly choosing its route so that the objective function increases at each stage.

Worked example 2.5

Solve the linear programming problem:

Maximise	$P = 2x + 3y$
subject to	$x + 2y \leqslant 40$
	$3x + 4y \leqslant 84$
	$5x + y \leqslant 55$
	$x \geqslant 0$
	$y \geqslant 0$

Solution

Graphical method

The feasible region can soon be drawn in the usual way. It is shown below with its vertices marked.

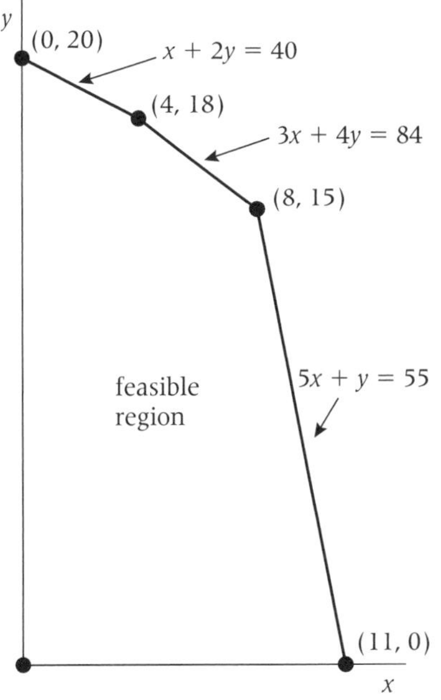

Then by using a 'profit line' or by calculating P at the vertices, we see that the maximum occurs at (4, 18) giving $P = 62$.

Simplex method

Slack variables s, t, u give:

$$P = 2x + 3y$$
$$x + 2y + s = 40$$
$$3x + 4y + t = 84$$
$$5x + y + u = 55$$
$$x \geqslant 0, y \geqslant 0, s \geqslant 0, t \geqslant 0, u \geqslant 0$$

P	x	y	s	t	u	
1	−2	−3	0	0	0	0
0	1	2	1	0	0	40
0	3	4	0	1	0	84
0	(5)	1	0	0	1	55

Interpretation

This represents $x = 0$, $y = 0$ with $P = 0$ (and $s = 40$, etc.)

Pivoting in x's column will have the effect of increasing x.

P	x	y	s	t	u	
1	0	$-2\frac{3}{5}$	0	0	$\frac{2}{5}$	22
0	0	$1\frac{4}{5}$	1	0	$-\frac{1}{5}$	29
0	0	($3\frac{2}{5}$)	0	1	$-\frac{3}{5}$	51
0	1	$\frac{1}{5}$	0	0	$\frac{1}{5}$	11

This represents $x = 11$, $y = 0$ with $P = 22$ (and $s = 29$, etc.)

Pivoting in y's column will have the effect of increasing y.

P	x	y	s	t	u	
1	0	0	0	$\frac{13}{17}$	$-\frac{1}{17}$	61
0	0	0	1	$-\frac{9}{17}$	($\frac{2}{17}$)	2
0	0	1	0	$\frac{5}{17}$	$-\frac{3}{17}$	15
0	1	0	0	$-\frac{1}{17}$	$\frac{4}{17}$	8

This represents $x = 8$, $y = 15$ with $P = 61$.

P	x	y	s	t	u	
1	0	0	0	$\frac{1}{2}$	0	62
0	0	0	1	$-4\frac{1}{2}$	1	17
0	0	1	0	$-\frac{1}{2}$	0	18
0	1	0	0	1	0	4

This represents $x = 4$, $y = 18$ with $P = 62$ which is now the maximum possible.

Comparing the two methods in the above solution you will see that the simplex method started at the origin (as always), moved anticlockwise around the feasible region to the vertex (11, 0), then to the vertex (8, 15) and finally to the vertex (4, 18) where the maximum of P occurs:

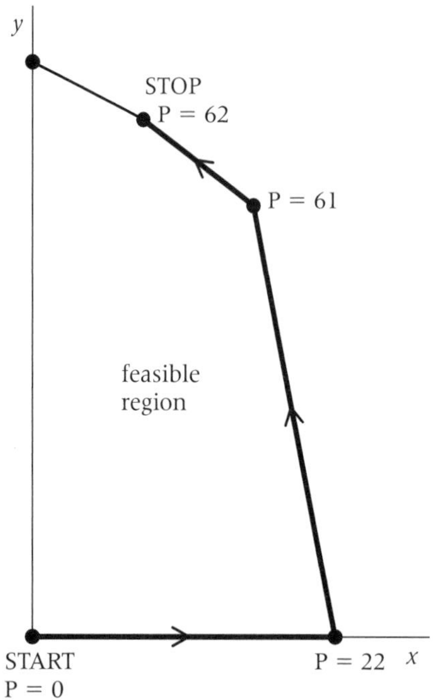

Interestingly, had we chosen to pivot with y first the route taken would have been clockwise around the feasible region and, in that example, it would have reached the maximum point with only two iterations instead of three.

In general, the simplex method:

- starts at the origin
- finds a route around the feasible region
- moves along an edge each time to an adjacent vertex
- increases the objective function at each stage
- stops when the maximum is reached.

The same is true (but harder to illustrate) in three dimensions. A linear programming problem with three variables can be illustrated with three mutually perpendicular axes in space. The feasible region is a convex polyhedron (or **simplex**) and the simplex method leads from the origin along edges to the maximum point, increasing the objective function at each stage:

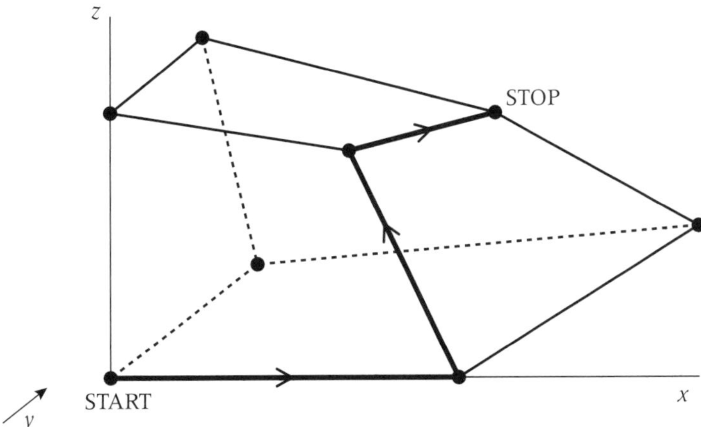

Mathematicians would argue that the same is true in n dimensions, but with more than three variables most people's geometric intuition will fail.

Worked exam question 2.6

Use the simplex method to solve the linear programming problem:

Maximise	$P = 5x + 2y$
subject to	$3x + y \leqslant 15$
	$2x + y \leqslant 12$
	$x \geqslant 0$
	$y \geqslant 0$

Interpret your initial simplex tableau and the tableau at the end of each iteration of the algorithm.

Solution

We introduce slack variables s and t to transform the problem to:

Maximise	$P = 5x + 2y$
subject to	$3x + y + s = 15$
	$2x + y + t = 12$
	$x \geqslant 0, y \geqslant 0, s \geqslant 0, t \geqslant 0$

The initial simplex tableau is:

P	x	y	s	t	
1	−5	−2	0	0	0
0	(3)	1	1	0	15
0	2	1	0	1	12

x and y are non-basic
$\therefore x = 0$ and $y = 0$
also $P = 0, s = 15, t = 12$

We can start by increasing either x or y, but we choose to increase x. The pivot position is as shown above (15/3 being less than 12/2). Dividing that row by 3 gives

P	x	y	s	t	
1	−5	−2	0	0	0
0	(1)	$\frac{1}{3}$	$\frac{1}{3}$	0	5
0	2	1	0	1	12

and using multiples of the pivot's row to get rid of the −5 and 2 in the pivot's column eventually gives:

P	x	y	s	t	
1	0	$-\frac{1}{3}$	$1\frac{2}{3}$	0	25
0	1	$\frac{1}{3}$	$\frac{1}{3}$	0	5
0	0	($\frac{1}{3}$)	$-\frac{2}{3}$	1	2

One iteration complete
y and s are non-basic
$\therefore y = 0$ and $s = 0$
also $P = 25$, $x = 5$, $t = 2$

The next pivot position is as shown above: multiplying that row by 3 gives:

P	x	y	s	t	
1	0	$-\frac{1}{3}$	$1\frac{2}{3}$	0	25
0	1	$\frac{1}{3}$	$\frac{1}{3}$	0	5
0	0	(1)	−2	3	6

Then using multiples of the pivot row to get rid of the $-\frac{1}{3}$ and $\frac{1}{3}$ in the pivot column gives

P	x	y	s	t	
1	0	0	1	1	27
0	1	0	1	−1	3
0	0	1	−2	3	6

Second iteration complete
s and t are non-basic
$\therefore s = 0$ and $t = 0$
also $P = 27$, $x = 3$, $y = 6$

Since there are no negative numbers in the top row we stop. The algorithm of the simplex method has taken us from $(0, 0)$ (with slack variables 15 and 12) to $(5, 0)$ (with slack variables 0 and 2) and finally to $(3, 6)$ (with both slack variables zero). During the process P increased from 0 to 25 to its maximum of 27 at $(3, 6)$.

EXERCISE 2D

1 In the solution of a linear programming problem, at one stage at the end of an iteration the tableau is as follows:

P	x	y	s	t	
1	0	−3	1	0	25
0	1	4	2	0	5
0	0	1	−2	1	6
0	0	−5	2	0	8

(a) Which point does this represent?

(b) What is the value of the objective function P at that point?

(c) What are the values of the slack variables at that point?

2 Use the simplex method to solve the linear programming problem:

Maximise	$P = x + 2y$
subject to	$4x + y \leqslant 18$
	$x + 3y \leqslant 21$
	$x \geqslant 0$
	$y \geqslant 0$

Interpret your initial simplex tableau and the tableau at the end of each iteration of the algorithm. [A]

3 Consider the linear programming problem:

Maximise	$P = 5x + 2y$
subject to	$3x + y \leqslant 15$
	$2x + y \leqslant 12$
	$x + 2y \leqslant 16$
	$x \geqslant 0$
	$y \geqslant 0$

(a) By introducing slack variables and pivoting first with x, use the simplex method to solve the problem.

(b) Sketch the feasible region and note clearly on your sketch the route taken by the process in **(a)**.

(c) How would the route have differed if you had pivoted with y first? [A]

2.6 Some general problems

The following chart shows what we have learned about the overall process of solving a linear programming problem by the simplex method:

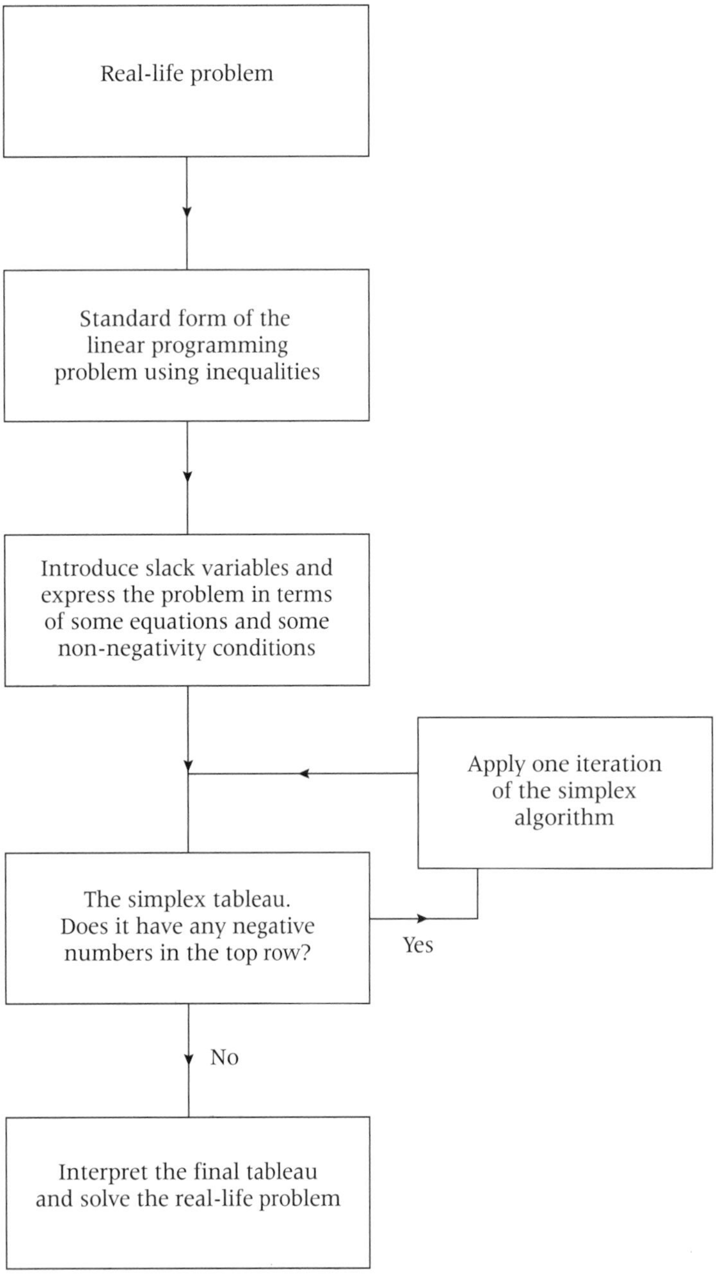

Real-life problem

↓

Standard form of the linear programming problem using inequalities

↓

Introduce slack variables and express the problem in terms of some equations and some non-negativity conditions

↓

The simplex tableau. Does it have any negative numbers in the top row?

Yes → Apply one iteration of the simplex algorithm → (return to the simplex tableau)

No ↓

Interpret the final tableau and solve the real-life problem

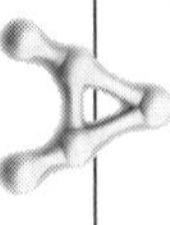

Each iteration of the simplex process increases the value of the objective function until it is maximised in the final tableau. The results can then be interpreted to solve the original real-life problem.

Here is one full worked example to illustrate the entire process.

Worked exam question 2.7

A holidaymaker wants to bring some wholesale packs of duty-free cigarettes and cigars into the country, in the boot of his car.

Each pack of cigarettes weighs a kilo, each pack of cigars weighs 3 kilos, and he dare not load more than 150 kilos altogether.

Each pack of cigarettes costs 100 francs, each pack of cigars costs 200 francs, and he has 11 000 francs to spend.

His boot will hold 80 packs of cigarettes or each pack of cigarettes can be replaced by two packs of cigars.

He will make £30 savings from each pack of cigarettes and £50 savings from each pack of cigars.

Use the simplex method to decide how many packs of each he should buy in order to make the most savings.

Solution

Let x be the number of packs of cigarettes and y the number of packs of cigars. Then the standard linear programming problem is to:

Maximise	$P = 30x + 50y$	
subject to	weight	$x + 3y \leqslant 150$
	cost:	$100x + 200y \leqslant 11\,000$
	space	$x + \frac{1}{2}y \leqslant 80$
		$x \geqslant 0$
		$y \geqslant 0$

The main inequalities tidy up to:

$$x + 3y \leqslant 150$$
$$x + 2y \leqslant 110$$
$$2x + y \leqslant 160$$

and the introduction of slack variables gives equations:

$$x + 3y + s = 150$$
$$x + 2y + t = 110$$
$$2x + y + u = 160$$

The simplex tableau is then:

P	x	y	s	t	u	
1	−30	−50	0	0	0	0
0	1	3	1	0	0	150
0	1	2	0	1	0	110
0	(2)	1	0	0	1	160

Increasing x gives the pivot position shown above (160/2 being the lowest). Dividing that row by 2 gives

P	x	y	s	t	u	
1	−30	−50	0	0	0	0
0	1	3	1	0	0	150
0	1	2	0	1	0	110
0	(1)	$\frac{1}{2}$	0	0	$\frac{1}{2}$	80

Adding/subtracting multiples of the pivot's row to the other rows to give 0s above the pivot leads to

P	x	y	s	t	u	
1	0	−35	0	0	15	2400
0	0	$2\frac{1}{2}$	1	0	$-\frac{1}{2}$	70
0	0	($1\frac{1}{2}$)	0	1	$-\frac{1}{2}$	30
0	1	$\frac{1}{2}$	0	0	$\frac{1}{2}$	80

One iteration is now complete. The new pivot position is shown ($30/1\frac{1}{2}$ being the lowest) and dividing the pivot's row by $1\frac{1}{2}$ gives:

P	x	y	s	t	u	
1	0	−35	0	0	15	2400
0	0	$2\frac{1}{2}$	1	0	$-\frac{1}{2}$	70
0	0	(1)	0	$\frac{2}{3}$	$-\frac{1}{3}$	20
0	1	$\frac{1}{2}$	0	0	$\frac{1}{2}$	80

Adding/subtracting multiples of the pivot's row to the other rows to give 0s above and below the pivot leads to

P	x	y	s	t	u	
1	0	0	0	$23\frac{1}{3}$	$3\frac{1}{3}$	3100
0	0	0	1	$-1\frac{2}{3}$	$\frac{1}{3}$	20
0	0	1	0	$\frac{2}{3}$	$-\frac{1}{3}$	20
0	1	0	0	$-\frac{1}{3}$	$\frac{2}{3}$	70

As there are no negative numbers in the top row this is the final tableau. It tells us that P takes its maximum of 3100 when $x = 70$ and $y = 20$ (the slack variables being 20, 0 and 0, respectively). Therefore the holidaymaker should take 70 packs of cigarettes and 20 packs of cigars in order to maximise his savings.

Some non-standard problems

This study of the simplex method has been restricted to standard maximising problems where the origin is in the feasible region (it then formed the starting point of the method). It is possible to generalise the instructions in the algorithm so that the method covers all linear programming problems, but that general form is beyond the scope of this course. However, one example is given where the origin is not a solution and we show how to adapt the problem.

Worked example 2.6

Consider the linear programming problem:

$$\begin{array}{ll}\text{Maximise} & P = 30x + 20y \\ \text{subject to} & 3x + y \leqslant 3800 \\ & 6x + 5y \leqslant 15\,100 \\ & x \geqslant 100 \\ & y \geqslant 500\end{array}$$

Show by introducing new variables how to transform this problem to a standard linear programming problem where the origin is a solution.

Solution

Let $X = x - 100$ and $Y = y - 500$. Then $x = X + 100$, $y = Y + 500$ and the problem transforms to:

$$\begin{array}{ll}\text{Maximise} & P = 30x + 20y = 30(X + 100) + 20(Y + 500) \\ \text{subject to} & 3(X + 100) + (Y + 500) \leqslant 3800 \\ & 6(X + 100) + 5(Y + 500) \leqslant 15\,100 \\ & X + 100 \geqslant 100 \\ & Y + 500 \geqslant 500\end{array}$$

which in turn reduce to:

$$\begin{array}{ll}\text{Maximise} & P = 30X + 20Y + 13\,000 \\ \text{subject to} & 3X + Y \leqslant 3000 \\ & 6x + 5y \leqslant 12\,000 \\ & X \geqslant 0 \\ & Y \geqslant 0\end{array}$$

This is now a standard problem with $(0, 0)$ in the feasible region, and hence the simplex method can be applied (the '+13 000' in P causes no problems – but you could of course maximise $30X + 20Y$ and add on the 13 000 later).

In fact we solved the equivalent problem in Worked exam question 2.4 where we found that $30X + 20Y$ had a maximum of 50 000 at $X = 333\frac{1}{3}$ and $Y = 2000$. Hence the original linear programming problem given in the question has the solution that P takes its maximum of 63 000 when $x = 433\frac{1}{3}$ and $y = 2500$.

Finally we consider just one minimising problem. It turns out that for every minimising linear programming problem there is a **dual problem** which is a maximising problem **with the same answers** for their objective functions. The duality theory of linear programming is beyond the scope of this course but we conclude with one example to illustrate this amazing link.

Worked example 2.7

Solve these two linear programming problems:

Minimise	$P = 21x + 12y$
subject to	$3x + y \geqslant 3$
	$x + 2y \geqslant 2$
	$x \geqslant 0$
	$y \geqslant 0$

Maximise	$Q = 3x + 2y$
subject to	$3x + y \leqslant 21$
	$x + 2y \leqslant 12$
	$x \geqslant 0$
	$y \geqslant 0$

Solution

We leave it as an exercise for you to solve these problems. The minimising one will have to be by graphical means and the maximising one can use either method.

You should find that P is minimised at $(\frac{4}{5}, \frac{3}{5})$ giving a minimum of **24**. On the other hand, Q is maximised at (6, 3) giving a maximum of **24**. So both problems give the same value for their objective functions.

What is the link between the two problems? Writing each as a small table with columns containing numbers/x/y we get

nos	x	y
	21	12
3	3	1
2	1	2

nos	x	y
	3	2
21	3	1
12	1	2

and you can see that the two tables are **transposes** of each other (the rows of one become the columns of the other).

A minimising and a maximising problem linked in this way are called **dual** problems and they always give the same answer.

The duality theory ensures that a given minimising problem can be transformed into a maximising one: hence our being able to solve maximising problems is actually sufficient.

EXERCISE 2E

1 Given the linear programming problem:

Maximise	$2x + y$
subject to	$x + 5y \leqslant 80$
	$x + y \leqslant 24$
	$3x + y \leqslant 64$
	$x \geqslant 5$
	$y \geqslant 0$

use a change of variables to transform it to a standard problem with $(0, 0)$ in the feasible region. Hence solve the problem by the simplex method. [A]

2 (a) Use a graphical method to solve the linear programming problem:

Minimise	$P = 2x + y$
subject to	$7x + 3y \geqslant 36$
	$x + y \geqslant 8$
	$3x + 5y \geqslant 30$

(b) Use the simplex method to solve the linear programming problem:

Maximise	$Q = 36x + 8y + 30z$
subject to	$7x + y + 3z \leqslant 2$
	$3x + y + 5z \leqslant 1$

[A]

(c) Write out a table for each of the problems in **(a)** and **(b)** and observe that the two problems are duals of each other.

3 A company manufactures two kinds of cloth A and B and uses three different colours of wool. The material required to make a unit length of each type of cloth and the total amount of wool of each colour that is available are shown in the table.

Requirements for unit length of cloth type		**Colour of wool**	**Wool available (kg)**
A (kg)	**B (kg)**		
4	1	Red	56
5	3	Green	105
1	2	Blue	56

The manufacturer makes a profit of £12 on a unit length of cloth A and a profit of £15 on a unit length of cloth B. How should he use the available material so as to make the largest possible profit?

(a) Solve the resulting problem by using the simplex algorithm.

(b) Confirm your answer to **(a)** by solving the problem graphically. [A]

MIXED EXERCISES

1 Use the simplex method to solve the linear programming problems:

(a)

Maximise	$P = 3x + 2y$
subject to	$2x + 3y \leqslant 24$
	$2x + y \leqslant 16$
	$y \leqslant 6$
	$x \geqslant 0$
	$y \geqslant 0$

[A]

(b)

Maximise	$P = x + 5y$
subject to	$4x + 3y \leqslant 12$
	$2x + 5y \leqslant 10$
	$x \geqslant 0$
	$y \geqslant 0$

[A]

(c)

Maximise	$P = x + y$
subject to	$3x + 4y \leqslant 12$
	$3x + 2y \leqslant 9$
	$x \geqslant 0$
	$y \geqslant 0$

[A]

2 Consider the linear programming problem:

Maximise	$P = 2x + 7y$
subject to	$5x + 2y \leqslant 25$
	$x + 2y \leqslant 13$
	$x \geqslant 0$
	$y \geqslant 0$

(a) Use the simplex method to solve the problem by first increasing x.

(b) Use the simplex method to solve the problem by first increasing y. [A]

(c) Sketch the feasible region of the problem and illustrate the routes taken by the simplex algorithm in **(a)** and **(b)**. [A]

3 (a) Solve each of these problems by the simplex method:

Maximise	$P = 10x + 12y + 8z$
subject to	$2x + 2y \leqslant 5$
	$5x + 3y + 4z \leqslant 15$
	$x \geqslant 0$
	$y \geqslant 0$
	$z \geqslant 0$

[A]

Maximise	$3x + 6y + 2z$
subject to	$3x + 4y + 2z \leqslant 2$
	$x + 3y + 2z \leqslant 1$
	$x \geqslant 0$
	$y \geqslant 0$
	$z \geqslant 0$

[A]

(b) (beyond syllabus) For each of the problems in **(a)** work out their dual minimising problems, solve them graphically, and confirm that dual pairs give the same answers for their objective function.

4 A linear programming problem is specified as:

Maximise	$P = 6x + 4y$
subject to	$x + 2y \leqslant 14$
	$x + y \leqslant 8$
	$2x + y \leqslant 11$
	$3x + y \leqslant 15$
	$x \geqslant 0$
	$y \geqslant 0$

(a) Solve the problem graphically.

(b) After some iterations of the simplex method the tableau is as shown opposite:

What point of the feasible region does this correspond to? Express P in terms of u and v and explain why this shows that $P = 36$ is not optimal.

P	x	y	s	t	u	v	
1	0	0	0	0	6	−2	36
0	0	0	1	0	−5	3	4
0	0	0	0	1	−2	1	1
0	0	1	0	0	3	−2	3
0	1	0	0	0	−1	1	4

(c) Carry out one further iteration of the simplex algorithm. [A]

5 A cycle manufacturer produces two types of mountain-bike: a basic Model X and a Super Model Y. Model X takes 6 effort-hours to make per unit, while Model Y takes 10 effort-hours per unit. There is a total of 450 effort-hours available per week for the manufacture of the two models.

Due to the difference in demand for the two models, handling and marketing costs are £20 per unit for Model X, but only £10 per unit for Model Y. The total funds available for these purposes are £800 per week.

Profits per unit for Models X and Y are £20 and £30 respectively. The objective is to maximise weekly profits by optimising the numbers of each model produced.

(a) The weekly profit is £P. The numbers of units of Model X and Model Y produced each week are x and y. Express P in terms of x and y. Also write down inequalities representing the constraints on production.

(b) By the simplex method, find the maximum obtainable profit and the numbers of each model manufactured which give this profit.

(c) If competition forces the manufacture to give a £5 discount on the price of Model X, resulting in a £5 reduction in profit, how are weekly profits now maximised? [A]

2

6 A maker of wooden furniture can produce three different types of furniture: sideboards, tables and chairs. Two machines are used in the production – a jigsaw and a lathe.

The manufacture of a sideboard requires 1 hour on the jigsaw and 2 hours on the lathe; a table requires 4 hours on the jigsaw and none on the lathe; a chair requires 2 hours on the jigsaw and 8 hours on the lathe.

The jigsaw can only operate 100 hours per week and the lathe for 40 hours per week. The profit made on a sideboard is £100, £40 on a table and £10 on a chair. In order to determine how best to use the two machines so as to maximise profits, formulate the problem as a linear programming problem, and solve it using the simplex method.

Is this realistic in practice? [A]

7 Use the simplex method to solve the linear programming problem:

Maximise	$P = x + 2y$
subject to	$2x + y \leqslant 30$
	$x + 3y \leqslant 30$
	$x \geqslant 0$
	$y \geqslant 0$

State the values of x, y, P and the slack variables initially and after each iteration of the algorithm. [A]

8 A linear programming problem is specified as:

Maximise	$P = 2x + y$
subject to	$6x + 5y \leqslant 60$
	$x + 2y \leqslant 17$
	$x \geqslant 0$
	$y \geqslant 0$

(a) Solve the problem by the simplex method, increasing x first.

(b) Solve the problem by the simplex method, increasing y first.

(c) Illustrate the routes taken by the algorithm in **(a)** and **(b)**.

(d) State the values of the slack variables at the optimal point. [A]

Key point summary

1 Given a real-life linear programming problem it can be expressed in terms of maximising (or minimising) an **objective function** subject to some **linear inequalities**. *p60*

2 By the introduction of **slack variables** (which measure the 'excess' in each non-trivial inequality), the problem reduces to some equations and some non-negativity conditions. *p61*

3 The standard maximising linear programming problem can then be expressed in the form of the **simplex tableau**. *p69*

4 The **simplex method** is an algorithm to be applied to the simplex tableau. Each iteration of the method consists of **pivoting** around a point chosen by numerical criteria. The process produces a new tableau and is repeated until the final tableau is reached with no negative entries in the top row. *p73*

5 Although we have only illustrated the simplex method for two (or sometimes three) variables with two (or sometimes three) constraints, in fact the method works for any number of variables and any number of constraints. *p76*

6 Each tableau represents a vertex of the feasible region. Its details are found by putting all the **non-basic** variables equal to 0 and solving the other equations. *p80*

7 Each iteration of the simplex method increases the value of the objective function until it is maximised in the final tableau. The results can then be interpreted to solve the original real-life problem. *p88*

2

Test yourself	What to review

To test each stage of the simplex method, consider this straightforward linear programming problem and answer the questions following it.

Ida Wick makes two types of candles to sell, Type A and Type B.

Each Type A requires 1 pack of wax, each Type B requires 3 packs of wax, and she has 20 packs of wax to use.

Each Type A takes 2 hours to make, each Type B takes 1 hour to make, and she has 10 hours to spare.

Ida makes £5 profit on each Type A candle and £2 profit on each Type B candle. How many of each type should she make in order to maximise her profit?

1 Introduce two variables x, y and write down an inequality arising from the amount of wax used and another inequality arising from the time available. What other trivial inequalities must your variables satisfy?	*Section 2.1 and Book D1, Chapter 4*
2 What is the objective function to be maximised?	*Section 2.1 and Book D1, Chapter 4*
3 Express the problem as a standard linear programming problem.	*Sections 2.1 and 2.2*
4 Introduce two slack variables and change the inequalities to some equations together with some non-negativity conditions.	*Section 2.3*
5 Form the simplex tableau. Which point does it represent?	*Sections 2.4 and 2.5*
6 Apply just one iteration of the simplex method by increasing x (i.e. by pivoting in x's column).	*Section 2.4*
7 What point does your new tableau represent? Explain how you know that the objective function is maximised there.	*Sections 2.4 and 2.5*
8 How many candles of each type should Ida make in order to maximise her profit, and what is that maximum?	*Section 2.1 and Book D1, Chapter 4*

Test yourself ANSWERS

1 x Type A, y Type B,
$x + 3y \leqslant 20$,
$2x + y \leqslant 10$,
$x \geqslant 0$, $y \geqslant 0$.

2 $P = 5x + 2y$.

3

Maximise	$P = x + 2y$
subject to	$x + 3y \leqslant 20$
	$2x + y \leqslant 10$
	$x \geqslant 0$
	$y \geqslant 0$

4 $x + 3y + s = 20$,
$2x + y + t = 10$.

5

P	x	y	s	t	
1	−5	−2	0	0	0
0	1	3	1	0	20
0	2	1	0	1	10

6

P	x	y	s	t	
1	0	$\frac{1}{2}$	0	$2\frac{1}{2}$	25
0	0	$2\frac{1}{2}$	1	$-\frac{1}{2}$	15
0	1	$\frac{1}{2}$	0	$\frac{1}{2}$	5

7 $y = 0$, $x = 5$; $(5, 0)$,
no negative numbers in top row.

8 5 Type A candles only; £25.

CHAPTER 3

Recurrence relations

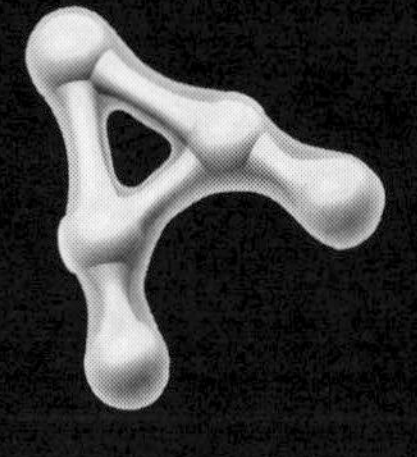

Learning objectives

After studying this chapter, you should be able to:

- recognise real problems which can be solved recursively
- set up an appropriate recurrence relation for any given problem
- solve a variety of first and second order recurrence relations
- apply your solutions to the real-life problems
- investigate long-term trends.

3.1 Introduction

In this chapter you will solve a selection of problems which are hard in themselves but can be solved by building up to them from previous situations.

For example the famous **Fibonacci sequence** is easy to define as:

0, 1, 1, 2, 3, 5, 8, 13, 21, ...

where, after the first two terms are given, subsequent terms are obtained by adding the two previous ones. But surely there must be a way of calculating the 1000th Fibonacci number without having to work out all the previous 999 numbers?

Similarly if you have £1000 savings which have interest added at 4% a year and, in addition, you add £100 to the savings each year, surely there must be a neat way of calculating your anticipated savings in 2025 without having to work out the total for each intermediate year?

Both those problems are typical of the ones which we shall solve using **recurrence relations**. In each case you can only express the answer in terms of previous ones and there is no obvious direct way of getting the answer you want.

The theory developed in this chapter is a very neat piece of pure mathematics with wide applications in statistics, applied mathematics, economics, geography, biology and physics.

3.2 Setting up the equation

Imagine that you are to jump from an aircraft and you want to free-fall for 600 metres. You know that in successive seconds you will fall:

5 metres during the 1st second

15 metres during the 2nd second

25 metres during the 3rd second

35 metres during the 4th second

⋮

How far will you fall during the nth second?
How far in total will you have fallen after n seconds?
How soon should you pull the rip-cord?

The answer to the first question is reasonably straightforward: we can see from the pattern that you will fall:

$10n - 5$ metres during the nth second

Now if we let u_1 be the **total** distance fallen in 1 second, u_2 be the **total** distance fallen in 2 seconds, u_3 the **total** distance fallen in 3 seconds, ... then we get:

$$u_2 = u_1 + \text{distance fallen during 2nd second} = 5 + 15 = 20$$

$$u_3 = u_2 + \text{distance fallen during 3rd second} = 20 + 25 = 45$$

$$u_4 = u_3 + \text{distance fallen during 4th second} = 45 + 35 = 80$$

⋮

In general

$$u_n = u_{n-1} + \text{distance fallen in the } n\text{th second} = u_{n-1} + 10n - 5$$

For the moment that does not help us to get a specific formula for u_n but we have learned that:

$$\boxed{u_n = u_{n-1} + 10n - 5 \quad (n > 1)}$$

This is called a **recurrence relation** as it is a relationship which is repeated over and over again. (Because it expresses the difference between successive u_ns it is also sometimes called a **difference equation**.) In general a recurrence relation expresses something like u_n in terms of earlier ones.

The recurrence relation quoted above is not quite complete. It would enable you to express u_{100}, say, in terms of u_{99}, which would then enable you to express it in terms of u_{98}, etc. But to actually be able to work out a numerical value of u_n you would also need to know the value of u_1 (which was 5). The extra information $u_1 = 5$ is known as an **initial condition**. So now the full story concerning your free-fall is:

$$u_1 = 5 \quad \text{and} \quad u_n = u_{n-1} + 10n - 5 \quad (n > 1)$$

3

In the next section you shall learn how to solve this recurrence relation in order to find a specific formula for u_n. Our task for the moment is simply to look at some problems and set up an appropriate recurrence relation and initial condition (or conditions) – solving the recurrence relations in subsequent sections.

You may be familiar with the puzzle called the **Tower of Hanoi** (sometimes known as the **Tower of Brahma**). The object of the puzzle is to transfer a pile of rings from one to another, one ring at a time. There is an intermediate rod on which to place rings during the process. At no stage is a larger ring allowed to be on top of a smaller one.

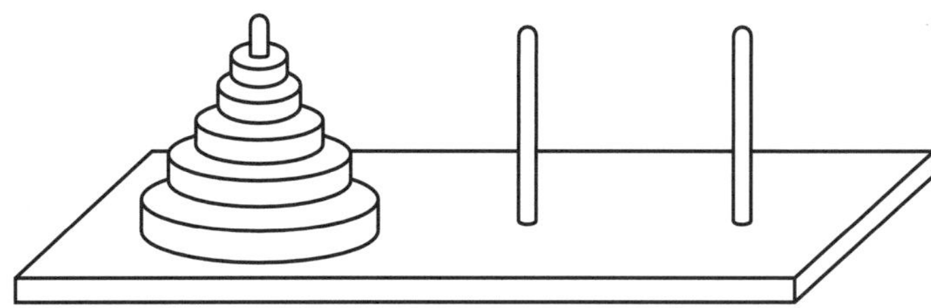

The Tower of Hanoi

Try it for yourself with just three rings. Then try it with four (your strategy with three will help). The puzzle comes from the Far East where the folklore is that in the temple of Benares a priest unceasingly moves a ring each day from one rod to another. They say that when he has finished moving a pile of 64 rings the world will end! There is some truth in that.

Worked example 3.1

Let u_n be the minimum number of moves needed to transfer a pile of n rings from one rod to another in the Tower of Hanoi puzzle. Find a recurrence relation for u_n.

Solution

Firstly, we can soon see that one ring can be transferred in just one move: so $u_1 = 1$.

Now imagine, for example, that you have learned how to move a pile of four rings in the most economical way, taking u_4 moves. Then you start again with a pile of five rings:

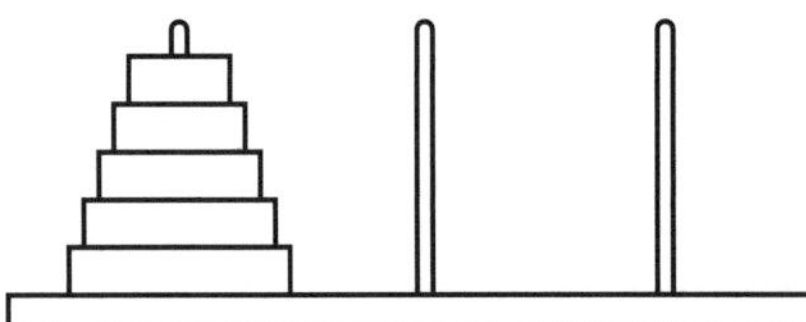

The most economical way of moving the five rings is to first transfer the top four to the intermediate rod (which you know how to do in just u_4 moves):

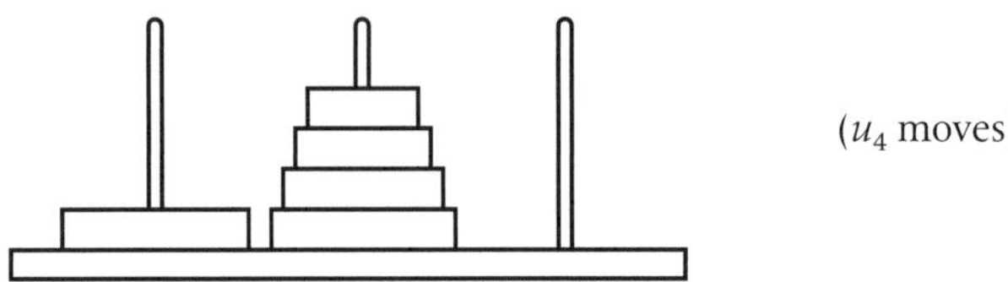

(u_4 moves)

Then move the largest ring to the final rod, taking one further move:

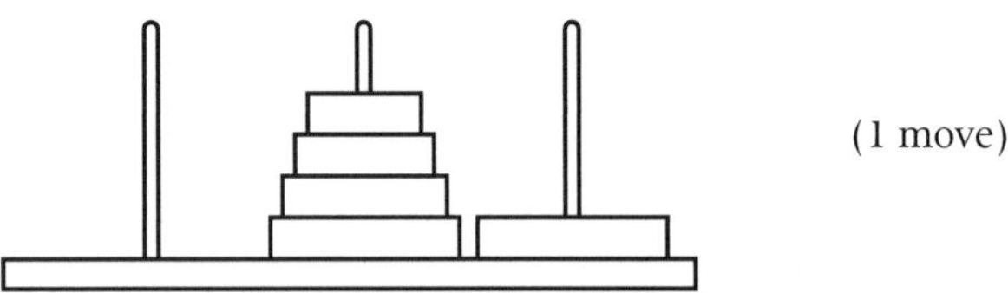

(1 move)

Finally, transfer the pile of four rods to the final rod (you can use the first rod as a resting place) taking a further u_4 moves:

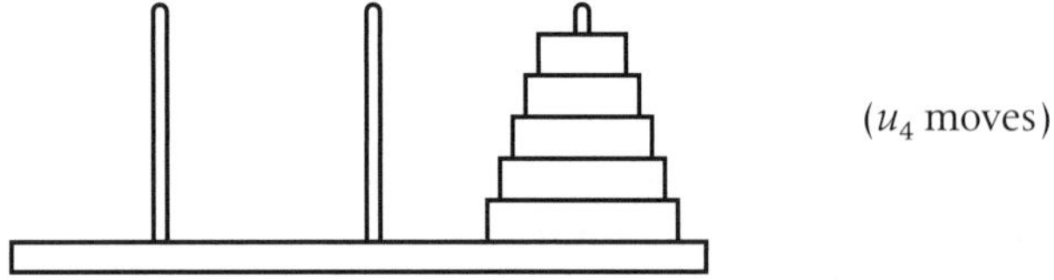

(u_4 moves)

There is no way that you can beat that process, which took $2u_4 + 1$ moves altogether. Hence, that is the minimum number of ways needed to move five rings; i.e.

$$u_5 = 2u_4 + 1.$$

Clearly, exactly the same argument would work for u_6 in terms of u_5, etc. In general the u_ns satisfy the recurrence relation:

$$u_1 = 1 \quad \text{and} \quad u_n = 2u_{n-1} + 1 \qquad (n > 1)$$

Again we shall actually solve that recurrence relation in the next section. But there are some variations on the way in which the relation can be presented, and you ought to be familiar with them. An equivalent answer to the one which we deduced in that worked example is:

$$u_1 = 1 \quad \text{and} \quad u_{n+1} = 2u_n + 1 \qquad (n \geqslant 1)$$

(The recurrence relation is telling us one value in terms of a previous one and the actual label used is irrelevant.) Another variation is that sometimes u_0 makes sense. In the Tower of Hanoi puzzle it would represent the number of ways needed to move 0 rings, and so of course it would be 0. Hence the initial condition could be given in terms of u_0 and our recurrence relation would then be

$$u_0 = 0 \quad \text{and} \quad u_n = 2u_{n-1} + 1 \qquad (n \geqslant 1)$$

or

$$u_0 = 0 \quad \text{and} \quad u_{n+1} = 2u_n + 1 \qquad (n \geqslant 0)$$

Note that all four versions will lead to exactly the same answer for u_n.

Worked example 3.2

In graph theory the **complete graph** K_n consists of n vertices with each joined to each of the others by a single edge. Let u_n be the number of edges of K_n. Find a recurrence relation for u_n.

Solution

We have already worked out u_n in graph theory in the course D1. But here we start again with the idea.

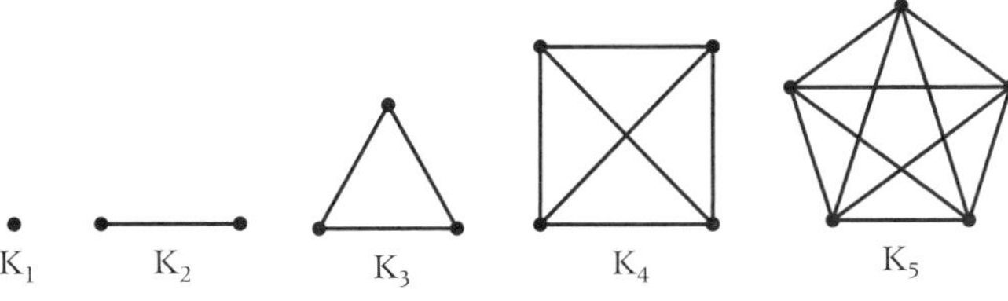

Firstly note that K_1 has no edges; i.e. $u_1 = 0$.

Now how can we build up, say, from K_4 to K_5? That would require the addition of one new vertex which would then have to be joined to the four previous vertices:

K_4
u_4 edges

K_5
$u_4 + 4$ edges

But K_5 has u_5 edges. Therefore:

$$u_5 = u_4 + 4$$

and in general

$$u_n = u_{n-1} + n - 1$$

(or $u_{n+1} = u_n + n$). Hence a recurrence relation for u_n is:

$$u_1 = 0 \quad \text{and} \quad u_n = u_{n-1} + n - 1 \qquad (n > 1)$$

Sometimes an answer is expressed in terms of more than one previous answer, as in the case of the **Fibonacci numbers**. These are attributed to the 13th century Italian mathematician *Leonardo Fibonacci* and they occur naturally in a range of problems on population and plant growth.

Worked example 3.3

The **Fibonacci numbers** are given by:

$$0, 1, 1, 2, 3, 5, 8, 13, 21, 34, 55, \ldots$$

where each is obtained by adding the previous two. Let $u_0 = 0$, $u_1 = 1$ and in general let u_n be the nth Fibonacci number. (Notice that the labelling in this case starts at 0 so 0 is the 0th Fibonacci number!) Write down a recurrence relation for u_n.

Solution

There is very little work to do here as we are told that u_n is the sum of the previous two Fibonacci numbers; i.e.

$$u_n = u_{n-1} + u_{n-2}.$$

That of course only works for u_2 onwards. Furthermore the process cannot get going until the first **two** terms have been given. So in this case the recurrence relation requires **two** initial conditions. Overall we get:

$$u_0 = 0,\ u_1 = 1 \quad \text{and} \quad u_n = u_{n-1} + u_{n-2} \qquad (n > 1)$$

3

EXERCISE 3A

1 Write down a recurrence relation for the *n*th term of each of these sequences. Note that in **(c)**, **(d)** and **(e)** each number is calculated from **two** previous ones:

(a) 1, 4, 7, 10, 13, ...

(b) 2, 5, 11, 23, 47, ...

(c) 0, 1, 2, 6, 16, 44, 120, ...

(d) 0, 1, 2, 5, 12, 29, 70, ...

(e) 16, 0, 8, 4, 6, 5, 5.5, 5.75, ...

2 On January 1st in the year 2000 Prudence put £1000 into a savings account and the money is growing by 4% a year. In addition, on each subsequent January 1st she intends to add a further £100. So, for example, on January 1st 2001 the account total is £1140. Let u_n be the amount in the account after she has put in her £100 on January 1st in the year $2000 + n$. Write down a recurrence relation for u_n.

3 The **triangular numbers** t_n are:

1, 3, 6, 10, 15, 21, ...

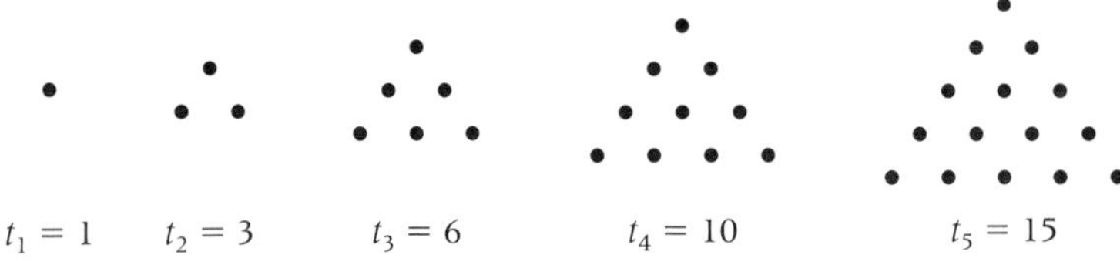

By observing how many dots have to be added to t_{n-1} to get t_n, write down a recurrence relation for t_n.

3.3 First order relations

Before proceeding it is worth recalling how to sum an **arithmetic series** and a **geometric series**. You will need to be familiar with both in some of our solutions.

An **arithmetic series** is a sum where there is a constant difference between the terms; e.g.

$$5 + 7 + 9 + 11 + \ldots + 73 + 75.$$

To work out this sum you could quote and apply the appropriate formula (involving n, a and d) but it is actually just as easy to remember that for such a neat series the average of all the terms is simply the average of the first and last term. Hence in the given example, where there are 36 terms of average $\frac{1}{2}(5+75)=40$, the sum is

$$\text{number of terms} \times \text{average} = 36 \times \tfrac{1}{2}(5+75) = 36 \times 40 = 1440.$$

A **geometric series** is a sum where each term is some fixed multiple of the previous term; e.g.

$$6 + 18 + 54 + 162 + \ldots + 6 \times 3^{99}.$$

Again you could work out this sum by quoting and applying the appropriate formula (involving n, a and r). But in practice it is very easy to make a mistake quoting that formula (for example in the given series n is 100 rather than 99). So, working from scratch, the given sum is:

$$S = 6 + \underbrace{\,18\,}_{\times 3} + 54 + 162 + \ldots + 6 \times 3^{99}.$$

and

$$3S = 18 + 54 + 162 + \ldots + 6 \times 3^{99} + 6 \times 3^{100}.$$

Hence subtracting the first expression from the second gives

$$2S = 6 \times 3^{100} - 6$$

and

$$S = 3(3^{100} - 1).$$

Whether you choose to use formulae or common-sense, make sure that you can sum arithmetic and geometric series.

Worked example 3.4

Calculate the sums of the series:

$$7 + 10 + 13 + 16 + \ldots + 301$$

and

$$10 + 15 + 22.5 + 33.75 + \ldots + 10 \times (1.5)^{17}.$$

3

Solution

using formulae

The arithmetic series

$$7 + 10 + 13 + \ldots + 301$$

has first term $a = 7$, common difference $d = 3$, and number of terms $n = 99$. Hence the formula:

$$S = \frac{n}{2}(2a + (n-1)d)$$

gives a sum of

$$S = \frac{99}{2}(2 \times 7 + 98 \times 3) = 15\,246$$

The geometric series:

$$10 + 15 + \ldots + 10 \times (1.5)^{17}$$

has first term $a = 10$, common ratio $r = 1.5$, and number of terms $n = 18$.

Hence the formula:

$$S = \frac{a(1 - r^n)}{1 - r}$$

gives

$$S = \frac{10(1 - (1.5)^{18})}{1 - 1.5} \approx 29\,538$$

from scratch

The arithmetic series

$$7 + 10 + 13 + \ldots + 301$$

has 99 terms of average

$$\tfrac{1}{2}(7 + 301) = 154.$$

Hence the total is

$$99 \times 154 = 15\,246$$

The geometric series:

$$S = 10 + 15 + \ldots + 10 \times (1.5)^{17}$$

has

$$1\tfrac{1}{2}S = 15 + \ldots + 10 \times (1.5)^{17} + 10 \times (1.5)^{18}$$

Hence subtracting the first from the second gives:

$$\tfrac{1}{2}S = 10 \times (1.5)^{18} - 10 \approx 14\,769$$

and

$$S \approx 29\,538$$

Now we are ready to continue with our study of recurrence relations. A recurrence relation which expresses each number in terms of **just one** previous number is called a **first order** recurrence relation. The examples of first order relations which we constructed in the previous section are:

Edges of K_n

$$u_1 = 0 \quad \text{and} \quad u_n = u_{n-1} + n - 1 \qquad (n > 1)$$

Free-fall

$$u_1 = 5 \quad \text{and} \quad u_n = u_{n-1} + 10n - 5 \qquad (n > 1)$$

Tower of Hanoi

$$u_1 = 1 \quad \text{and} \quad u_n = 2u_{n-1} + 1 \qquad (n > 1)$$

We shall now proceed to solve these recurrence relations. A 'bare hands' approach is simply to keep reapplying the formula, gradually working backwards to the initial value. This is known as **recursion** or **iteration**.

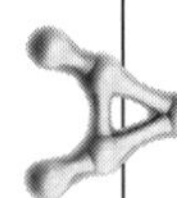

A **first order** recurrence relation of the form:

$$u_1 = a, \ u_n = ku_{n-1} + f(n) \ (n > 1)$$

can be solved by **recursion** or **iteration**, expressing u_{n-1} in terms of u_{n-2}, etc. The resulting expression for u_n can sometimes be simplified using **arithmetic** or **geometric series**.

Worked example 3.5

The number of edges, u_n, of the complete graph K_n satisfies the recurrence relation

$$u_1 = 0 \quad \text{and} \quad u_n = u_{n-1} + n - 1 \quad (n > 1)$$

By iterating with the recurrence relation find a specific formula for u_n in terms of n.

Solution

The recurrence relation works for n and for $n - 1$ and for $n - 2$ ... to give:

$$\begin{aligned} u_n &= u_{n-1} + n - 1 \\ u_{n-1} &= u_{n-2} + n - 2 \\ u_{n-2} &= u_{n-3} + n - 3 \\ &\vdots \end{aligned}$$

and so working back from n by putting these together gives:

$$\begin{aligned} u_n &= u_{n-1} + n - 1 \\ &= (u_{n-2} + n - 2) + n - 1 \\ &= u_{n-2} + (n - 2) + (n - 1) \\ &= (u_{n-3} + n - 3) + (n - 2) + (n - 1) \\ &= u_{n-3} + (n - 3) + (n - 2) + (n - 1) \\ &\vdots \\ &= u_1 + 1 + 2 + \ldots + (n - 3) + (n - 2) + (n - 1) \\ &= 0 + 1 + 2 + \ldots + (n - 3) + (n - 2) + (n - 1) \end{aligned}$$

This last expression is an arithmetic series with sum $\frac{1}{2}n(n - 1)$ and so we have deduced that $u_n = \frac{1}{2}n(n - 1)$. (This confirms our answer from graph theory.)

3

Worked exam question 3.1

A free-faller jumps from a plane and the distance she has fallen after n seconds satisfies the recurrence relation:

$$u_1 = 5 \quad \text{and} \quad u_n = u_{n-1} + 10n - 5 \quad (n > 1)$$

(a) By repeated application of the relation, find a specific formula for u_n in terms of n.

(b) The free-faller wants to break a record by dropping 2000 metres before pulling the rip-cord of her parachute. After how many seconds should she pull the cord?

Solution

(a) The recurrence relation tells us that:

$$\begin{aligned} u_n &= u_{n-1} + 10n - 5 \\ u_{n-1} &= u_{n-2} + 10(n-1) - 5 \\ u_{n-2} &= u_{n-3} + 10(n-2) - 5 \\ &\vdots \end{aligned}$$

Therefore:

$$\begin{aligned} u_n &= u_{n-1} + 10n - 5 \\ &= (u_{n-2} + 10(n-1) - 5) + 10n - 5 \\ &= u_{n-2} + 10[(n-1) + n] - 5 \times 2 \\ &= (u_{n-3} + 10(n-2) - 5) + 10[(n-1) + n] - 5 \times 2 \\ &= u_{n-3} + 10[(n-2) + (n-1) + n] - 5 \times 3 \\ &\vdots \\ &= u_1 + 10[2 + 3 + \ldots + (n-1) + n] - 5(n-1) \end{aligned}$$

Then, using the initial condition that $u_1 = 5$ and summing the arithmetic progression $2 + 3 + \ldots + n$ gives

$$u_n = 5 + 10 \times (n-1) \times \tfrac{1}{2}(n+2) - 5(n-1)$$

which tidies up to the delightfully neat answer $u_n = 5n^2$.

(Check: $u_1 = 5 = 5.1^2$, $u_2 = u_1 + 15 = 20 = 5.2^2$, $u_3 = u_2 + 25 = 45 = 5.3^2$, etc.)

(b) After n seconds she has fallen $5n^2$ metres. So she will have fallen 2000 metres after n seconds, where:

$$5n^2 = 2000, \quad n^2 = 400 \quad \text{and} \quad n = 20.$$

Therefore she should pull the rip-cord after 20 seconds.

The process of iteration (or reapplying the relation over-and-over again) is very long-winded and so, in practice, there are standard formulae which you can quote to save you the effort. We shall give a formula for solving those first order recurrence relations, which are of the form:

$$u_n = ku_{n-1} + c$$

constant (pointing to k) constant (pointing to c)

In general we can give the solution of such a recurrence relation:

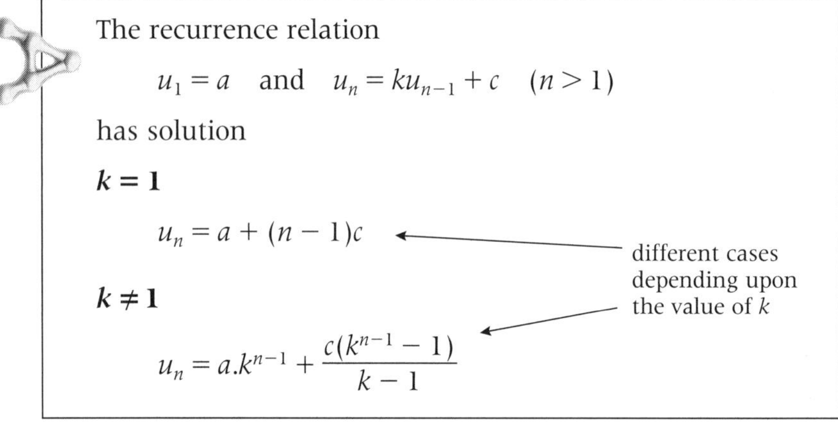

The recurrence relation

$$u_1 = a \quad \text{and} \quad u_n = ku_{n-1} + c \quad (n > 1)$$

has solution

$k = 1$

$$u_n = a + (n-1)c$$

$k \neq 1$

$$u_n = a.k^{n-1} + \frac{c(k^{n-1} - 1)}{k - 1}$$

Now if you are given such a first order recurrence relation to solve, you can simply use the formula.

Worked exam question 3.2

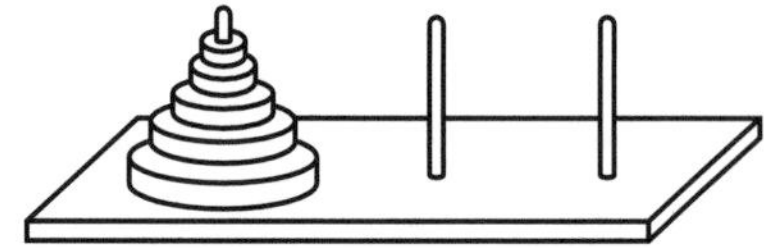

In the Tower of Hanoi puzzle the number of moves, u_n, required to move a pile of n rings satisfies the recurrence relation

$$u_1 = 1 \quad \text{and} \quad u_n = 2u_{n-1} + 1 \quad (n > 1)$$

(a) Solve the recurrence relation to express u_n in terms of n.

(b) According to legend the priests of Benares are moving a pile of 64 rings at one a day. Approximately how long will it take them to complete the puzzle?

3

Solution

(a) The given recurrence relation

$$u_n = 2u_{n-1} + 1$$

is of the right form and we can apply the formula with $k = 2$, $c = 1$ and $a = 1$ (the value of u_1). Hence the solution is:

$$\begin{aligned} u_n &= a.k^{n-1} + \frac{c(k^{n-1} - 1)}{k - 1} \\ &= 2^{n-1} + \frac{1(2^{n-1} - 1)}{2 - 1} \\ &= 2.2^{n-1} - 1 \\ &= 2^n - 1. \end{aligned}$$

(Quick check: it takes one move for one ring, which **is** $2^1 - 1$, and three moves for two rings, which **is** $2^2 - 1$, etc.)

(b) The number of moves required for 64 rings is $2^{64} - 1$ which is approximately 18 447 000 000 billion. At one a day that would take 50 million billion years!

The given general formula for solving certain first order equations assumed that the initial condition was given in terms of u_1. If instead it is given in terms of u_0, then the formula has to be adapted slightly. It does not really have to be remembered afresh if you just realise that to get from the 0th term instead of the 1st you have to increase the n in the solution by 1 to give the following.

The recurrence relation

$$u_0 = a \quad \text{and} \quad u_n = ku_{n-1} + c \quad (n \geqslant 1)$$

has solution

$\boldsymbol{k = 1}$

$$u_n = a + nc$$

$\boldsymbol{k \neq 1}$

$$u_n = a.k^n + \frac{c(k^n - 1)}{k - 1}$$

Worked exam question 3.3

The population of dolphins in a Scottish bay is currently about 1000 pairs. Each year 5% of them die and 6% of the pairs produce a pair of baby dolphins. In addition 10 pairs join the population each year from neighbouring waters.

(a) Let p_n be the number of pairs of dolphins n years from now. Write down a recurrence relation in p_n and solve it.

(b) Approximately how many dolphins will there be 10 years from now?

(c) New fishing methods in the Scottish Isles mean that a further 3% of the dolphins die in the fishing nets each year. How does that effect your recurrence relation in **(a)**? Solve the revised recurrence relation and use your solution to predict when the dolphin population will reach 750 pairs.

Solution

(a) p_0 = number of pairs now = 1000

and

$$p_n = p_{n-1} - \underset{\text{deaths}}{\underset{\uparrow}{0.05p_{n-1}}} + \underset{\text{births}}{\underset{\uparrow}{0.06p_{n-1}}} + \underset{\text{new}}{\underset{\uparrow}{10}} = 1.01p_{n-1} + 10$$

This is a standard first order relation with $a = 1000$, $k = 1.01$ and $c = 10$.
Therefore by the formula quoted above the solution is:

$$p_n = 1000(1.01)^n + \frac{10((1.01)^n - 1)}{1.01 - 1} = 2000(1.01)^n - 1000.$$

(b) It follows from our answer in **(a)** that:

$$p_{10} = 2000\,(1.01)^{10} - 1000 \simeq 1209.$$

(c) The revised recurrence relation is:

$$p_n = 0.98p_{n-1} + 10$$

and the new solution turns out to be

$$p_n = 500\,(0.98)^n + 500$$

The population reaching 750 pairs means $p_n = 750$ which happens when:

$$500\,(0.98)^n = 250 \quad \text{or} \quad 0.98^n = 0.5$$

Hence

$$n.\log(0.98) = \log(0.5) \quad \text{and} \quad n = \frac{\log(0.5)}{\log(0.98)} \simeq 34$$

and the population will reach 750 pairs in about 34 years' time.

You will have noticed that the formula for the solution of linear first order relations was given in two cases, $k = 1$ and $k \neq 1$. The case $k = 1$ turns out to be trivial and you can certainly solve such recurrence relations without using the formula:

Worked example 3.6

Find the nth term of the sequence

$$4, 7, 10, 13, \ldots$$

Solution

Since the terms go up in threes it is fairly natural to compare the terms with:

$$3, 6, 9, 12, \ldots$$

and you see immediately that the nth term of the given sequence is $3n + 1$.

In the unlikely event that you felt the need to use recurrence relations, the terms of the sequence satisfy

$$u_1 = 4 \quad \text{and} \quad u_n = u_{n-1} + 3.$$

By the general formula with $a = 4$, $k = 1$ and $c = 3$ we get the solution:

$$u_n = a + (n - 1)c = 4 + 3(n - 1) = 3n + 1$$

as before.

That example shows that the $k = 1$ case is trivial and is rarely used. The $k \neq 1$ case is much more useful and it is reasonably straightforward to produce using our iterating method:

Given: $u_1 = a \quad \text{and} \quad u_n = ku_{n-1} + c$

To deduce: $u_n = ak^{n-1} + \dfrac{c(k^{n-1} - 1)}{k - 1}$

We have:

$$\begin{aligned} u_n &= ku_{n-1} + c \\ &= k(ku_{n-2} + c) + c \\ &= k^2u_{n-2} + kc + c \\ &= k^2(ku_{n-3} + c) + kc + c \\ &= k^3u_{n-3} + k^2c + kc + c \\ &\;\vdots \\ &= k^{n-1}u_1 + k^{n-2}c + k^{n-3}c + \ldots + kc + c \\ &= ak^{n-1} + c\underbrace{(k^{n-2} + k^{n-1} + \ldots + k + 1)}_{\text{geometric series}} \\ &= ak^{n-1} + \frac{c(k^{n-1} - 1)}{k - 1} \end{aligned}$$

as expected. Of course for such standard linear relations there will now be no need to go through that iterating process because we have the result summarised as a general formula which can be quoted whenever needed.

EXERCISE 3B

1 Solve each of the following recurrence relations:

(a) $u_1 = 5, \quad u_n = u_{n-1} + 4 \quad (n > 1)$

(b) $u_1 = 1, \quad u_n = 2u_{n-1} + 3 \quad (n > 1)$

(c) $u_1 = 0, \quad u_n = \frac{1}{2}u_{n-1} + 10 \quad (n > 1)$

(d) $u_0 = 2, \quad u_n = u_{n-1} + 4 \quad (n \geqslant 1)$

(e) $u_0 = 1, \quad u_n = 2u_{n-1} - 1 \quad (n \geqslant 1)$.

2 Tessa has just put £1000 into a Building Society savings account which has a fixed interest rate of 5%. In addition, on each anniversary of opening the account she is going to add a further £200. Use a recurrence relation to find a formula for how much will be in the account n years from now. When will the amount in the account first exceed £5000?

3 The population of foxes in Tallyshire is currently about 100 pairs. Each year 30% of them die and 20% of the pairs produce a pair of baby foxes. In addition 20 pairs join the population each year from neighbouring counties.

(a) Let p_n be the number of pairs of foxes n years from now. Write down a recurrence relation in p_n and solve it.

(b) What will happen to the fox population in the long term?

(c) Fox-hunting is to be banned in Tallyshire thus halving the death rate. How does this effect your recurrence relation in **(a)**? Solve the revised recurrence relation and use your solution to predict the fox population in 10 years' time.

4 In the algorithm for the Chinese postperson problem (Section 1.3) the odd vertices had to be paired together. For example, with four vertices A, B, C, D there were three pairings

AB/CD, AC/BD, AD/BC.

Let p_n be the number of possible pairings of $2n$ vertices. Show that:

$$p_1 = 1, \quad p_n = (2n - 1)p_{n-1} \quad (n > 1)$$

and deduce by iteration that:

$$p_n = 1.3.5 \ldots (2n - 1) = \frac{(2n)!}{2^n.n!}.$$

3

5 [harder] In the late 19th century Arthur Cayley proved that the number of trees with 100 labelled vertices is 100^{98} (with similar results for any number of vertices). The key to proving this difficult result is to let t_n denote the number of trees on 100 labelled vertices in which the first vertex is joined to all except n of the other vertices. Then it can be shown that for $n > 1$:

$$t_n = \frac{99(99-n)}{n} t_{n-1}$$

Use an iterating process to deduce that:

$$t_n = \frac{99^n.98.97 \ldots (99-n)}{n(n-1)(n-2) \ldots 1} = \binom{98}{n} 99^n.$$

If you wish, it is then possible to deduce that the number of trees on 100 labelled vertices is 100^{98}.

3.4 Second order relations – homogeneous

A **second order** recurrence relation is one in which each number is expressed in terms of **two** previous numbers. In this section we shall restrict attention to **linear** second order recurrence relations of the form:

$$u_n = pu_{n-1} + qu_{n-2}$$

constant (p) constant (q)

In addition this relation is **homogeneous**, meaning that every term involves one of the us. In the next section we shall extend our study to non-homogeneous relations of the form:

$$u_n = pu_{n-1} + qu_{n-2} + \mathrm{f}(n)$$

for various functions f.

We have already met one homogeneous linear second order recurrence relation, namely the one governing the Fibonacci numbers:

Fibonacci numbers

$$u_0 = 0, \ u_1 = 1 \quad \text{and} \quad u_n = u_{n-1} + u_{n-2} \quad (n > 1)$$

which is of the form given above with $p = q = 1$.

Worked example 3.7

There are n discs in a circle and we wish to colour each disc with one of three colours and to do it in such a way that no two adjacent discs are the same colour.

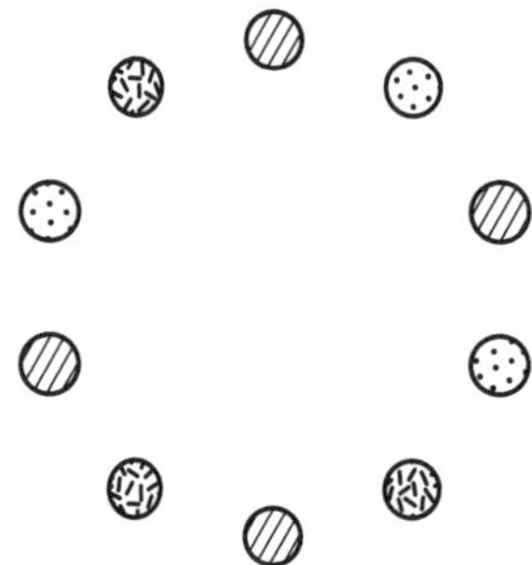

Let u_n denote the number of ways of doing the colouring. Show that u_n satisfies the recurrence relation

$$u_2 = u_3 = 6 \quad \text{and} \quad u_n = u_{n-1} + 2u_{n-2} \quad (n > 3)$$

Solution

Although putting two discs 'in a circle' is rather meaningless it is reasonable that:

u_2 = number of ways of colouring two discs $= 3 \times 2 = 6$
u_3 = number of ways of colouring three discs $= 3 \times 2 \times 1 = 6$

The general relation is quite tricky (and more than you would be asked to deduce in an exam). The trick is to pick one particular disc (the bottom one, say) and to break down the u_n colourings into two types:

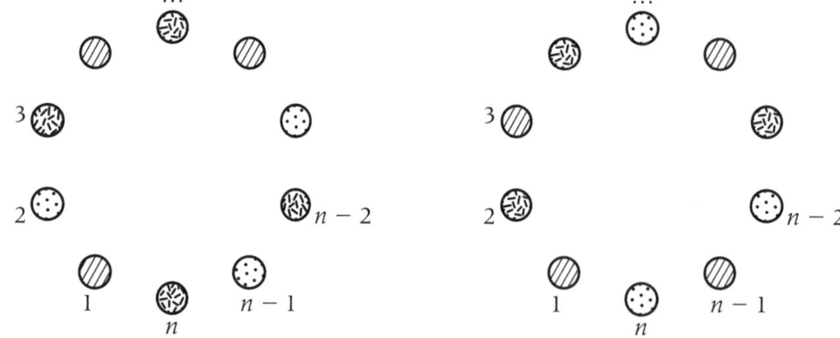

Type I: 1 and $n - 1$ different colours **Type II:** 1 and $n - 1$ the same colour

All the Type 1 patterns can be obtained from any correct colouring of a circle of $n - 1$ discs, with the nth disc slipped in between the first and $(n - 1)$st in the one colour that is different from both of them. Hence there are u_{n-1} Type I colourings of n discs.

All the Type II patterns can be obtained from any correct colouring of a circle of $n - 2$ discs with the $(n - 1)$st and nth then put in place, with the $(n - 1)$st coloured the same colour as the first and the nth coloured in either of the two other colours. Hence there $2u_{n-2}$ Type II colourings of n discs.

Therefore the total number of colourings of n discs, obtained by adding the Type I and Type II patterns, is given by:

$$u_n = u_{n-1} + 2u_{n-2}$$

as required.

So now how do we solve recurrence relations like

$$u_n = u_{n-1} + u_{n-2}$$

and

$$u_n = u_{n-1} + 2u_{n-2}$$

(each with two given initial conditions)? There is a standard procedure to follow in order to solve such recurrence relations:

To solve the recurrence relation: $u_n = pu_{n-1} + qu_{n-2}$
I: form the quadratic equation: $x^2 - px - q = 0$ (the **auxiliary equation**)
II: find the roots α and β of the auxiliary equation
III: then u_n has the **general solution**: **$\alpha \neq \beta$** $u_n = A\alpha^n + B\beta^n$ **$\alpha = \beta$** $u_n = (A + Bn)\alpha^n$ (two cases depending on whether α and β are different or not)
IV: to find the values of the constants A and B use the two initial conditions

Worked example 3.8

A sequence is defined by the recurrence relation:

$$u_0 = 3,\ u_1 = 7 \quad \text{and} \quad u_n = 5u_{n-1} - 6u_{n-2} \quad (n > 1).$$

State u_2 and u_3 and solve the recurrence relation to find a formula for u_n.

Solution

The terms u_2 and u_3 are obtained by applying the recurrence relation with $n = 2$ and $n = 3$, respectively:

$$u_2 = 5u_1 - 6u_0 = 5 \times 7 - 6 \times 3 = 17$$
$$u_3 = 5u_2 - 6u_1 = 5 \times 17 - 6 \times 7 = 43.$$

To solve the recurrence relation we shall carefully follow the procedure I–IV given above.

I: From $u_n = 5u_{n-1} - 6u_{n-2}$ the auxiliary equation is:

$$x^2 - 5x + 6 = 0.$$

II: The roots of the auxiliary equation are $\alpha = 3$ and $\beta = 2$.

III: $\alpha \neq \beta$ and so the general solution is:

$$u_n = \mathrm{A}3^n + \mathrm{B}2^n$$

for some constants A and B.

IV: To find A and B we use the initial conditions. In this case $u_0 = 3$ and so using the formula from III with $n = 0$ gives:

$$u_0 = 3 = \mathrm{A}3^0 + \mathrm{B}2^0 = \mathrm{A} + \mathrm{B}.$$

Similarly, $u_1 = 7$ and so using the formula from III with $n = 1$ gives

$$u_1 = 7 = \mathrm{A}3^1 + \mathrm{B}2^1 = 3\mathrm{A} + 2\mathrm{B}.$$

Solving the two equations:

$$\mathrm{A} + \mathrm{B} = 3 \quad \text{and} \quad 3\mathrm{A} + 2\mathrm{B} = 7$$

gives A = 1 and B = 2. Hence:

$$u_n = \mathrm{A}3^n + \mathrm{B}2^n = 1.3^n + 2.2^n = 3^n + 2^{n+1}$$

and the final answer is that

$$\boxed{u_n = 3^n + 2^{n+1}}$$

(Check: that would give $u_2 = 3^2 + 2^3 = 17$, which fits the value calculated earlier.)

Worked exam question 3.4

The Fibonacci numbers satisfy the recurrence relation:

$$u_0 = 0, \ u_1 = 1 \quad \text{and} \quad u_n = u_{n-1} + u_{n-2} \quad (n > 1).$$

(a) Solve the recurrence relation to obtain an explicit formula for the nth Fibonacci number.

(b) Although the Fibonacci numbers become very large, the ratio:

$$\frac{u_n}{u_{n-1}}$$

of each number divided by its previous one settles down to a particular value. State the value correct to two decimal places.

Solution

(a) Again we shall follow the procedure I–IV given earlier.

I: From $u_n = u_{n-1} + u_{n-2}$ the auxiliary equation is:

$$x^2 - x - 1 = 0.$$

II: The roots of the auxiliary equation are

$$\alpha = \frac{1+\sqrt{5}}{2} \text{ and } \beta = \frac{1-\sqrt{5}}{2}$$

III: $\alpha \neq \beta$ and so the general solution is:

$$u_n = \mathrm{A}\left(\frac{1+\sqrt{5}}{2}\right)^n + \mathrm{B}\left(\frac{1-\sqrt{5}}{2}\right)^n$$

for some constants A and B.

IV: To find A and B we use the initial conditions. In this case $u_0 = 0$ and so using the formula from III with $n = 0$ gives:

$$u_0 = 0 = \mathrm{A}\left(\frac{1+\sqrt{5}}{2}\right)^0 + \mathrm{B}\left(\frac{1-\sqrt{5}}{2}\right)^0 = \mathrm{A} + \mathrm{B}.$$

Similarly, $u_1 = 1$ and so using the formula from III with $n = 1$ gives

$$u_0 = 1 = \mathrm{A}\left(\frac{1+\sqrt{5}}{2}\right)^1 + \mathrm{B}\left(\frac{1-\sqrt{5}}{2}\right)^1 = \frac{\mathrm{A}(1+\sqrt{5})}{2} + \frac{\mathrm{B}(1-\sqrt{5})}{2}$$

Solving the two equations:

$$\mathrm{A} + \mathrm{B} = 0 \quad \text{and} \quad \mathrm{A}(1+\sqrt{5}) + \mathrm{B}(1-\sqrt{5}) = 2$$

gives $\mathrm{A} = 1/\sqrt{5}$ and $\mathrm{B} = -1/\sqrt{5}$. Hence the solution is:

$$\boxed{u_n = \frac{1}{\sqrt{5}}\left(\frac{1+\sqrt{5}}{2}\right)^n - \frac{1}{\sqrt{5}}\left(\frac{1-\sqrt{5}}{2}\right)^n}$$

(It seems strange to have $\sqrt{5}$ in the answer. But if you use the solution to calculate u_7, for example, on a calculator then you do get the Fibonacci number 13.)

(b) We have seen that:

$$u_n = \frac{1}{\sqrt{5}}\left(\frac{1+\sqrt{5}}{2}\right)^n - \frac{1}{\sqrt{5}}\left(\frac{1-\sqrt{5}}{2}\right)^n \approx 0.45((1.62)^n - (-0.62)^n).$$

Now for large n the term $\pm(0.62)^n$ shrinks to nothing – try it on a calculator. Therefore for large n:

$$u_n \approx 0.45(1.62)^n$$

and hence $u_n/u_{n-1} \approx 1.62$.

In both the previous examples the roots of the auxiliary equation were different. The method still works if the roots are equal or complex (i.e. involving the square roots of negative numbers, although that is beyond the scope of this course) and our final example shows how to use the procedure I–IV in the case when the roots are equal.

Worked exam question 3.5

A chemical process produces liquid helium. The volume produced during the first day was 400 litres, the volume produced during the second day was 1200 litres and every day after that the amount produced during day n was four times the increase in going from day $n-2$ to day $n-1$. Write this information as a recurrence relation and find the volume of liquid helium produced during the 10th day.

Solution

Let u_n be the number of litres of liquid helium produced during day n. Then the given information can be written as:

$$u_1 = 400,\ u_2 = 1200 \text{ and } u_n = 4(u_{n-1} - u_{n-2}) = 4u_{n-1} - 4u_{n-2}\ (n > 2)$$

We now follow the procedure I–IV to solve this recurrence relation.

I: From $u_n = 4u_{n-1} - 4u_{n-2}$ the auxiliary equation is:

$$x^2 - 4x + 4 = 0.$$

II: The roots of the auxiliary equation are $\alpha = 2$ and $\beta = 2$.

III: $\alpha = \beta$ and so the appropriate rule from III tells us that the general solution is:

$$u_n = (\text{A} + \text{B}n)2^n$$

for some constants A and B.

IV: To find A and B we use the initial conditions. In this case $u_1 = 400$ and so using the formula from III with $n = 1$ gives:

$$u_1 = 400 = (\text{A} + \text{B}.1)2^1 = 2\text{A} + 2\text{B}.$$

Similarly, $u_2 = 1200$ and so using the formula from III with $n = 2$ gives:

$$u_2 = 1200 = (\text{A} + \text{B}.2)2^2 = 4\text{A} + 8\text{B}.$$

These equations reduce to:

$$\text{A} + \text{B} = 200 \quad \text{and} \quad \text{A} + 2\text{B} = 300$$

which give A = 100 and B = 100. Hence:

$$\boxed{u_n =}\ (\text{A} + \text{B}n)2^n = \boxed{100(1 + n)2^n}$$

(Check: that would give $u_3 = 100 \times 4 \times 2^3 = 3200$ which equals what you get from:

$$u_3 = 4u_2 - 4u_1 = 4 \times 1200 - 4 \times 400 = 3200.)$$

Finally, we are asked for the volume produced on the 10th day, which is:

$$u_{10} = 100 \times 11 \times 2^{10} = 1\,126\,400.$$

3

As in the case of the first order relations, it is straightforward to prove that the general solution which we have been using will always work. We shall restrict attention to showing that, if α is a root of the auxiliary equation and A is any constant, then $A\alpha^n$ will be a solution of the recurrence relation. (It then follows in a straightforward way that if β is the other root then $A\alpha^n + B\beta^n$ also works.)

Given: α is a root of $x^2 - px - q = 0$ and A is a constant.

To deduce: $u_n = A\alpha^n$ satisfies the recurrence relation

$$u_n = pu_{n-1} + qu_{n-2}$$

You have that:

$$u_n = A\alpha^n$$

and so:

$$u_{n-1} = A\alpha^{n-1}$$

$$u_{n-2} = A\alpha^{n-2}$$

Therefore:

$$u_n - pu_{n-1} - qu_{n-2} = A\alpha^n - pA\alpha^{n-1} - qA\alpha^{n-2} = A\alpha^{n-2}(\alpha^2 - p\alpha - q)$$

But α is a root of $x^2 - px - q = 0$; in other words:

$$\alpha^2 - p\alpha - q = 0$$

Hence:

$$u_n - pu_{n-1} - qu_{n-2} = 0$$

and:

$$u_n = pu_{n-1} + qu_{n-2}$$

as expected. Therefore you have that $A\alpha^n$ is a solution of the recurrence relation. You shall not have to reproduce this proof: generally you simply quote the result and work through the procedures I–IV.

EXERCISE 3C

1 Solve the second order recurrence relations:

(a) $u_0 = 4, u_1 = 5$ and $u_n = 3u_{n-1} - 2u_{n-2}$ $(n > 1)$;

(b) $u_1 = 0, u_2 = 16$ and $u_n = 8u_{n-1} - 16u_{n-2}$ $(n > 1)$;

(c) $u_1 = 2, u_2 = 0$ and $u_n = 4u_{n-2}$ $(n > 1)$;

(d) $u_0 = 4, u_2 = 4$ and $u_n = 3u_{n-1} - 2u_{n-2}$ $(n > 1)$.

2 There are n discs in a circle and each has to be coloured in one of three colours such that no two adjacent discs are the same colour. If u_n denotes the number of ways of colouring all the discs, then it satisfies the recurrence relation:

$$u_2 = 6,\ u_3 = 6 \quad \text{and} \quad u_n = u_{n-1} + 2u_{n-2} \quad (n > 3).$$

Solve this recurrence relation to find a formula for u_n, and confirm by actually counting the colourings that your answer is correct for $n = 4$. [A]

3 A population of wild rabbits started with 50 pairs at the beginning of month 1 which grew to 80 pairs at the beginning of month 2. Each month after that every living pair of rabbits produces one other pair, and then those rabbits who are two months old all die.

Let r_n denote the number of pairs of rabbits alive at the beginning of month n. Write down and solve a recurrence relation in r_n.

In which month will the population exceed 1000?

4 (a) Let u_n denote the number of ways of colouring a row of n discs, each one being red or blue, with no two consecutive reds. By considering how many of those colourings have the nth disc blue and how many of those colourings have the nth disc red, show that:

$$u_1 = 2,\ u_2 = 3 \quad \text{and} \quad u_n = u_{n-1} + u_{n-2} \quad (n > 3).$$

(b) Solve the recurrence relation in **(a)** and confirm by counting the colourings that your answer is correct in the case $n = 4$. [A]

5 (a) [harder] Let u_n denote the number of ways of colouring a row of n discs, each one being red, blue or yellow, with no two consecutive reds and no two consecutive blues. Show that:

$$u_1 = 3,\ u_2 = 7 \quad \text{and} \quad u_n = 2u_{n-1} + u_{n-2} \quad (n > 2).$$

(b) Solve the recurrence relation in **(a)** and confirm by counting the colourings that your answer is correct in the case $n = 4$. [A]

3

3.5 Second order relations – non-homogeneous

In this section we shall solve second order recurrence relations of the form

$$u_n = pu_{n-1} + qu_{n-2} + f(n)$$

The procedure to follow is an adaptation of one for homogeneous relations (where $f(n)$ was 0) – it includes the extra stage II*.

To solve the recurrence relation: $u_n = pu_{n-1} + qu_{n-2} + f(n)$
I: form the auxiliary equation: $x^2 - px - q = 0$
II: find the roots α and β of the auxiliary equation
II*: find any one **particular solution** $u_n = P(n)$ which satisfies the original recurrence relation
III: then u_n has the **general solution**: **$\alpha \neq \beta$** $u_n = A\alpha^n + B\beta^n + P(n)$ **$\alpha = \beta$** $u_n = (A + Bn)\alpha^n + P(n)$
IV: to find the values of the constants A and B use the two initial conditions

Worked example 3.9

Solve the recurrence relation:

$$u_0 = 6,\ u_1 = 10 \quad \text{and} \quad u_n = u_{n-1} + 6u_{n-2} + 1 - 6n \quad (n > 1)$$

Solution

Note firstly that the given recurrence relation:

$$u_n = u_{n-1} + 6u_{n-2} + 1 - 6n$$

is of the form:

$$u_n = pu_{n-1} + qu_{n-2} + f(n)$$

with $p = 1, q = 6$ and $f(n) = 1 - 6n$. To solve the relation we follow steps I–IV from the above procedure.

I: The auxiliary equation is:

$$x^2 - x - 6 = 0.$$

II: It has roots $\alpha = 3$, $\beta = -2$.

II*: This is the new stage: it involves finding just one **particular solution** which satisfies

$$u_n = u_{n-1} + 6u_{n-2} + 1 - 6n.$$

Finding such a function usually involves a bit of informed guesswork. In this case the '$+ 1 - 6n$' leads us to try for a $u_n = P(n)$ of the form $a + bn$. Then $u_{n-1} = a + b(n-1)$, etc, and trying these in the recurrence relation gives:

$$\begin{array}{ccccccc} u_n & = & u_{n-1} & + & 6u_{n-2} & + & 1 - 6n \\ \downarrow & & \downarrow & & \downarrow & & \downarrow \\ a + bn & = & (a + b(n-1)) & + & 6(a + b(n-2)) & + & 1 - 6n \end{array}$$

which tidies up to:

$$13b - 6a - 1 = 6(b-1)n.$$

But this has to work **for all *n***. How can that happen? Only if the right-hand side never changes, which means that the coefficient of n must be 0. Hence:

$$b - 1 = 0 \quad \text{and} \quad 13b - 6a - 1 = 0$$

which gives $b = 1$ and $a = 2$. So the **one** particular solution that we are looking for is:

$$u_n = 2 + n.$$

III: In II we saw that $\alpha = 3$ and $\beta = -2$. Since $\alpha \neq \beta$ the general solution will be:

$$u_n = \mathrm{A}\alpha^n + \mathrm{B}\beta^n + \mathrm{P}(n) = \mathrm{A}3^n + \mathrm{B}\,(-2)^n + 2 + n.$$

IV: The final stage is to use the initial conditions to find A and B. We are given that $u_0 = 6$ and so putting $n = 0$ in the expression for u_n derived in III we get:

$$u_0 = 6 = \mathrm{A}3^0 + \mathrm{B}(-2)^0 + 2 + 0 = \mathrm{A} + \mathrm{B} + 2.$$

Similarly, we are given that $u_1 = 10$ and so putting $n = 1$ in the expression for un derived in III we get:

$$u_1 = 10 = \mathrm{A}3^1 + \mathrm{B}(-2)^1 + 2 + 1 = 3\mathrm{A} - 2\mathrm{B} + 3.$$

This gives us the two equations in A and B:

$$\mathrm{A} + \mathrm{B} = 4 \quad \text{and} \quad 3\mathrm{A} - 2\mathrm{B} = 7$$

which solve to give A = 3 and B = 1. Hence (at last!) the solution of the given recurrence relation is:

$$u_n = 3.3^n + (-2)^n + 2 + n$$

which tidies up to

$$\boxed{u_n = 3^{n+1} + (-2)^n + 2 + n}$$

Finding one particular function of n which works in a recurrence relation (at stage II*) relies on making a reasonable guess about the form the solution should take. The only types of relations which we shall meet, and the corresponding particular solutions to try, are given in the table below.

When looking for a particular function to work in:

$$u_n = pu_{n-1} + qu_{n-2} + f(n)$$

For f(n) of the form	Try a particular solution of the form
constant	constant
n, $2n - 1$, etc.	$a + bn$
n^2, $2n^2 + n - 1$, etc.	$a + bn + cn^2$
k^n	ak^n

(In any unusual cases advice will be given to help find a particular solution. For example, if the suggested particular solution happens to satisfy $u_n = pu_{n-1} + qu_{n-2}$, then an alternative one will be needed.)

Worked exam question 3.6

A retired author lives on his royalties. His income in the nth year of retirement is u_n, where u_n satisfies the recurrence relation:

$$u_n = 0.75u_{n-1} + 0.25u_{n-2} + \frac{600}{2^n} \quad (n > 2).$$

(a) Find the general solution of this recurrence relation.

(b) In the first year of retirement his income was £21 000 and in the second year of retirement it was £32 000. Find a formula for his income in the nth year of retirement.

(c) What will his income settle down to in the long term?

Solution

For part **(a)** we must work through I, II, II* and III of the procedure to give us the general solution. Then for part **(b)** we will follow step IV and use the given initial conditions.

I: The auxiliary equation is:

$$x^2 - 0.75x - 0.25 = 0 \quad \text{or} \quad 4x^2 - 3x - 1 = 0$$

II: It has roots $\alpha = 1$, $\beta = -\frac{1}{4}$.

II*: We must find just one particular solution which satisfies:

$$u_n = 0.75u_{n-1} + 0.25u_{n-2} + \frac{6000}{2^n}$$

and the table above suggests trying

$$u_n = \frac{a}{2^n} \quad \text{(giving } u_{n-1} = \frac{a}{2^{n-1}}\text{, etc.)}$$

Substituting these in the recurrence relations gives:

$$\begin{array}{ccccccc} u_n & = & 0.75u_{n-1} & + & 0.25u_{n-2} & + & \frac{6000}{2^n} \\ \downarrow & & \downarrow & & \downarrow & & \downarrow \\ \frac{a}{2^n} & = & \frac{0.75a}{2^{n-1}} & + & \frac{0.25a}{2^{n-2}} & + & \frac{6000}{2^n} \end{array}$$

which tidies up to:

$$a = 1.5a + a + 6000$$

and hence $a = -4000$. So the particular solution is:

$$-\frac{4000}{2^n}.$$

III: In II we saw that $\alpha = 1$ and $\beta = -\frac{1}{4}$. Since $\alpha \neq \beta$ the general solution will be of the form:

$$u_n = \mathrm{A}\alpha^n + \mathrm{B}\beta^n + \mathrm{P}(n) = \mathrm{A}1^n + \mathrm{B}\,(-\tfrac{1}{4})^n - \frac{4000}{2^n}.$$

Hence, in answer to **(a)**, the general solution is:

$$u_n = \mathrm{A} + \frac{\mathrm{B}}{(-4)^n} - \frac{4000}{2^n}.$$

IV: The final stage is to use the initial conditions to find A and B. We are given that $u_1 = 21\,000$ and so putting $n = 1$ in the general solution we get:

$$u_1 = 21\,000 = \mathrm{A} - \tfrac{1}{4}\mathrm{B} - 2000.$$

Similarly, we are given that $u_2 = 32\,000$ and so putting $n = 2$ in the general solution gives:

$$u_2 = 32\,000 = \mathrm{A} + \tfrac{1}{16}\mathrm{B} - 1000.$$

This gives us the two equations in A and B:

$$4\mathrm{A} - \mathrm{B} = 92\,000 \quad \text{and} \quad 16\mathrm{A} + \mathrm{B} = 528\,000$$

which solve to give A = 31 000 and B = 32 000. Hence the required formula for the author's retirement income is:

$$\boxed{u_n = 31\,000 + \frac{32\,000}{(-4)^n} - \frac{4000}{2^n}}$$

(c) As n gets large the denominators of $\pm 4^n$ and 2^n will make those parts shrink to nothing. Hence in the longer term the income will tend towards £31 000.

Worked exam question 3.7

The famous **Chinese ring puzzle** consists of a tangle of rings and strings on a bar, as shown. The object of the puzzle is to untangle the strings and to let all the rings hang freely.

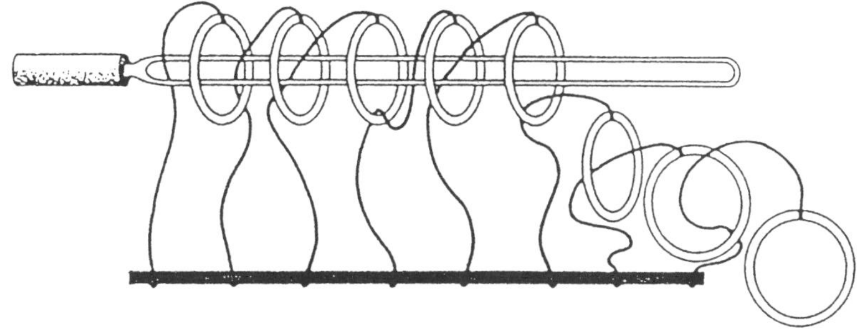

The procedure for untangling rings is complicated: let us assume that for n rings it takes m_n moves of a ring on or off the bar. For example, to untangle the eighth ring you have to remove rings 1–6 (taking m_6 moves), remove ring 8 (taking one move) and put back on rings 1–6 (taking m_6 moves again). That would leave you with ring 8 hanging freely and seven rings back on the bar waiting to be untangled. Explain briefly why this implies that

$$m_8 = m_7 + 2m_6 + 1$$

and write down the corresponding general relation for m_n. Hence use the fact that $m_0 = 0$ and $m_1 = 1$ to find a formula for m_n.

Solution

The untangling process described took $2m_6 + 1$ moves and reduced the eight-ring situation to the seven-ring situation. A further m_7 moves would then complete the puzzle. Hence:

$$m_8 = m_7 + 2m_6 + 1$$

and in general:

$$m_n = m_{n-1} + 2m_{n-2} + 1.$$

We now work through I–IV of the procedure to solve the recurrence relation.

I: The auxiliary equation is:

$$x^2 - x - 2 = 0.$$

II: It has roots $\alpha = 2$, $\beta = -1$.

II*: We must find just one particular solution which satisfies:

$$m_n = m_{n-1} + 2m_{n-2} + 1.$$

and the earlier table suggests trying:

$$m_n = \text{constant} = a, \text{ say.}$$

Hence $m_{n-1} = m_{n-2} = a$ also and substituting these in the recurrence relation gives:

$$\begin{array}{ccccccc} m_n & = & m_{n-1} & + & 2m_{n-2} & + & 1 \\ \downarrow & & \downarrow & & \downarrow & & \downarrow \\ a & = & a & + & 2a & + & 1 \end{array}$$

which gives $a = -\frac{1}{2}$. So the particular solution is $m_n = -\frac{1}{2}$.

III: In II we saw that $\alpha = 2$ and $\beta = -1$. Since $\alpha \neq \beta$ the general solution will be of the form:

$$m_n = \text{A}\alpha^n + \text{B}\beta^n + \text{P}(n) = \text{A}2^n + \text{B}\,(-1)^n - \tfrac{1}{2}.$$

IV: The final stage is to use the initial conditions to find A and B. We are given that $m_0 = 0$ and so putting $n = 0$ in the general solution we get:

$$m_0 = 0 = \text{A} + \text{B} - \tfrac{1}{2}.$$

Similarly, we are given that $m_1 = 1$ and so putting $n = 1$ in the general solution gives:

$$m_1 = 1 = 2\text{A} - \text{B} - \tfrac{1}{2}.$$

The two equations in A and B give $\text{A} = \frac{2}{3}$ and $\text{B} = -\frac{1}{6}$. Hence the number of moves required for n rings is given by:

$$m_n = \tfrac{2}{3} \times 2^n - \tfrac{1}{6} \times (-1)^n - \tfrac{1}{2}$$

which tidies up to:

$$\boxed{m_n = \frac{2^{n+1}}{3} - \begin{cases} \frac{1}{3} & (n \text{ odd}) \\ \frac{2}{3} & (n \text{ even}) \end{cases}}$$

(This may look rather peculiar but it **is** always an integer. In fact it is the 'integer part' of $2^{n+1}/3$.)

EXERCISE 3D

1 Solve the following recurrence relations:

(a) $u_0 = 0$, $u_1 = -2$ and $u_n = -u_{n-1} + 6u_{n-2} + 12 \ (n > 1)$

(b) $u_1 = 7$, $u_2 = 21$ and $u_n = 5u_{n-1} - 4u_{n-2} - 2^{n-1} \ (n > 2)$

(c) $u_0 = 4$, $u_1 = 12$ and $u_n = 6u_{n-1} - 9u_{n-2} + 4(n-1) \ (n > 1)$.

2 A new bacteria has started to grow in a hospital laboratory. Each spore produces new spores, four of which become detectable 1 year later and 12 of which become detectable 2 years later. In addition 30 new spores have been brought into the laboratory each year since 1992.

(a) If u_n is the number of detectable spores of the bacteria at the end of the year $1990 + n$, show that u_n satisfies the recurrence relation:

$$u_n = 4u_{n-1} + 12u_{n-2} + 30 \quad (n > 1).$$

(b) Find the general solution of the recurrence relation in **(a)**.

(c) Given that there were no spores of bacteria at the end of 1990 and just two at the end of 1991, find a formula for u_n. [A]

3 A new internet company's profits will grow very rapidly but will also be affected by its growth in previous years. It is anticipated that in the nth year after it is formed its profits will be p_n million pounds, where p_n satisfies the recurrence relation

$$p_n = p_{n-1} - \tfrac{1}{4}p_{n-2} + (n + 2)^2 \quad (n > 1).$$

Given that the company started with £19 million profits and in its first year made £22 million profit, find a formula for p_n. In which year are the profits expected to exceed £500 million for the first time?

MIXED EXERCISES

1 Solve the recurrence relation:

$$u_1 = 1, \quad u_n = \tfrac{1}{2}u_{n-1} + 1 \quad (n > 1).$$

2 Use iteration to solve:

$$u_1 = 1, \quad u_n = u_{n-1} + n \quad (n > 1).$$

3 The sequence $u_0, u_1, u_2, \ldots$ is defined by

$$u_0 = 1, \quad u_n = u_{n-1} + \frac{1}{2^n}.$$

Use recursion with this equation to write down u_n as a sum and then calculate the sum.
What does u_n tend to as n gets large? [A]

4 An ancient puzzle involves arranging tiles in a pattern. It takes one move to arrange one tile but thereafter to arrange n tiles you have to

(i) arrange $n - 1$ tiles
(ii) move the nth tile once
(iii) arrange $n - 1$ tiles again
(iv) move the nth tile once
(v) arrange $n - 1$ tiles again.

Let t_n denote the number of moves needed to arrange n tiles. Write down and solve a recurrence relation in t_n. [A]

5 Solve the recurrence relation:

$$u_0 = 1,\ u_1 = 2 \quad \text{and} \quad u_n = u_{n-1} + 6u_{n-2} \quad (n > 1).$$

6 Solve the recurrence relation:

$$u_1 = 0,\ u_2 = 9 \quad \text{and} \quad u_n = 6u_{n-1} - 9u_{n-2} \quad (n > 1).$$

7 A simple primitive organism takes 1 hour to mature and then from the end of the second hour onwards it produces two offspring each hour. Let u_n denote the number of organisms after n hours. Write down a recurrence relation in u_n and find its general solution.

Given that initially there are no organisms but that one is introduced at the end of the first hour, find u_n. [A]

8 To get to the centre of the Maths Maze you have to encounter many junctions, each with a five-way choice. Two of the choices take you one junction closer to the centre and the other three take you two junctions closer to the centre. Eventually, when one junction away from the centre, there is just one route to the centre. How many routes are there to the centre when two junctions away? Show that the number r_n of routes when n junctions away from the centre satisfies the recurrence relation

$$r_1 = 1,\ r_2 = 5 \quad \text{and} \quad r_n = 2r_{n-1} + 3r_{n-2} \quad (n > 2).$$

Hence find a formula for r_n. [A]

9 The growth in number of neutrons in a nuclear reaction is modelled by the recurrence relation $u_{n+1} = 6u_n - 8u_{n-1}$, with initial values $u_1 = 2$, $u_2 = 5$, where u_n is the number at the beginning of the time interval $n (n = 1, 2, \ldots)$. Find the solution for u_n and hence, or otherwise, determine the value of n for which the number reaches 10 000. [A]

10 In an experiment the pressure of gas in a container is measured each second and the pressure (in standard units) after n seconds is denoted by p_n. The measurements satisfy the recurrence relation $p_0 = 6$, $p_1 = 3$, and $p_{n+2} = \frac{1}{2}(p_{n+1} + p_n)$ $(n \geqslant 0)$. Find an explicit formula for p_n in terms of n, and state the value to which the pressure settles down in the long term. [A]

11 A population subject to natural growth and harvesting is modelled by the recurrence relation $u_{n+1} = (1 + \alpha)u_n - k2^n$. Here u_n denotes the population size at time n and α and k are positive numbers. If $u_0 = a$, find the solution for u_n in terms of n, α, a and k.

(a) With no harvesting ($k = 0$), $a = 100$ and $\alpha = 0.2$, determine the smallest value of n for which $u_n \geqslant 200$.

(b) With $k = 1$, $a = 200$ and $\alpha = 0.2$,

(i) Show that $u_n = (201.25)(1.2)^n - (1.25)2^n$

(ii) What is the long term future of the population?

(iii) Determine the value of n which gives the greatest population. [A]

12 In a new colony of geese there are 10 pairs of birds, none of which produce eggs in their first year. In each subsequent year, pairs of birds which are in their second or later year have, on average four eggs (two male and two female). Assuming no deaths, show that the recurrence relation which describes the geese population at the beginning of each year is $u_1 = 0$, $u_2 = 10$ and $u_n = u_{n-1} + 2u_{n-2}$ $(n > 2)$. If, in addition, 10 pairs of young geese are introduced in each of the second year onwards. Adapt and solve the relation to find a formula for the number of geese at the beginning of year n. When will the number of geese first exceed 1000? [A]

13 A ternary sequence is a sequence of numbers, each of which is 0, 1, or 2. (For example, 1002 and 1111 are four-digit ternary sequences.) Let u_n be the number of n-digit ternary sequences which do not contain two consecutive 0s. By considering the number of such sequences which begin with 0, and the number which begin with 1 or 2, find a second-order linear recurrence relation for u_n, and write down appropriate initial conditions.

For a harder exercise, find u_n. [This would be easier working with u_0 and u_1 rather than u_1 and u_2: which value of u_0 makes the recurrence relation work?]

14 **(a)** Find the general solution of the recurrence relation:

$$u_n = 7u_{n-1} - 10u_{n-2}$$

(b) Find a particular solution of the form $an2^n$ for the recurrence relation:

$$u_n = 7u_{n-1} - 10u_{n-2} - 3.2^{n-1}$$

(c) Solve the recurrence relation:

$u_0 = 6$, $u_1 = 29$ and $u_n = 7u_{n-1} - 10u_{n-2} - 3.2^{n-1}$ $(n > 1)$ [A]

15 Solve the recurrence relation:

$u_0 = 1$, $u_1 = 11$ and $u_n = 10u_{n-1} - 25u_{n-2} + 16n - 40$ $(n > 1)$ [A]

16 [harder] Let:

$$v_n = \binom{n-1}{0} + \binom{n-2}{1} + \binom{n-3}{2} + \ldots$$

(until the terms become zero). Show that $v_1 = v_2 = 1$ and $v_n = v_{n+1} + v_{n-2}$ $(n > 2)$. What can you deduce about the sequence $v_1, v_2, v_3, v_4, \ldots$?

17 [investigations]

(a) How many ways are there of arranging n identical 1×2 rectangles into a $2 \times n$ rectangle?

(b) The life of a bee is quite amazing. There are basically three types of bee:

- **queen** a fertile female
- **worker** an infertile female
- **drone** a fertile male.

Eggs are either fertilised, resulting in queens and workers or unfertilised, resulting in drones.

Trace back the ancestors of a drone. Find the numbers of ancestors back to the nth generation. The generation tree has been started for you below:

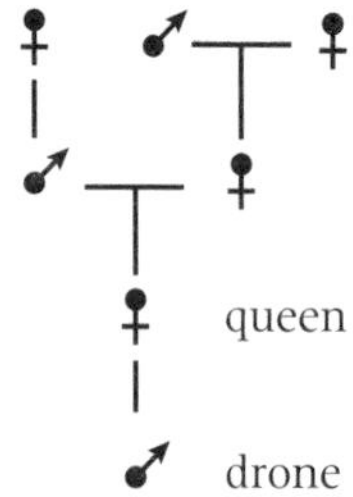

18 [beyond syllabus]

Solve the recurrence relation:

$u_0 = 5, u_1 = 0, u_2 = 8$ and $u_n = 2u_{n-1} + u_{n-2} - 2u_{n-3}$ $(n > 2)$ [A]

(It has auxiliary equation $x^3 - 2x^2 - x + 2 = 0$.)

3

Key point summary

1 A **first order** recurrence relation of the form: p110

$$u_1 = a, \quad u_n = ku_{n-1} + f(n)$$

can be solved by **recursion** or **iteration**, expressing u_{n-1} in terms of u_{n-2}, etc. The resulting expression for u_n can sometimes be simplified using **arithmetic** or **geometric series**.

2 In the special case: p113

$$u_1 = a, \quad u_n = ku_{n-1} + c$$

the solution is given by:

$k = 1$

$$u_n = a + (n - 1)c$$

$k \neq 1$

$$u_n = ak^{n-1} + \frac{c(k^{n-1} - 1)}{k - 1}$$

3 The recurrence relation: p119

$$u_n = pu_{n-1} + qu_{n-2}$$

has **general solution**:

$$u_n = \mathrm{A}\alpha^n + \mathrm{B}\beta^n$$

where $\alpha \neq \beta$ are the roots of the auxiliary equation

$$x^2 - px - q = 0.$$

In the case where $\alpha = \beta$ the general solution is:

$$u_n = (\mathrm{A} + \mathrm{B}n)\alpha^n.$$

The constants A and B can be found using the initial conditions (typically, the values of u_1 and u_2).

4 The recurrence relation: p125

$$u_n = pu_{n-1} + qu_{n-2} + f(n)$$

has general solution given by:

$$\begin{pmatrix}\text{general solution of} \\ u_n = pu_{n-1} + qu_{n-2} + f(n)\end{pmatrix} = \begin{pmatrix}\text{general solution of} \\ u_n = pu_{n-1} + qu_{n-2}\end{pmatrix} + \begin{pmatrix}\textbf{particular solution} \text{ of} \\ u_n = pu_{n-1} + qu_{n-2} + f(n)\end{pmatrix}$$

Once again the constants can be found by using the initial conditions.

Test yourself	What to review
Solve the following recurrence relations:	
1 $u_1 = 1, \quad u_n = u_{n-1} + 2n - 1 \quad (n > 1)$, by recursion.	*Section 3.3, including arithmetic series*
2 $u_1 = 2, \quad u_n = 2u_{n-1} - 1 \quad (n > 1)$.	*General formula in Section 3.3*
3 (a) $u_1 = 1, u_2 = 7$ and $u_n = -u_{n-1} + 2u_{n-2} \quad (n > 2)$. **(b)** $u_0 = 1, u_1 = 1$ and $u_n = \frac{2}{3}u_{n-1} - \frac{1}{9}u_{n-2} \quad (n > 1)$.	*Procedure in Section 3.4*
4 (a) $u_0 = 3.8, u_1 = 6.9$ and $u_n = \frac{3}{2}u_{n-1} - \frac{1}{2}u_{n-2} + 3^n \quad (n > 2)$. **(b)** $u_0 = 1, u_1 = 5$ and $u_n = 2u_{n-1} - u_{n-2} + 6 \quad (n > 1)$.	*Procedure and table of particular solutions in Section 3.5*

Test yourself ANSWERS

1 $u_n = n^2$.

2 $u_n = 2^n - 2^{n-1} + 1 \; (= 2^{n-1} + 1)$.

3 (a) $u_n = 3 + (-2)^n$, **(b)** $u_n = \dfrac{(1 + 2n)}{3^n}$.

4 (a) $u_n = 1 + \dfrac{1}{2^n} + 1.8 \times 3^n$, **(b)** $u_n = 1 + n + 3n^2$.

CHAPTER 4

Codes

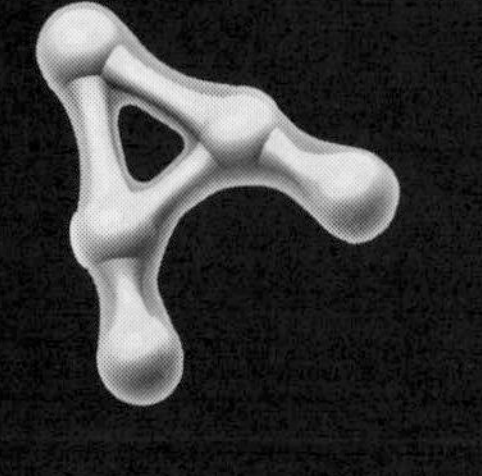

4

Learning objectives

After reading this chapter, you should be able to:

- appreciate the role of codes in a highly technological society
- understand why particular designs are used for particular codes
- understand the need for error detection and correction
- understand how and why check digits are used
- find the Hamming distance of a binary code
- understand what is meant by a linear code
- construct and use a parity check matrix.

4.1 Introduction

In the past you have probably played at sending secret coded messages to your friends. One simple example is to have a password such as 'enigmas' (which can change regularly) and then to code messages using the following substitutions for the letters:

A B C D E F G   H I J K L M N O P Q R S T U V W X Y Z
E N I G M A S   B C D F H J K L O P Q R T U V W X Y Z

Then the message 'this is not a code' would actually be sent as

TBCRCRKLTEILGM

and the receiver of the message, who also knew the password, could decode it.

Interestingly enough, this is **not** what mathematicians would call a code, to them it is a cipher. The branch of mathematics involved with sending **secret** messages is known as **cryptography**. The subject of **codes** is simply devoted to translating messages into a form suitable for sending. Historical examples include the Morse code (creating sound messages of 'dots' and 'dashes' sent on a special machine and used extensively in two world wars) and semaphore (for sending messages from one ship to another within sight by holding flags in certain positions). Neither code was secret: in each case the 'codeword' (dots and dashes or flag positions) representing each letter of the alphabet was standard and well known so that anyone receiving the message could decode it.

However, with the advent of the 'information age', the internet and satellite technology have consigned those old codes to history and replaced them with much more sophisticated codes. For example, we can code each item on a supermarket shelf so that a machine can 'read' it at the checkout, or we can code pictures of Mars taken by a satellite into an electronic message to be transmitted back to Earth. Although you might not have appreciated it, many aspects of life today depend on the effective use of codes. Examples include

bar codes;
satellite transmission;
post codes;
book codes;
bank codes;
computer codes;
internet communication;
compact disc reproduction;
digital television;
⋮

Whilst the average member of the public does not need to know how these codes are designed or how they work, it has become a very important subject for mathematicians to study.

The crux of the study is to design modern codes so that if an error occurs in their transmission, then the receiver will detect that this has happened (such as when the scanner misreads a bar code at the supermarket checkout). In more sophisticated codes the receiver might even be able to correct the errors! This happens with the very weak satellite messages received from Mars which can still be used to create good pictures, or with a scratched CD which can still create perfect reproduction.

It is very hard to imagine how a machine can detect and correct errors in messages which it receives. The underlying mathematics was first developed by *Claude Shannon* in 1948, but he could have had no idea how this would lead to the widespread use of electronic codes today. This chapter introduces you to the fascinating subject of codes and their error-correcting capabilities.

4.2 Historical perspective

Although codes have now become indispensable to modern life, they are not a new invention, and our study will start with two codes which have been around for some time.

Braille

Braille is a method of writing that can be used by blind people. It was invented in 1829 by the Frenchman, *Louis Braille* (1809–1852). When he was 3 years old he lost the sight of one eye while playing with one of his father's knives (his father was a harness maker), and soon lost his sight completely.

An earlier system for soldiers passing messages in the dark had been developed by another Frenchman, *Charles Barbier*, and this used up to 12 embossed dots, six vertical in two rows, as shown opposite. Each letter is made up of a pattern of raised dots which the reader can feel with his fingers. *Braille* revised the pattern by using a base of **six** positions, three vertical in two rows, as shown opposite.

The following questions are posed in order to make you start to think about the practicalities of designing a code.

4

Worked example 4.1

1 How many different arrangements of raised dots are possible in Braille (ranging from no dots at all to all six)?

2 How many different arrangements of raised dots are possible in Barbier's system (ranging from no dots at all to all 12)?

3 How many of the arrangements of raised dots in Braille use

- 1 dot?
- 2 dots?
- 3 dots?
- 4 dots?
- 5 dots?
- 6 dots?

4 Why would the arrangement with no dots raised be impractical?

5 How many arrangements with just one dot raised could effectively be used in a code?

6 Why is Braille superior to Barbier's system?

Solution

1 For each of the six positions you have to decide whether there is a dot or not; i.e. a two-way choice six times, giving $2^6 = 64$ arrangements.

2 Similarly, there are $2^{12} = 4096$ combinations in Barbier's system.

3 1 dot: 6 arrangements
2 dots: 15 arrangements

(You could just count these directly or note that it is the number of ways of choosing two from six where order does not matter, giving an answer of 6.5/2.)

3 dots: 10 arrangements
4 dots: 15 arrangements

(it is equivalent to choosing two **not** to use)

5 dots: 6 arrangements
6 dots: 1 arrangement

Check: the total is 63 which, with the arrangement of no dots, gives 64 as in **(a)**.

4 A blind person has to 'feel' the letters: an arrangement of no dots would be indistinguishable from there being no message.

5 Just one because the reader would have to have some idea of position in order to distinguish two arrangements each consisting of one dot. (In a similar way certain pairs of raised dots would be hard to distinguish.)

6 The alphabet plus other symbols needed in a code amount to 50 items at most. Even with the restrictions mentioned in **3** and **5** Braille offers sufficient different combinations. Learning any more would be impractical anyway.

The full alphabet for Braille is given below and you can see how it avoids some of the problems we have already discussed.

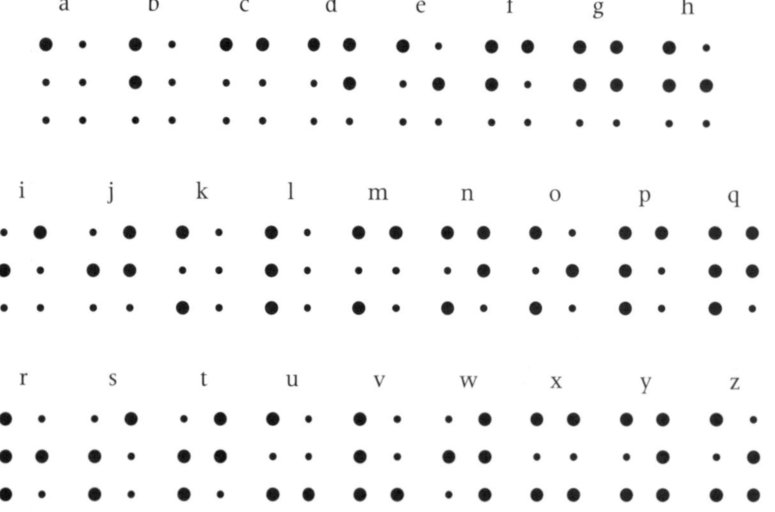

Morse code

This was designed in America by *Samuel Morse*, 1791–1872, and was first used in 1844 for the telegraph line between Baltimore and Washington. Although modern technology has superseded the need for morse code as a form of communication, the 'SOS' code is still universally used for shipping in distress.

In the Morse code the combinations of dots and dashes for each letter are as follows:

a	b	c	d	e	f	g	h
•–	–•••	–•–•	–••	•	••–•	––•	••••

i	j	k	l	m	n	o	p	q
••	•–––	–•–	•–••	––	–•	–––	•––•	––•–

r	s	t	u	v	w	x	y	z
•–•	•••	–	••–	•••–	•––	–••–	–•––	––••

Worked example 4.2

Give an example to show that pauses need to be left between the letters of a Morse code in order to make the message unambiguous.

Solution

There are many possibilities, such as

••–•••–

which can be read as either 'east' or 'feet'.

EXERCISE 4A

1 A code for the visual passing of messages consists of representing letters of the alphabet by placing each of your arms in one of the four positions 'north-east', 'north-west', 'south-east' and 'south-west'. One possible arrangement is illustrated.

(a) How many combinations are possible if the two arms are indistinguishable from distance and if both arms can be in the same position?

(b) How many combinations are possible if the two arms are indistinguishable from a distance and if the two arms must be in different positions?

(c) Suggest ways in which to change the code to increase the number of combinations to be sufficient for a working language.

2 A code consists of changing each letter to a **codeword** consisting of a string of dots and dashes, where each codeword uses the same number of symbols. How many symbols must there be in each codeword in order to give sufficient codewords for a working language?

3 A code is required to display letters and digits using a liquid crystal display as found on most calculators. For example attempts at an A and an 8 are shown. How many different combinations are possible? Why are some impractical, and how could you improve the display?

4 The list below show the International Morse Code (in 'dots and dashes') for some letters of the alphabet.

Using these letters only.

(a) give an example to show that in Morse Code even a single error can go undetected;

(b) give an example of seven dots and dashes to show that, unless a pause is left between letters, a message received in Morse Code may be decoded in more than one way. [A]

4.3 Modern codes

Some of the current codes which we take for granted in modern life are described below. They were largely designed to be used with modern technology.

Postcodes

Much of the mail in the UK is now sorted automatically. This has been made possible by the introduction of postcodes, which were started in 1966 and are now used throughout the UK.

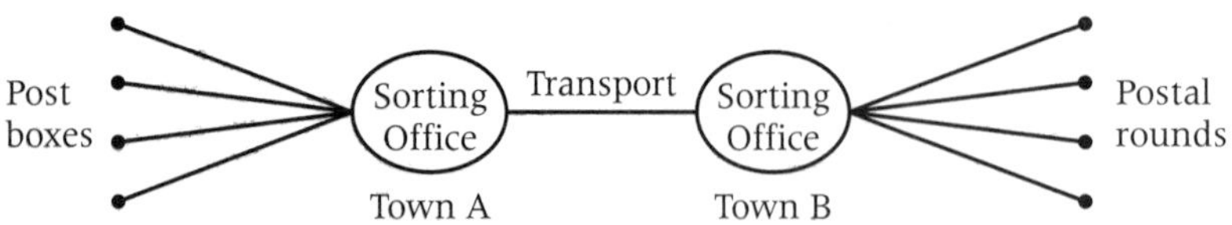

After collection, letters are sorted at the local sorting office into **areas** and **districts**. They are then forwarded to the appropriate sorting office where they are sorted again into **sectors** and **units**.

The postcode shown opposite illustrates these aspects.

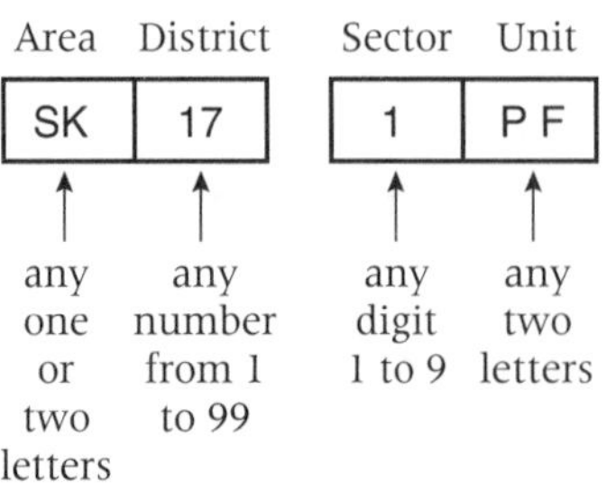

Worked example 4.3

1 In the format of the postcodes given above, how many different possibilities are there?

2 If in fact the codes are restricted to 100 areas and each area has an average of 20 districts, and each of the 9 sectors has an average 100 units, how many different postcodes are there?

3 Assuming that there are approximately 24 million mailing addresses in the UK, how many on average share the same postcode?

Solution

1 $(26^2 + 26) \times 99 \times 9 \times 26^2 \approx 423$ million.

2 $100 \times 20 \times 9 \times 100 = 1.8$ million.

3 $\frac{24}{1.8} \approx 13$ addresses per postcode.

Have you noticed that your mail has a pattern of blue dots on the envelope? This is because the Royal Mail have translated the postcode into another code which can be read automatically by sorting machines – another example of a modern code!

Bar codes

Bar codes are nearly universal today, being used in just about every industry. They were first suggested for automation in grocery stores in 1932 in the thesis of a Harvard Business School student, but it was not until the 1950s that the idea of a scanner installed at checkouts was conceived. It took another two decades for a combination of technology advancement and economic pressure to bring about the commercial use of bar codes and optical readers in retail trading. In 1973 the UPC (Universal Product Code) was adopted as a standard. In 1976 a variation as the EAN (European Article Numbers) was also standardised.

Three examples of eight-digit EAN symbols are shown in the margin. These are used by large stores for their own brands. Each bar code consists of:

- left-hand guard
- left-hand four numbers
- centre guard
- right-hand four numbers
- right-hand guard.

8-digit EAN

Looking at the code for each digit, you will notice that the representation of a digit is dependent on whether it is on the left- or right-hand side. In fact, each representation is designed using a seven module system. For example, a left-hand side 5 is shown magnified below the codes (the dashes are shown here to emphasise the seven module design – they are not actually shown on the code).

Each number has two white and two black strips of varying thickness but following the rules that:

(a) the first module must be white

(b) the last module must be black

(c) there are in total either three or five black modules.

A convenient way of representing each number is given by using 0 (white) 1 (black) giving 0 1 1 0 0 0 1 for 5, as shown. The codes for the right-hand digits are obtained from the left-hand versions by interchanging blacks and white (or 0s and 1s).

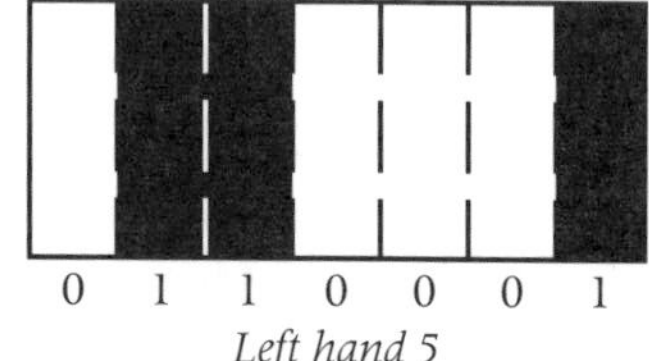

Left hand 5

Worked example 4.4

With the rules listed above, how many different possible left-hand arrangements are there?

Solution

There are just ten possible arrangements. In fact they are used for the digits 0–9 as illustrated:

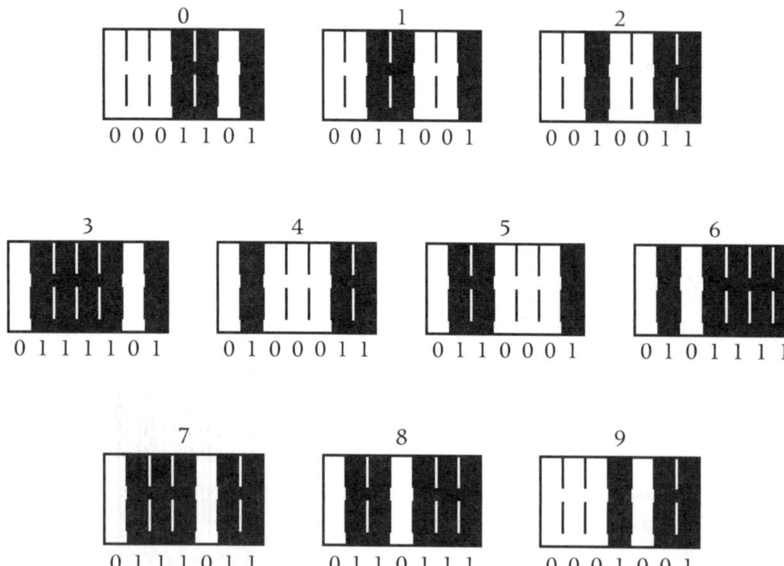

Now let us consider the more extensive **13-digit EAN**.

Examples of this code are found on many grocery products. Three such codes are shown opposite.

The first digit, which as you can see is not represented directly in the code, together with the second digit, indicates the country in which the article number was allocated; e.g. 50 represents the UK, 31 represents France, etc. The next five digits are issued to a particular manufacturer, and the next five identify the product. The final number is a 'check digit': we shall investigate these in the next section.

As we saw in the solution of the previous worked example, in the eight-digit EAN there is a prescribed way of denoting left-hand digits. For the 13-digit EAN the rules are rather more complicated. First we need the following bar-code representations of digits in three versions:

digit	A	B	C
0			
1			
2			
3			
4			
5			
6			
7			
8			
9			

In 13-digit EAN all six right-hand numbers are coded using rule C above, but the six left-hand numbers are coded using a combination of rules A and B. The combination varies and is determined by the first digit. For example for UK code (beginning 50), its left-hand (uncoded) digit is 5 and this determines that the next six digits are coded using the rules A, B, B, A, A, B, respectively. Check for yourselves that the UK code illustrated above follows the pattern:

5	0	1	0	0	3	1	6	6	1	0	3	8
uncoded	A	B	B	A	A	B	C	C	C	C	C	C

Worked example 4.5

1 What is the relationship between the rules A, B and C?

2 The supermarket scanner might read bar codes upside down. Might this cause problems?

3 In the 13-digit EAN code if the leading digit is not 0 the pattern for the remaining 12 digits consists of some mixture of three As and three Bs, followed by six Cs. How many such patterns are there? If, in addition, the first coded digit uses pattern A, how many such patterns are there?

Solution

1 The rules A are the ones given earlier for the left-hand digits of the eight-digit EAN code. Rule C is then rule A with blacks and whites interchanged: it is the one used for the right-hand digits in the eight-digit EAN code. Rule B is the same as rule C but with the modules in reverse order – it is the 'upside-down' version of C.

2 In both the eight-digit and 13-digit codes any bar code differs from all possible upside-down versions. For example, some of the left-hand digits use three or five black modules whereas all the right-hand digits use two or four. So the computerised scanner will recognise which way up the code was meant to be.

3 There are $\binom{6}{3} = \frac{6.5.4}{3.2.1} = 20$ ways of choosing three positions for As from the six possible positions. In half of those A will be first, so there are 10 such arrangements. (Alternatively there are $\binom{5}{2} = \frac{5.4}{2.1}$ ways of choosing positions for the other two As from the remaining five places.)

ISBN book numbers

Every book published is given an International Standard Book Number (ISBN) and you can usually find a book's number quoted on its cover (often together with its bar code translation). The ISBN is made up of the following components:

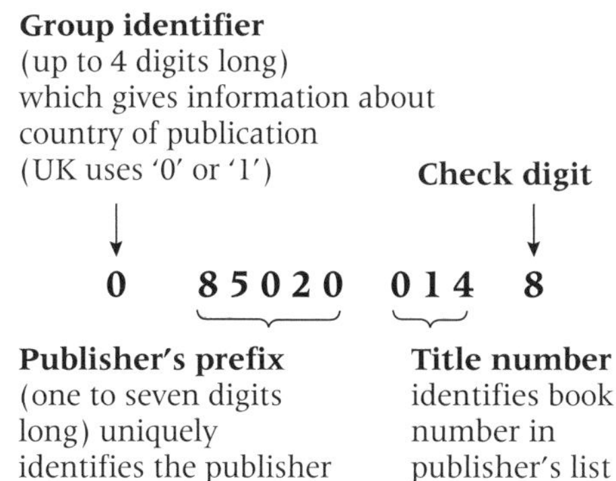

As with the case of bar codes, there is a 'check digit': we shall discuss the role of these in the next section.

Computing codes

There are many codes used in computing, but the most commonly used code is ASCII (American Standard Code for Information Interchange), The code is summarised below. It is in ascending binary order in each section.

This code is not particularly efficient and for computers with limited memory space (e.g. hand-held calculators) often different codes are used.

Character	Code
Space	010 0000
0	011 0000
1	011 0001
2	011 0010
3	011 0011
...	... ...
...	... ...
9	011 1001
+	010 1011
−	010 1101
=	011 1101
A	100 0001
B	100 0010
...	... ...
O	100 1111
P	101 0000
Q	101 0001
...	... ...
...	... ...
Z	101 1010

ASCII code

Huffman codes

A **Huffman code** is another way of coding a limited selection of letters or numbers into binary form.

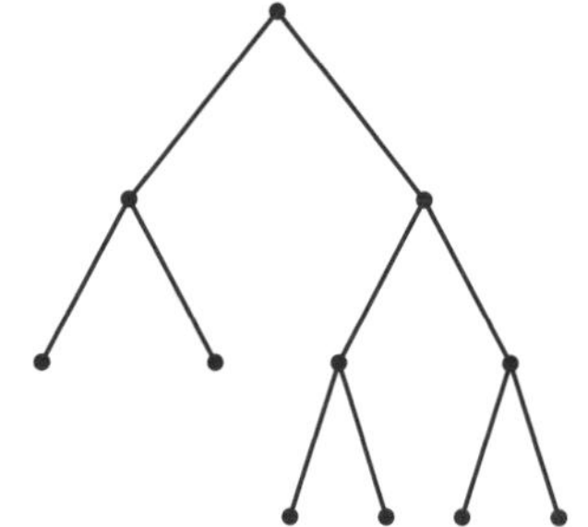

Recall from the course D1 that a **tree** is a graph which is connected but which has no cycles. The tree illustrated has just one vertex of degree 2 and all the other vertices have degree 3 or 1. Any such tree can be illustrated in that 'bifurcating' way with the vertex of degree 2 at the top and, as you move downwards, each junction offering a two-way choice.

If you need to code n characters (e.g. letters or digits) into binary form using a Huffman code you first need one of these 'bifurcating' trees with n vertices of degree 1. So if you simply wanted a code for six letters A, B, C, D, E, F then the previous tree would be suitable. You would then write the six letters by the six vertices of degree 1 and label all the edges as shown.

In addition, for practical reasons which will become clear, you would assign more frequently occurring letters higher up in the tree. So a reasonable way of constructing a Huffman code for A–F with the above tree is now shown:

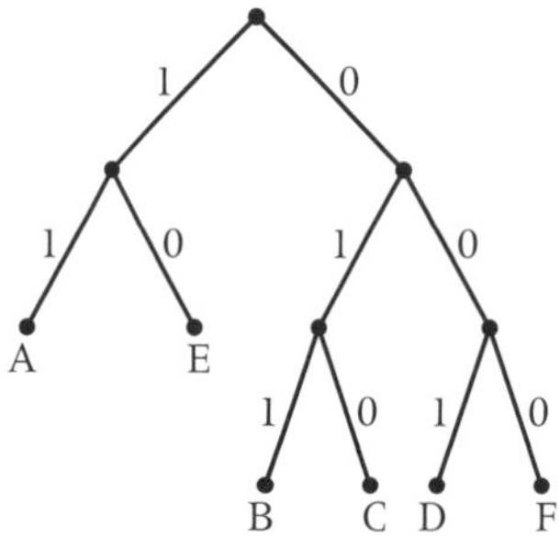

The way to code each letter is now clear: simply read the path of edges from the top to the appropriate vertex. In your tree that gives:

A : 11   B : 011   C : 010   D : 001   E : 10   F : 000

Then, for example, the code for the word 'beef' is:

0111010000

The neat thing about the Huffman codes is the process of decoding. Supposing that you had just received the above message. To decode it start at the top of the tree and follow the path 01110... for as long as you can. In fact you reach B after 011. So then start again with the rest of the message 1010000.

After 10 that leads you to E so start again with 10000, etc. In this way you can decode the message as 'beef' and begin to see that, even without spaces between letters, a message received in a Huffman code can be decoded unambiguously.

You will also have seen why frequently occurring letters are put higher up the tree – the effect is that their codes are shorter.

EXERCISE 4B

1 Consider the codes for the digits 0–9 given under rules A, B and C for the 13-digit EAN bar code.

(a) If one module of a rule A code was misread (i.e. black instead of white or vice-versa) could it be mistaken for another rule A digit?

(b) If one module of a rule A code was misread (i.e. black instead of white or vice-versa) could it be mistaken for another digit under rule C?

(c) If one module of a rule A code was misread (i.e. black instead of white or vice-versa) could it be mistaken for another digit under rule B?

2 Here is part of a binary code:

A : 0 B : 1111 C : 1110 D : 111 E : 1
F : 1101 G : 1011 H : 1010 I : 11 ...

Discuss its limitations.

3 The ASCII code is a binary code in which each codeword consists of six binary digits. Design a code covering all letters but using only five binary digits in each codeword. How many unused strings of 0s and 1s are left for other symbols?

4 Design an efficient Huffman code for the letters E, A, T, M, N, P where they are given in decreasing order of frequency (i.e. E is the most frequently-used letter and P the least).

5 **(a)** We wish to design a Huffman code for just four letters. One possible tree is as shown opposite:

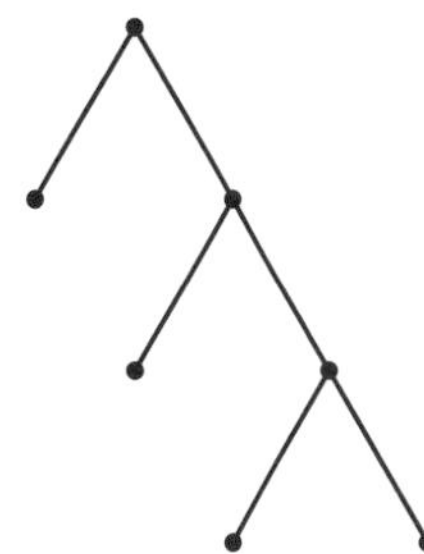

Illustrate the other four trees which could also be used.

(b) When using the tree illustrated opposite for the letters C, O, D, E, the word 'code' became 010010001. Place the four letters in the appropriate positions on that tree.

(c) Show that the message 010010001 could not correspond to the word 'code' with any of the other possible Huffman codes found in **(a)**. [A]

6 A Huffman code is needed for n letters. Assume that the tree used has a total of m vertices.

(a) How many of those m vertices are of degree 1?

(b) How many of the vertices are of degree 2?

(c) The remaining vertices are of degree 3 – how many?

(d) Use the previous parts to show that the sum of all the vertex degrees equals:

$$n + 2 + 3(m - n - 1)$$

(e) In any graph the sum of the vertex degrees is closely related to the number of edges. Use that relationship to prove that $m = 2n - 1$. [A]

(In other words a Huffman code for n letters needs a tree with $2n - 1$ vertices.)

4.4 Check digits

Many modern codes employ a checking device to detect some of the errors which might be made in writing or reading a number. For example, the ISBN numbers referred to in the previous section actually consist of nine digits with an additional check digit at the end.

In this case, the check digit is designed so that any one error in the previous nine digits is spotted. It is calculated in the following way.

Multiply the first nine numbers by 10, 9, 8, …, 2, respectively and find the sum of the resulting numbers. The check number is the smallest number that needs to be added to this total so that it is exactly divisible by 11.

For the example referred to earlier:

Check digit
↓
ISBN 0 85020 014 8

$$0.10 + 8.9 + 5.8 + 0.7 + 2.6 + 0.5 + 0.4 + 1.3 + 4.2 = 135$$

so the check digit must be 8, since 143 is divisible by 11. Note that if the number 10 is needed for the check digit, the symbol X is used.

Worked example 4.6

1 Determine the check digits for the following ISBN numbers:

1 8699330 00 c 1 7135 2272 d

2 There is one error in this ISBN number:

1 869932 23 8

List all the possible correct numbers.

3 In these ISBN numbers two adjacent digits have been transposed:

0 12431 035 5 1 7864 3290 X

What are the possible correct numbers?

Solution

1 For the first number:

$$1.10 + 8.9 + 6.8 + 9.7 + 9.6 + 3.5 + 1.4 + 0.3 + 0.2 = 266$$

and so $c = 9$ to make the total 275 (= 11.25). Similarly:

$$1.10 + 7.9 + 1.8 + 3.7 + 5.6 + 2.5 + 2.4 + 7.3 + 2.2 = 175$$

and so $d = 1$ to make the total 176 (= 11.16).

2 For the given number:

$$1.10 + 8.9 + 6.8 + 9.7 + 9.6 + 3.5 + 2.4 + 2.3 + 3.2 + 8 = 290$$

which is 4 more than a multiple of 11. To reduce the total by 4 we can make any **one** of the following changes:

1.10 + 8.9 + 6.8 + 9.7 + 9.6 + 3.5 + ②.4 + 2.3 + ③.2 + ⑧

(② reduce by 1; ③ reduce by 2; ⑧ reduce by 4)

Alternatively, reducing the total of 290 by 15 or 26 or 37 or 48 or ... will give a multiple of 11, as will increasing the total by 7 or 18 or 29 or 40 or .... Therefore any one of the following changes will also produce viable ISBN numbers:

①.10 + 8.9 + ⑥.8 + 9.7 + ⑨.6 + ③.5 + 2.4 + ②.3 + 3.2 + 8

(① increase by 4; ⑥ reduce by 6; ⑨ reduce by 8; ③ reduce by 3; ② increase by 6)

Therefore any of the following ISBN numbers could have been intended:

1 869931 23 8 1 869932 21 8 1 869932 23 4 1 809932 23 8

1 869132 23 8 1 869902 23 8 5 869932 23 8 1 869932 83 8

3 Here

$$0.10 + 1.9 + 2.8 + 4.7 + 3.6 + 1.5 + 0.4 + 3.3 + 5.2 + 5 = 100$$

which is 1 more (or 10 less) than a multiple of 11. In general, the effect of transposing two digits a and b is to change part of the calculation of the check digit as follows:

$$n.a + (n - 1).b \quad \text{becomes} \quad n.b + (n - 1).a$$

which increases the total by $b - a$ or decreases it by $a - b$. So in this case we are looking for two adjacent digits ab of 0 12431 035 5 with $a = b + 1$. (Then shunting a forward one place and b back one place will decrease the total of 100 to 99.) There are just two possibilities:

0 12431 035 5 or 0 12431 035 5

giving the correct ISBN number as:

0 12341 035 5 or 0 12430 135 5

Similarly, for 1 7864 3290 X,

$$1.10 + 7.9 + 8.8 + 6.7 + 4.6 + 3.5 + 2.4 + 9.3 + 0.2 + 10 = 263$$

which is 1 less than a multiple of 11 and so we require adjacent digits ab with $a = b - 1$. The only possibility is:

1 7864 3290 X

giving a correct ISBN number of:

1 8764 3290 X

As with ISBN numbers, bar codes incorporate a check digit, again the last one. For eight–digit EAN bar codes it is chosen so that

3 × (1st + 3rd + 5th + 7th number + (2nd + 4th + 6th + 8th number) is exactly divisible by 10.

For example, for the eight-digit EAN bar code:

0033 7793

it means that:

$$3 \times (0 + 3 + 7 + 9) + (0 + 3 + 7 + 3) = 3 \times 19 + 13 = 70$$

is exactly divisible by 10.

13-digit EAN codes use a similar method as 8-digit EAN codes for determining the check digit, except that all 13 numbers are included, so that the number

$$3 \times (2\text{nd} + 4\text{th} \ldots + 12\text{th number}) + (1\text{st} + 3\text{rd} + \ldots + 13\text{th number})$$
must be divisible by 10.

Worked exam question 4.1

With the rules for check digits quoted above [which would be given in an exam]:

1 calculate the check digits of these EAN bar codes:

5021 422c 2 365491 65011d;

2 find the possible bar codes which can lead to:

6071 5922 or 1 034965 800250

with just one error;

3 find the possible bar codes which can lead to:

6071 5922 or 1 034 965 800250

with just one transposition of two adjacent digits.

Solution

1 We need:

$$3 \times (5 + 2 + 4 + 2) + (0 + 1 + 2 + c) = 42 + c$$

to be divisible by 10 and so c is 8. Similarly, we need:

$$3 \times (3 + 5 + 9 + 6 + 0 + 1) + (2 + 6 + 4 + 1 + 5 + 1 + d) = 91 + d$$

to be divisible by 10 and so d is 9.

2 Here 3 × odd positions + evens gives:

$$3 \times (6 + 7 + 5 + 2) + (0 + 1 + 9 + 2) = 72$$

and so the total exceeds a multiple of 10 by 2 or 12 or 22 or …, and it is less than a multiple of 10 by 8 or 18 or 28 or …. Any change to a digit in an even position will change the total by the corresponding amount, but any increase or decrease of a digit in an odd position will have three times the effect on the total. Hence to change the total of 72 to a multiple of 10 we must make any one of the following changes:

reduce one by 4 (6, 7, 5) — reduce one by 2 (9, 2)

$$3 \times (6 + 7 + 5 + 2) + (0 + 1 + 9 + 2) = 72$$

increase by 6 (2) — increase one by 8 (0, 1)

Hence the correct 8-digit EAN number is one of:

2071 5922	6031 5922	6071 1922	6071 5722
6071 5920	6071 5982	6871 5922	6079 5922

For the given 13-digit EAN number 3 × even positions + odds gives

$$3 \times (0 + 4 + 6 + 8 + 0 + 5) + (1 + 3 + 9 + 5 + 0 + 2 + 0) = 89$$

and so we need to subtract 9 (there is no way that a single digit or 3 × digit can give 19 or 29 or 39 ...) or, similarly, to add 1 or 21. Hence to make a correct number we have to make one of the following changes:

reduce one by 3 (4, 6, 8, 5) — reduce by 9 (9)

$$3 \times (0 + 4 + 6 + 8 + 0 + 5) + (1 + 3 + 9 + 5 + 0 + 2 + 0) = 89$$

increase one by 7 (0, 0) — increase one by 1 (1, 3, 5, 0, 2, 0)

Therefore the correct number could be any one of these:

1 031965 800250	1 034935 800250	1 034965 500250
1 034965 800220	1 034065 800250	1 734965 800250
1 034965 807250	2 034965 800250	1 044965 800250
1 034966 800250	1 034965 810250	1 034965 800350
	1 034965 800251	

3 Transposing two digits a and b in either code changes their contribution to the total from:

$3a + b$ to $a + 3b$

and so the change is 2(a - b). So with 6071 5922 and:

$$3 \times (6 + 7 + 5 + 2) + (0 + 1 + 9 + 2) = 72$$

The total must be decreased by 2 or 12 or increase it by 8 or 18. Hence we want two adjacent digits where the one in the odd position is 1 more or 6 more than its neighbour, or we want adjacent digits where the one in the odd position is 4 less or 9 less than its neighbour. The only possibilities are:

6071 5922 and 6071 5922

giving the correct number as 0671 5922 or 6017 5922.

In the case of 1 034965 800250, which gave the odd total 89, any switching of adjacent pairs will change the total by an even amount and so it can never be divisible by 10. Hence no 13-digit EAN number can have resulted in the given number with just one transposition of adjacent vertices.

4

EXERCISE 4C

1 Calculate the check digits for the following numbers:

(a) ISBN number 2 3409 8751 *a*

(b) eight-digit EAN number 3401 231 *b*

(c) 13-digit EAN number 3 452100 62108 *c*.

2 A shop tries to order a book with ISBN number 0 876 00123 4 but is told that there is an error.

(a) If the error is in the check digit, what is the correct ISBN number?

(b) If the error is in the very first digit, what is the correct ISBN number?

(c) If the error arises from the transposition of two adjacent digits, what is the correct ISBN number? [A]

3 At a supermarket checkout the scanner fails to read an eight-digit EAN bar code and so the cashier reads the label and types the number 3401 2589 but the computer still tells him that an error has occurred.

(a) If the error is in the check digit, what is the correct number?

(b) If the error is in a digit other than the check digit and the cashier has typed too high a number, what is the correct number?

(c) If the error arises from the transposition of two adjacent digits, what are the three possible correct numbers? [A]

4.5 Error detection and correction

You saw in the previous section how check digits for ISBN numbers and bar codes are used to detect errors. This section looks at codes relevant to data transmission, for example the transmission of pictures from Mars to the Earth, and shows how such codes are designed in order to detect (and in some cases correct) errors.

To take an example, in TV broadcasting the message for transmission is a picture in the studio. The camera converts this into a 625-row array of packages of information, each package denoting a particular colour. This array, in the form of an electrical signal, is broadcast via antennae and the atmosphere, and is finally interpreted by the receiving set in the living room. The picture seen there differs somewhat from the original, errors having corrupted the information at various stages in the channel of communication. These errors may result in effects varying from subtle changes of colour tone to what looks like a violent snowstorm. Technically, the errors are all classified as **noise**.

A model of data transmission is shown below:

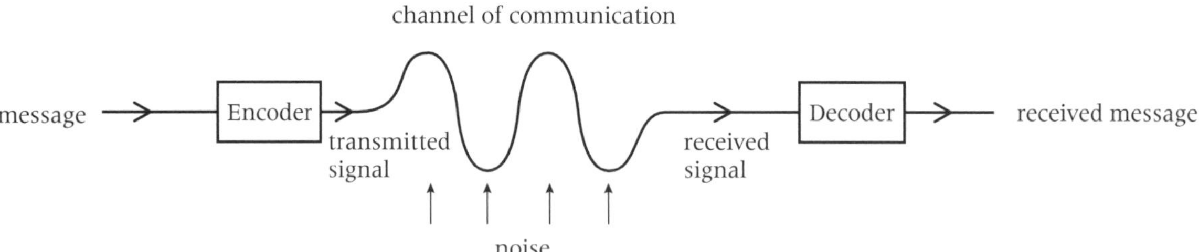

Normally, the message is encoded, the signal transmitted to the receiver, and then decoded with a received message. It is in the transmission that noise can affect the signal.

For example, the Mariner 9 spacecraft in 1971 sent television pictures of the planet Mars across a distance of 84 million miles. Despite a very low power transmitter, the space-probe managed to send data which eventually resulted in very high quality pictures being shown on our screens. This was in part largely due to the sophisticated coding system used: when the message was received, having been changed by noise, the receiver was still able to work out what was intended. In other words it could **detect** and **correct** errors.

The same theory of error-correcting codes now enables television signals to be coded. Then, provided you have a digital decoder, your receiver can work out the intended picture even if errors have occurred. It is this application of codes that has lead to digital television.

Our study of error-correcting codes will be restricted to **binary codes** in which each **codeword** is a string of 0s and 1s. This is because all the important codes are used for electronic transmission where an electric pulse or lack of it is translated into a 1 or 0.

In addition we shall restrict attention to codes in which each codeword uses the same number of symbols: this is called the **length** of the code.

As a very simple example, imagine that we only ever want to send four messages 'North', 'South', 'East' or 'West'. The simplest binary code with four codewords has length 2. One example would be:

N : 00　　S : 01　　E : 10　　W : 11

That would be fine if there were no possibility of noise; i.e. if the messages were always received without errors. But an error in a single bit (or binary digit) will completely change the meaning of the message. For example a single error in 'North' (00) could result in it being read as 'South' (01) or 'East' (10).

The easiest way to adapt that code is to introduce a check digit. We shall simply add a third digit to each codeword and we shall do it so that the sum of all three bits in each codeword is even. That leads us to the following binary code of length 3:

N : 000　　S : 011　　E : 101　　W : 110

Now if a single error occurs in the transmission of a codeword, the receiver will know that an error has occurred. This is because any single error will cause the total of the digits to be odd. So, for example, a single error in the transmission of 'South' (011) will result in 111 or 001 or 010, none of which is an acceptable codeword. However, the receiver will not be able to tell what message was intended. For example if the received message is 111 with just one error then the intended message might have been 011 ('South') or 101 ('East') or 110 ('West'). So with just a single error the receiver will know that an error has occurred but will then have to ask for the message to be repeated.

Sometimes (as with satellite or television transmission) it is impossible to ask for the message to be repeated and so an even better code is needed. Consider the following version of a N/S/E/W code – it is a binary code of length 6:

N : 000111　　S : 011010　　E : 101100　　W : 110001

Although this code has twice the length of the previous one, it can now detect **and correct** a single error. For example supposing that the received message is 111001. Since this is not one of the four codewords the receiver knows that an error has occurred. But what was the intended message?

'North'? (000111)	This would need five changes to make it into the received message 111001.
'South'? (011010)	This would need three changes to make it into the received message 111001.
'East'? (101100)	This would need three changes to make it into the received message 111001.
'West'? (110001)	This would need just one change to make it into the received message 111001.

On the assumption that the equipment is reasonably reliable and that one error is far more likely than three or five, in this case the receiver will assume that the intended message was 'West'. This is called **nearest word decoding**.

By now you should be beginning to get a feel for what is the important characteristic of a code for the determination of the errors that can be detected and corrected. The crucial concept is that of **distance** between codewords.

The **distance** d between any two codewords in a code is defined as the number of actual differences between the codewords. For example, in the previous N/S/E/W code the distance between the codewords for 'North' and 'South' is given by:

$$d(000111, 011010) = 4$$

since they differ in four places as shown:

```
N : 0 0 0 1 1 1
      × × ×   ×
S : 0 1 1 0 1 0
```

Worked example 4.7

For each pair of codewords in the code:

N : 000111　　S : 011010　　E : 101100　　W : 110001

find the distance between them. Deduce that if a codeword of this word is transmitted and up to three errors occur during transmission, then the receiver will be able to detect that an error has occurred.

Solution

N–S : $d(000111, 011010) = 4$
N–E : $d(000111, 101100) = 4$
N–W : $d(000111, 110001) = 4$
S–E : $d(011010, 101100) = 4$
S–W : $d(011010, 110001) = 4$
E–W : $d(101100, 110001) = 4$

```
N : 0 0 0 1 1 1
    ×   ×   × ×
E : 1 0 1 1 0 0
```

Hence it takes four changes to make one codeword into another. Therefore if a codeword is transmitted with one, two or three errors then the resulting string of 0s and 1s will **not** be a codeword. Hence the receiver will know that something has gone wrong and will be able to detect that an error has occurred.

That example was unusual, with every pair of codewords being distance 4 apart. In general, the **Hamming distance** δ of a code is defined as the **minimum** distance between any two codewords in the code. So the above example has Hamming distance 4.

> The distance between two codewords is the number of places in which they differ. The **Hamming distance** of a code is the smallest distance between two different codewords of the code

4

Worked exam question 4.2

Determine the Hamming distance for the code with codewords:

11000, 00101, 10101, 11111.

Explain why this code could not even detect a single error.

Solution

You must find distances between all the codewords:

$d(11000, 00101) = 4$
$d(11000, 10101) = 3$
$d(11000, 11111) = 3$
$d(00101, 10101) = 1$ ← Hamming distance, the minimum of the distances
$d(00101, 11111) = 3$
$d(10101, 11111) = 2$

The code cannot detect a single error because, for example, a single error in 00101 could result in 10101 which is still an acceptable codeword. Hence the receiver would not realise that anything was wrong.

Worked exam question 4.3

Codes A and B have the codewords listed below:

A	B
000000	0000
001110	0011
010101	0101
011011	0110
100011	1001
101101	1010
110110	1100
111000	1111

1 Find the Hamming distance of each code.

2 Show that both codes can detect errors if a single error occurs in a codeword.

3 Which of the two codes can **correct** errors if a single error occurs in a codeword? Explain your answer.

Solution

1 A check of all pairs of codewords in A show that any pair differ in at least three places. The minimum of three happens, for example, with

$$d(010101, 011011) = 3$$

Similarly, each pair in B differ in at least two places and

$$d(0101, 0110) = 2$$

Hence code A has Hamming distance 3 and code B has Hamming distance 2.

```
0 1 0 1 0 1
    × × ×
0 1 1 0 1 1

0 1 0 1
    × ×
0 1 1 0
```

2 Since in each case the Hamming distance is greater than 1 it is impossible to change one codeword into another with just one change. So a single error in a codeword will result in a string of 0s and 1s which is **not** a codeword and therefore the receiver will realise that an error has occurred.

3 In code B a single error could result in the string 0111 being received. Although the receiver would know that an error had occurred, it could not decide whether codeword 0101 or codeword 0110 was intended. So code B cannot correct single errors. On the other hand, in code A if a single error occurs in a codeword then we have the following situation:

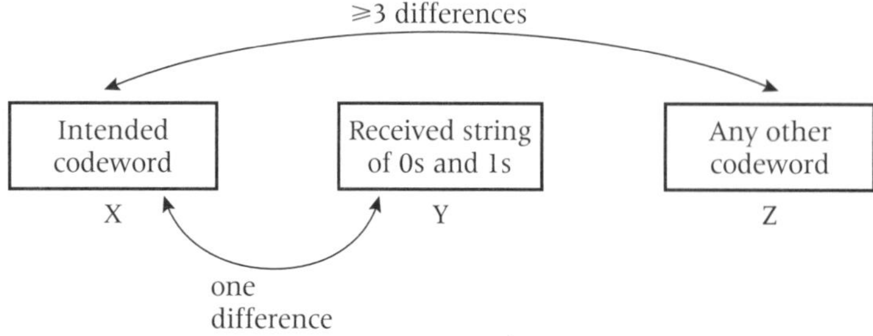

Since it takes one change from X to Y but at least three from X to Z, it must take at least two changes to get from Y to Z. In other words the closest codeword to Y is definitely X, and nearest word decoding will result in the receiver interpreting Y correctly as X. Hence code A can correct errors if a single error occurs.

Worked exam question 4.4

A code has codewords including:

11010010
01010101
10000111
10101010

and the distances between any two of its codewords are four or eight.

1 What is the Hamming distance of the code?

2 Show that if one, two or three errors occur in the transmission of a codeword, then the receiver will be able to detect that an error has occurred.

3 Give an example of a string of eight 0s and 1s which a receiver would know was incorrect and yet would be unable to correct.

4 How many errors in a codeword can be detected and corrected? Give reasons for your answer.

Solution

1 The minimum of all the distances is 4.

2 If the received string has one, two or three errors then (as it takes at least four changes to make one codeword into another) the received string will not be another codeword. Hence the receiver will know that an error has occurred.

3 Consider 11010001. Then

$$d(11010001, 11010010) = 2$$

↑ first codeword

and

$$d(11010001, 01010101) = 2$$

↑ second codeword

Hence (as all distances between codewords are at least four) 11010001 is not a codeword. So if received it would be clear that an error had occurred. But it would be impossible to tell whether the first or second codeword was intended.

4 Just one error in a codeword can be corrected (two or more being ruled out by **3**). Then

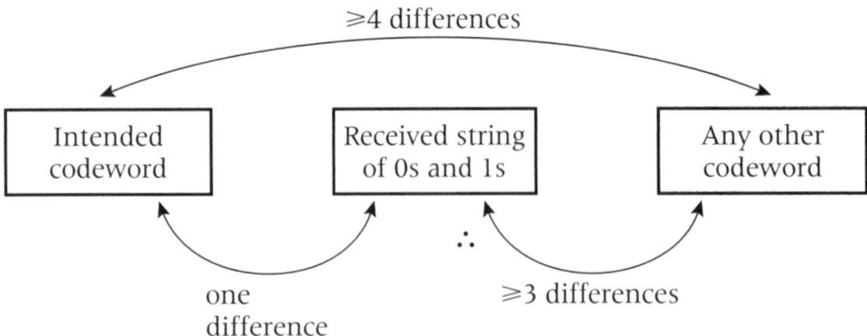

Hence the intended codeword is simply the codeword which is the 'nearest' one to the received string.

Are you beginning to see the connection between the Hamming distance of a code and the number of errors in a codeword which it can detect and correct? Imagine, for example, a code with Hamming distance of 60 (not an unreasonable figure for sophisticated telecommunications codes). Then if up to 59 errors occurred in a codeword the received string of 0s and 1s would not be a codeword and the receiver would realise that an error had occurred.

On the other hand there is a string of 0s and 1s which is distance 30 from two different codewords – so if that string was the received message it would not be clear which codeword was intended. Hence the code cannot correct 30 errors in a codeword. However, if only 29 errors were made then we would have:

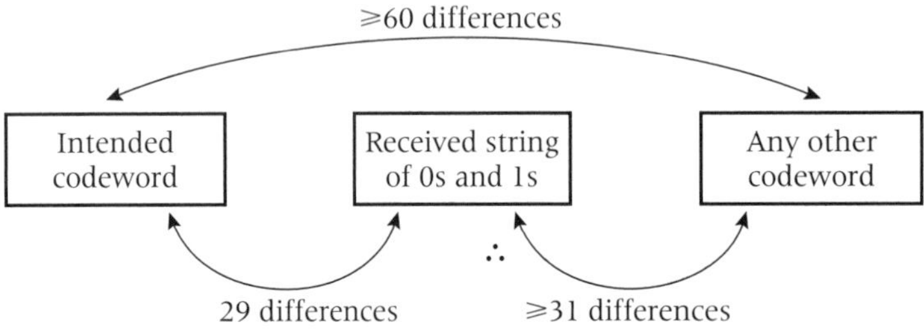

Therefore the receiver would know that the codeword 'nearest' to the received string was the correct one.

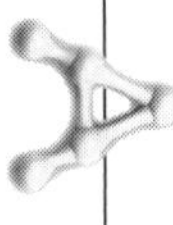

A code of Hamming distance δ can:
(a) detect errors if fewer than δ occurs in any codeword
(b) detect **and correct** errors if fewer than $\frac{1}{2}\delta$ occur in any codeword.

A little thought will show you that the result is true whether δ is even or odd.

Worked exam question 4.5

A code of length 10 has just the four codewords:

0000000000
0110110001
1001001110
1111111111

1 Find the Hamming distance of the code.

2 Up to how many errors in a codeword can be detected?

3 Up to how many errors in a codeword can be simultaneously detected and corrected?

4 A new codeword is formed by replicating each codeword; e.g. the second codeword becomes:

01101100010110110001

Up to how many errors in a codeword can this new code simultaneously detect, and up to how many can it correct?

5 Briefly describe how to to construct a code of four codewords which can simultaneously detect and correct up to nine errors in a codeword.

Solution

1 $d(0000000000, 0110110001) = 5$

$d(0000000000, 1001001110) = 5$

$d(0000000000, 1111111111) = 10$

$d(0110110001, 1001001110) = 10$

$d(0110110001, 1111111111) = 5$

$d(1001001110, 1111111111) = 5$

$\therefore$ Hamming distance $= 5$

2 The code can detect up to four errors per codeword.

3 The code can correct up to two errors per codeword.

4 New Hamming distance is 10: hence it can detect up to nine errors per codeword and correct up to four.

5 Replicating the code again will give four codewords of length 40 and a Hamming distance of 20. It will therefore be able to correct up to nine errors per codeword.

We now know the theory of error-correcting codes, but how in practice do we construct codes and how do we mechanically decode received messages? We answer these questions in the next two sections.

EXERCISE 4D

1 The '2 out of 5' code consists of all possible strings of five 0s and 1s which include exactly two 1s.

(a) List all the codewords of the code.

(b) Why is this a useful code for transmitting numerical data?

(c) Find the Hamming distance of the code.

(d) Up to how many errors in a codeword can this code detect? [A]

2 A code has seven codewords

1101000
0110100
0011010
0001101
1000110
0100011
1010001

(a) The distance between any two words of the code is the same. What is that distance?

(b) Explain why if three errors occur in the transmission of a codeword, then the receiver will know that an error has occurred.

(c) How many errors in a codeword would a receiver be able to correct and detect?

3 A code has the following eight codewords:

0000000
0011101
0101011
0110110
1000111
1011010
1101100
1110001

What is the length and Hamming distance of this code? State its error-correcting capabilities. [A]

4.6 Linear codes

In this section we intend to generate some useful codes by algebraic means. You first need a simple piece of algebra concerning the addition of the bits of our codes. Throughout this section the addition of binary digits is given by:

$$0 + 0 = 0$$
$$0 + 1 = 1$$
$$1 + 0 = 1$$
$$1 + 1 = 0$$

This is given for use in codes and is not quite binary addition (where there would have been a 1 'carried' in 1 + 1). In fact it is called **addition modulo 2**. In a sense this new addition is just a measure of whether the two things being added are the same, the answer being 0 for 'yes' and 1 for 'no'. The algebra enables you to deal with equations. For example if:

$$1 + x = 0$$

then adding 1 to both sides gives:

$$1 + 1 + x = 1 + 0 \quad \text{and} \quad x = 1$$

(which could be thought of in modulo 2 arithmetic as '-1' is just 1).

The addition extends to adding up any two codewords of the same length:

e.g. 0011101 + 0111010 = 0100111

We can now use this algebra to construct codes.

Worked example 4.8

1 Write out all binary codewords of the form $x_1 x_2 x_3 x_4 x_5$ where:

$$x_1 + x_2 = 0$$
$$x_1 + x_3 + x_5 = 0$$
$$x_2 + x_4 = 0$$

2 Show that your answers to **1** form a code with Hamming distance equal to 2.

3 Show that any two of the codewords add up to give another codeword.

4

Solution

1 The equation:

$$x_1 + x_2 = 0$$

simply tells us that x_1 and x_2 are the same, and the equation:

$$x_2 + x_4 = 0$$

tells us that x_2 and x_4 are the same. So all our codewords will look like:

11–1– or 00–0–.

In the case of 11–1–, where $x_1 = 1$, the equation:

$$x_1 + x_3 + x_5 = 0$$

tells us that:

$$1 + x_3 + x_5 = 0 \quad \text{and so} \quad x_3 + x_5 = 1$$

and x_3, x_5 are different. This gives:

11110 and 11011.

Similarly, in the case of 00–0–, where $x_1 = 0$, the equation:

$$x_1 + x_3 + x_5 = 0$$

tells us that:

$$x_3 + x_5 = 0$$

and so x_3, x_5 are the same. This gives:

00101 and 00000.

Hence the four codewords are:

11110	00101
11011	00000

2 $d(11110, 11011) = 2$ $d(11011, 00101) = 4$

$d(11110, 00101) = 4$ $d(11011, 00000) = 4$

$d(11110, 00000) = 4$ $d(00101, 00000) = 2$

$\therefore$ Hamming distance $= 2$

3 We should check that adding any two codewords does give a codeword. But if you add a codeword to itself you get 00000 which **is** a codeword, so we need not check those cases. Similarly, if you add 00000 to any codeword then the answer is the same codeword, so we need not check those cases. That leaves:

$$11110 + 11011 = 00101$$
$$11110 + 00101 = 11011$$
$$11011 + 00101 = 11110$$

and so in call cases the sum of two codewords is a codeword.

A code is called **linear** if whenever you add two codewords the answer is also a codeword. Hence the code in Worked example 4.8 is linear. Indeed it is typical of the linear codes which we shall meet because it was **generated** by some linear equations.

The definition of a linear code requires that even if you add a codeword to itself the answer must be a codeword. But if you add a codeword to itself you just get the zero codeword 000...0.

A **linear** code is one in which the sum of any two codewords is a codeword. A linear code must contain the zero codeword.

Worked exam question 4.6

Write out all codewords of the form $x_1 x_2 x_3 x_4 x_5 x_6$ where

$$x_1 + x_2 = 0 \qquad x_4 + x_5 = 0$$

$$x_2 + x_3 = 0 \qquad x_5 + x_6 = 0$$

and find the Hamming distance of the code.
Confirm by addition that the code is linear.

Solution

The equations simply tells us that x_1, x_2, x_3 the same and that x_4, x_5, x_6 are the same. This gives four codewords:

111111 000111

111000 000000

which has Hamming distance 3.

Now as the zero codeword is there, the only additions of codewords which need to be checked are:

111111 + 111000 = 000111

111111 + 000111 = 111000

111000 + 000111 = 111111

and as each answer is a codeword the code is linear.

Worked exam question 4.7

Eight codewords form a linear code. Seven of the codewords are given as:

00000 11010

00111 11101

00110 11100

11011

1 What is the remaining codeword?

2 The codewords $x_1 x_2 x_3 x_4 x_5$ are generated by two linear equations, one involving two xs and the other involving three xs. Write down two equations which generate the code.

Solution

1 You might just spot a pattern to determine which codeword is missing or, more systematically, you could add pairs of codewords to try to find a new answer. For example, adding the second and third codewords gives:

$$00111 + 00110 = 00001$$

which is not in the list. Hence the missing codeword is 00001.

2 It is clear that in each codeword the first two bits are the same; i.e.

$$x_1 + x_2 = 0.$$

The second equation is trickier. Whenever $x_1 = 0$ the third and fourth bits are the same, but whenever $x_1 = 1$ the third and fourth bits are different; i.e.

$$x_1 + x_3 + x_4 = 0.$$

EXERCISE 4E

1 A code has the following codewords:

0000000	1000111
0011101	1011010
0101011	1101100
0110110	1110001

Show that the code is linear.

2 List all the codewords $x_1\,x_2\,x_3\,x_4\,x_5$ which satisfy:

$$x_1 + x_2 + x_3 = 0 \quad \text{and} \quad x_1 + x_3 + x_4 = 0.$$

Confirm that the code is linear and state its Hamming distance.

3 (For investigation)

(a) How many possible codewords are there of length n if all combinations of 0s and 1s are allowed?

(b) Given a linear code and a new linear equation which is satisfied by some of the codewords but not others, what proportion of the codewords satisfy the new equation?

(c) Show that the number of codewords in any linear code equals a power of 2.

4 Eight codewords form a linear code. Seven of the codewords are given as:

000000	111100
010100	101011
000011	111111
010111	

(a) What is the remaining codeword?

(b) The codewords $x_1\,x_2\,x_3\,x_4\,x_5\,x_6$ are generated by three linear equations, each involving two xs. Write down three equations which generate the code. [A]

4.7 The parity check matrix

When we first considered error-correcting codes in Section 4.5 we looked at the simple example:

N : 000111 S : 011010 E : 101100 W : 110001

and tried to work out what the received message:

111001

meant. By comparing it with each of the codewords we found that it was 'nearest' to 110001 (W):

N	S	E	W
0 0 0 1 1 1	0 1 1 0 1 0	1 0 1 1 0 0	1 1 0 0 0 1
× × × × ×	× × ×	× × ×	×
1 1 1 0 0 1	1 1 1 0 0 1	1 1 1 0 0 1	1 1 1 0 0 1
			nearest

In practice codes have hundreds of codewords and so the above process of comparing every received string with every codeword would be very time-consuming (even if computer-aided).

In this section we investigate a neat systematic way of correcting received messages when using a **linear** code. Our method will involve matrix multiplication which, although it may be new to you, is reasonably straightforward in this context. As before we are working 'modulo 2' so that any even answer gives us 0 and any odd answer gives us 1.

A linear code is determined by some linear equations. For example the code with codewords:

0000
0011
1101
1110

consists of all those which satisfy:

$$x_1 + x_2 = 0$$
$$x_2 + x_3 + x_4 = 0.$$

We can write these equations in the form of a table or **matrix**:

$$\begin{pmatrix} 1 & 1 & 0 & 0 \\ 0 & 1 & 1 & 1 \end{pmatrix} \begin{pmatrix} x_1 \\ x_2 \\ x_3 \\ x_4 \end{pmatrix} = \begin{pmatrix} 0 \\ 0 \end{pmatrix}$$

matrix

Each equation is represented by a row of the matrix. For example, to read the first equation go along the first row and down the column of xs multiplying corresponding pairs. Then add all the products together. That gives:

$$1.x_1 + 1.x_2 + 0.x_3 + 0.x_4$$

(which is just $x_1 + x_2$). To see what this equals look at the top number on the right-hand side, namely 0. Hence the first row represents the equation:

$$x_1 + x_2 = 0$$

as required. Similarly the second row represents:

$$0.x_1 + 1.x_2 + 1.x_3 + 1.x_4 = 0 \quad \text{or} \quad x_2 + x_3 + x_4 = 0$$

as required.

Worked example 4.9

1 Write in matrix form the following equations in $x_1, x_2, x_3, x_4, x_5, x_6$.

$$\begin{aligned} x_1 + x_3 &= 0 \\ x_2 + x_3 + x_6 &= 0 \\ x_5 + x_6 &= 0. \end{aligned}$$

2 What equations are represented by the matrix equation:

$$\begin{pmatrix} 1 & 1 & 1 & 0 & 0 \\ 0 & 1 & 0 & 1 & 1 \\ 0 & 0 & 1 & 1 & 0 \end{pmatrix} \begin{pmatrix} x_1 \\ x_2 \\ x_3 \\ x_4 \\ x_5 \end{pmatrix} = \begin{pmatrix} 0 \\ 0 \\ 0 \end{pmatrix} ?$$

3 Which of the following satisfies the matrix equation given in **2**:

11001 11101 10110 01010?

Solution

1

$$\begin{pmatrix} 1 & 0 & 1 & 0 & 0 & 0 \\ 0 & 1 & 1 & 0 & 0 & 1 \\ 0 & 0 & 0 & 0 & 1 & 1 \end{pmatrix} \begin{pmatrix} x_1 \\ x_2 \\ x_3 \\ x_4 \\ x_5 \\ x_6 \end{pmatrix} = \begin{pmatrix} 0 \\ 0 \\ 0 \end{pmatrix}$$

2 $x_1 + x_2 + x_3 = 0$

$x_2 + x_4 + x_5 = 0$

$x_3 + x_4 = 0$

3 You could try each of the given string of 0s and 1s in each of the traditional equations or, better still, you could get used to testing them directly in the matrix equation. Remember that an equation is obtained by reading its row and multiplying each of the numbers with its corresponding entry in the column. For example, replacing the column of xs by a column formed from the first codeword 11001 gives:

$$\begin{pmatrix} 1 & 1 & 1 & 0 & 0 \\ 0 & 1 & 0 & 1 & 1 \\ 0 & 0 & 1 & 1 & 0 \end{pmatrix} \begin{pmatrix} 1 \\ 1 \\ 0 \\ 0 \\ 1 \end{pmatrix} = \begin{pmatrix} 1.1 + 1.1 + 1.0 + 0.0 + 0.1 \\ 0.1 + 1.1 + 0.0 + 1.0 + 1.1 \\ 0.1 + 0.1 + 1.0 + 1.0 + 0.1 \end{pmatrix} = \begin{pmatrix} \text{even} \\ \text{even} \\ \text{even} \end{pmatrix} = \begin{pmatrix} 0 \\ 0 \\ 0 \end{pmatrix}$$

and so 11001 does satisfy the equations. However, following the same process with 11101 gives:

$$\begin{pmatrix} 1 & 1 & 1 & 0 & 0 \\ 0 & 1 & 0 & 1 & 1 \\ 0 & 0 & 1 & 1 & 0 \end{pmatrix} \begin{pmatrix} 1 \\ 1 \\ 1 \\ 0 \\ 1 \end{pmatrix} = \begin{pmatrix} 1.1 + 1.1 + 1.1 + 0.0 + 0.1 \\ 0.1 + 1.1 + 0.1 + 1.0 + 1.1 \\ 0.1 + 0.1 + 1.1 + 1.0 + 0.1 \end{pmatrix} = \begin{pmatrix} \text{odd} \\ \text{even} \\ \text{odd} \end{pmatrix} = \begin{pmatrix} 1 \\ 0 \\ 1 \end{pmatrix}$$

and so 11101 does not satisfy the equations. You can check 10111 and 01010 for yourselves.

Given a linear code and the linear equations which generate it, the matrix representing those equations is called the **parity check matrix** of the code. For example in Worked exam question 4.7 we looked at the code with codewords:

00000
00111
00110
11011
11010
11101
11100

and found that it was generated by the equations:

$$x_1 + x_2 = 0$$
$$x_1 + x_3 + x_4 = 0.$$

Hence this code has a parity check matrix:

$$\begin{pmatrix} 1 & 1 & 0 & 0 & 0 \\ 1 & 0 & 1 & 1 & 0 \end{pmatrix}$$

Note that it is not unique, for example the second equation could have been replaced by:

$$x_2 + x_3 + x_4 = 0,$$

thus giving a different parity check matrix.

4

The parity check matrix can be used to check and correct received messages.

There is no point in switching from one representation of the equations to another unless it teaches us something new. Let us look again at the calculations we did in Worked example 4.9. Essentially in part **2** we had a code whose codewords had to satisfy the matrix equation:

$$\begin{pmatrix} 1 & 1 & 1 & 0 & 0 \\ 0 & 1 & 0 & 1 & 1 \\ 0 & 0 & 1 & 1 & 0 \end{pmatrix} \begin{pmatrix} x_1 \\ x_2 \\ x_3 \\ x_4 \\ x_5 \end{pmatrix} = \begin{pmatrix} 0 \\ 0 \\ 0 \end{pmatrix}$$

and in part **3** we had to check whether the following were codewords:

11001 11101 10110 01010.

This is like being given the parity check matrix of the code and some received messages to check. For example, is 11001 a codeword? Yes, because we saw that:

$$\begin{pmatrix} 1 & 1 & 1 & 0 & 0 \\ 0 & 1 & 0 & 1 & 1 \\ 0 & 0 & 1 & 1 & 0 \end{pmatrix} \begin{pmatrix} 1 \\ 1 \\ 0 \\ 0 \\ 1 \end{pmatrix} = \begin{pmatrix} 0 \\ 0 \\ 0 \end{pmatrix}$$

On the other hand is 11101 a codeword of the code? No because we saw that:

$$\begin{pmatrix} 1 & 1 & 1 & 0 & 0 \\ 0 & 1 & 0 & 1 & 1 \\ 0 & 0 & 1 & 1 & 0 \end{pmatrix} \begin{pmatrix} 1 \\ 1 \\ 1 \\ 0 \\ 1 \end{pmatrix} = \begin{pmatrix} 1 \\ 0 \\ 1 \end{pmatrix}$$

If the message 11101 had been received then this process would show that it is not a codeword and that an error had occurred. But how could you find the nearest codeword to correct it to? The key is in the answer to the matrix equation:

$$\begin{pmatrix} 1 & 1 & 1 & 0 & 0 \\ 0 & 1 & 0 & 1 & 1 \\ 0 & 0 & 1 & 1 & 0 \end{pmatrix} \begin{pmatrix} 1 \\ 1 \\ 1 \\ 0 \\ 1 \end{pmatrix} = \begin{pmatrix} 1 \\ 0 \\ 1 \end{pmatrix}$$

the answer equals the third column of the matrix

∴ there is an error in the third bit

and the intended message should have been 11**0**01

4

Worked exam question 4.8

A linear code has codewords:

110001
110110
101010
101101
011011
011100
000111
000000

1 By looking at:
- the 1st, 2nd and 3rd bits of each codeword
- the 1st, 5th and 6th bits of each codeword
- the 3rd, 4th and 5th bits of each codeword

find a parity check matrix for the code.

2 Use your matrix to correct the message:

111010110110101111

Solution

1 You will see that in all the codewords the suggested triples of bits add to an even number; i.e. to 0 modulo 2. Hence the equations which determine the codewords are:

$$x_1 + x_2 + x_3 = 0$$
$$x_1 + x_5 + x_6 = 0$$
$$x_3 + x_4 + x_5 = 0$$

giving a parity check matrix

$$\begin{pmatrix} 1 & 1 & 1 & 0 & 0 & 0 \\ 1 & 0 & 0 & 0 & 1 & 1 \\ 0 & 0 & 1 & 1 & 1 & 0 \end{pmatrix}$$

2 The received message, split into strings of length 6, is:

111010 110110 101111

and we test each of those strings with the parity check matrix:

111010

$$\begin{bmatrix} 1 & 1 & 1 & 0 & 0 & 0 \\ 1 & 0 & 0 & 0 & 1 & 1 \\ 0 & 0 & 1 & 1 & 1 & 0 \end{bmatrix} \begin{bmatrix} 1 \\ 1 \\ 1 \\ 0 \\ 1 \\ 0 \end{bmatrix} = \begin{bmatrix} 1.1 + 1.1 + 1.1 + 0.0 + 0.1 + 0.0 \\ 1.1 + 0.1 + 0.1 + 0.0 + 1.1 + 1.0 \\ 0.1 + 0.1 + 1.1 + 1.0 + 1.1 + 0.0 \end{bmatrix} = \begin{bmatrix} \text{odd} \\ \text{even} \\ \text{even} \end{bmatrix} = \begin{bmatrix} 1 \\ 0 \\ 0 \end{bmatrix}$$

Therefore there is an error in the second place and the string should be corrected to 101010.

110110

$$\begin{bmatrix} 1 & 1 & 1 & 0 & 0 & 0 \\ 1 & 0 & 0 & 0 & 1 & 1 \\ 0 & 0 & 1 & 1 & 1 & 0 \end{bmatrix} = \begin{bmatrix} 1 \\ 1 \\ 0 \\ 1 \\ 1 \\ 0 \end{bmatrix} = \begin{bmatrix} 1.1 + 1.1 + 1.0 + 0.1 + 0.1 + 0.0 \\ 1.1 + 0.1 + 0.0 + 0.1 + 1.1 + 1.0 \\ 0.1 + 0.1 + 1.0 + 1.1 + 1.1 + 0.0 \end{bmatrix} = \begin{bmatrix} \text{even} \\ \text{even} \\ \text{even} \end{bmatrix} = \begin{bmatrix} 0 \\ 0 \\ 0 \end{bmatrix}$$

and so this string is correct.

101111

$$\begin{bmatrix} 1 & 1 & 1 & 0 & 0 & 0 \\ 1 & 0 & 0 & 0 & 1 & 1 \\ 0 & 0 & 1 & 1 & 1 & 0 \end{bmatrix} = \begin{bmatrix} 1 \\ 0 \\ 1 \\ 1 \\ 1 \\ 1 \end{bmatrix} = \begin{bmatrix} 1.1 + 1.0 + 1.1 + 0.1 + 0.1 + 0.1 \\ 1.1 + 0.0 + 0.1 + 0.1 + 1.1 + 1.1 \\ 0.1 + 0.0 + 1.1 + 1.1 + 1.1 + 0.1 \end{bmatrix} = \begin{bmatrix} \text{even} \\ \text{odd} \\ \text{odd} \end{bmatrix} = \begin{bmatrix} 0 \\ 1 \\ 1 \end{bmatrix}$$

Therefore there is an error in fifth place and the string should be corrected to 101101. Overall the corrected message is then:

101010110110101101

We conclude our work on linear codes and parity check matrices with a few miscellaneous comments.

Firstly note that we have only illustrated the use of parity check matrices for the correction of single errors, where the non-zero column had to be matched to a column of the parity check matrix. The method extends to any number of errors but it requires the non-zero column to be matched to a **sum** of columns of the parity check matrix and this is beyond the scope of this current course.

Another question which may have crossed your mind is how to be sure that we have found all the necessary equations for a linear code and not included any redundant ones. In general there are 2^n strings of 0s and 1s of length n. Each equation rules out half the possibilities and so a linear code of length n generated by one equation will have 2^{n-1} codewords, a second independent equation will reduce that to 2^{n-2} codewords, etc. Hence if a linear code of length n actually has 2^k codewords then it must have been generated by $n-k$ independent equations. The parity check matrix will then have $n-k$ rows and n columns. The code is then said to have **dimension** k and **efficiency** (or **rate**) k/n.

4

> The number of codewords in a linear code is always a power of 2: if it has 2^k codewords and is of length n then its parity check matrix has $n - k$ rows and n columns.

For example, to have a code consisting of 32 codewords ($= 2^5$) we need the code to be of length 5 or more. If it has length 5 then every combination of 0s and 1s is used as a codeword, every bit of information counts and the code has efficiency 5/5 = 1; i.e. it is totally efficient. However it has absolutely no error-correcting capabilities. On the other hand if a code has 32 codewords has length 9 (when 5 would do) then it has efficiency 5/9 (but, if constructed carefully, much better error-correcting capabilities). So the design of good codes calls for a balance between the efficiency and the error-correcting capabilities. This is beyond our current scope but details can be found in the *Further reading*.

We conclude with one example to illustrate these terms.

Worked example 4.10

A linear code has codewords:

110001
110110
011100
011011
101101
101010
000111
000000

State its length, dimension and efficiency. Also state how many independent equations generate the code and the size of its parity check matrix.

Solution

This code has:

length	6	(n)
number of codewords	2^3	(2^k)
dimension	3	(k)
efficiency	0.5	(k/n)
generating equations	3	$(n-k)$
rows of parity check matrix	3	$(n-k)$
columns of parity check matrix	6	(n)

EXERCISE 4F

1 Let C be the code with the parity check matrix:

$$\begin{pmatrix} 1 & 0 & 1 & 0 \\ 1 & 1 & 0 & 1 \end{pmatrix}$$

Find the codewords of C and write down the Hamming distance of C.

2 Consider the linear code whose eight codewords are as follows:

0011101	0101011
0110110	1000111
1011010	1101100
1110001	0000000.

(a) Find the distance between any two codewords, and hence find the Hamming distance of the code.

(b) Find the number of errors in a transmitted codeword which can be detected and corrected by this code.

(c) A codeword is transmitted and the binary word 1001100 is received. Which codeword is most likely to have been transmitted? [A]

3 The eight codewords of a linear code are as follows:

0000000	1100101
0011101	1111000
1001011	0110011
1010110	0101110

(a) State the Hamming distance of this code.

(b) How many errors per received codeword can this code:

(i) correct, **(ii)** detect?

(c) A codeword is transmitted and the binary word 0100101 is received. Which of the eight codewords is most likely to have been the one transmitted?

4 Show that the code:

000000	101011
000111	101100
011001	110010
011110	110101

is linear and find a parity check matrix. Use it to decode the received message 010110.

MIXED EXERCISES

1 Suggest a way of adapting the Morse code so that it has an error-detecting capability.

2 Each letter in the Braille alphabet can be written as a binary string of length 6, with raised dots being referred to as 1s:

$$\begin{matrix} x_1 \bullet & \bullet\, x_4 \\ x_2 \bullet & \bullet\, x_5 \\ x_3 \bullet & \bullet\, x_6 \end{matrix} \longrightarrow x_1x_2x_3x_4x_5x_6$$

For example: a

(a) Give the binary representation of b–f

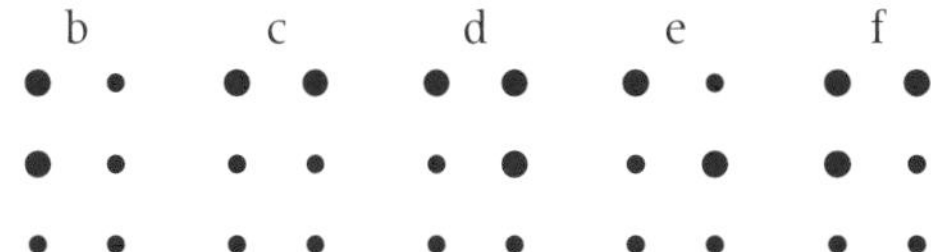

(b) Show that the code has no error-detecting capability.
(c) How could some sort of check be built in to the system?

4

3 A bank issues eight-digit account numbers where the last digit is a check digit. In a number of the form:

abcdefgh

the check digit h is non-zero and is chosen so that:

$$8a + 7b + 6c + 5d + 4e + 3f + 2g + h$$

is divisible by 9.

(a) Find the check digits of the numbers:

5432 815x and 5301 225y

(b) A single error has occurred in the number:

1043 5182.

Give the seven possible numbers which might have been intended.

(c) A single transposition of two adjacent digits has occurred to give the number:

1043 5182.

What was the correct number? [A]

4 The tree illustrated is used as a Huffman code for the letters A, B, C, D, E.

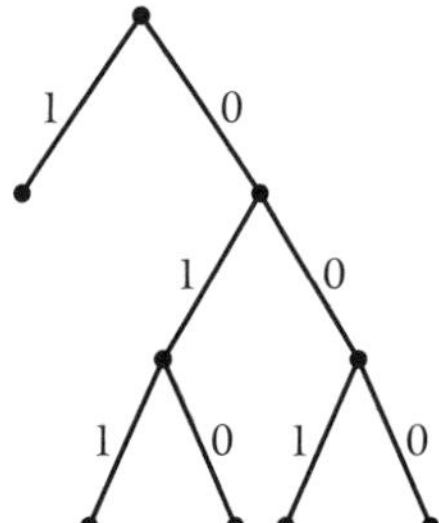

In this code the word BEAD becomes:

0101011000.

(a) What does the word DACE become?

(b) Decode the message:

00011000

(c) In another Huffman code for just the five letters A–E, A uses one digit, B uses two digits and C uses three digits. How many digits do D and E use? [A]

5 The codewords of three codes A, B, and C are listed:

A	B	C
0000000	0010111	00000000
1101001	0100110	00001111
0101010	0110001	00110011
1000011	1000101	01010101
1001100	1010010	01100110
0100101	1100011	01011010
1100110	1110100	00111100
0001111	0001011	11111111
1110000		11110000
0011001		11001100
1011010		10101010
0110011		10011001
0111100		10100101
1010101		11000011
0010110		
1111111		

(a) For each code state its length.

(b) Calculate the Hamming distance of each code.

(c) How many errors per codeword can each code detect? How many can it correct?

(d) Just one of the codes is linear. Which one?

(e) In one case the addition of two further codewords will make the code linear. Decide which code and find the two codewords.

6 A code has codewords:

000000 111000 000111 111111.

(a) Show that the code is linear and state its Hamming distance.

(b) Construct a parity check matrix for the code and use it to check and correct the message:

000101111111000110. [A]

7 Show that the code with codewords:

0000000000
0110110010
1001001101
1111111111

is a linear code. Construct a parity check matrix for it and use the matrix to check and correct the message:

100000110111110110010. [A]

8 The code C has parity-check matrix:

$$\begin{pmatrix} 0 & 0 & 0 & 1 & 1 & 1 & 1 \\ 0 & 1 & 1 & 0 & 0 & 1 & 1 \\ 1 & 0 & 1 & 0 & 1 & 0 & 1 \end{pmatrix}$$

(a) What is the length of the code?

(b) How many codewords does it have?

(c) Give five of its codewords.

(d) A codeword of C is transmitted and incorrectly received as 0111000. Find the possible error and the transmitted codeword, assuming that only one error has occurred. [A]

9 Consider the code whose codewords are:

0000000000
1111111111
0110110010
1001001101

(a) How many errors does this code simultaneously correct and detect?

(b) If a message is received as 0110111111, which codeword is most likely to have been transmitted?

(c) Is this code a linear code?

(In each part, give reasons for your answer.)

4

10 One codeword of a code is 1001110. The other words are obtained by repeatedly moving the front digit to the back giving:

1001110
0011101

and so on.

(a) List the seven words of the code.

(b) What is the Hamming distance of this code?

(c) How many errors in a codeword can be simultaneously detected and corrected? Give a brief reason for your answer.

(d) Show that the code is not linear. What is the minimum number of codewords which need to be added to make this code linear?

(e) The matrix:

$$\begin{pmatrix} 1 & 0 & 1 & 1 & 0 & 0 & 0 \\ 1 & 1 & 1 & 0 & 1 & 0 & 0 \\ 1 & 1 & 0 & 0 & 0 & 1 & 0 \\ 0 & 1 & 1 & 0 & 0 & 0 & 1 \end{pmatrix}$$

is a parity check matrix for this code. Show how to use it to correct the received message

0110111111010000111111. [A]

11 Consider the linear code C whose eight codewords are as follows:

0000000000	1001011100
0100101110	1101110010
0010010111	1011001011
0110111001	1111100101

(a) What is the Hamming distance of this code? How many errors in a transmitted codeword can this code simultaneously correct and detect?

(b) The matrix

$$\begin{pmatrix} 1 & 0 & 0 & 1 & 0 & 0 & 0 & 0 & 0 & 0 \\ 0 & 1 & 0 & 0 & 1 & 0 & 0 & 0 & 0 & 0 \\ 1 & 0 & 1 & 0 & 0 & 1 & 0 & 0 & 0 & 0 \\ 1 & 1 & 0 & 0 & 0 & 0 & 1 & 0 & 0 & 0 \\ 1 & 1 & 1 & 0 & 0 & 0 & 0 & 1 & 0 & 0 \\ 0 & 1 & 1 & 0 & 0 & 0 & 0 & 0 & 1 & 0 \\ 0 & 0 & 1 & 0 & 0 & 0 & 0 & 0 & 0 & 1 \end{pmatrix}$$

is a parity check matrix for C. Use it to decode the received word 0010000111. [A]

12 A linear code has eight codewords, six of which are as follows:

001110
010101
011011
100011
101101
110110

(a) Find the other two codewords.

(b) State the Hamming distance of the code.

(c) Given that the sum of the 2nd, 3rd and 4th bits is always even, and that the sum of the last three bits is always even, find a third connection and write the conditions as three linear equations in x_1, x_2, x_3, x_4, x_5, and x_6.

(d) Construct a parity-check matrix for C and use it to check and correct the message 111101011011011110.

4

Key point summary

1 A **Huffman code** assigns letters to the vertices of degree 1 of a 'bifurcating' tree. *p148*

2 You will not be expected to remember details of the Morse code, Braille, bar codes or ISBN numbers but you should understand the general principles. In particular you should understand the concept of a **check digit**. *p150*

3 The **distance** between two codewords is the number of places in which they differ. The **Hamming distance** of a code is the smallest distance between two different codewords of the code. *p159*

4 If a code has Hamming distance δ then it can **detect** errors if fewer than δ occur in any codeword and it can **correct** errors if fewer than $\frac{1}{2}\delta$ occur in any codeword. The method of decoding is to choose the **nearest codeword**. *p162*

5 A **linear code** is one in which the sum of any two codewords (modulo 2) is a codeword. A linear c ode must include the zero codeword and have 2^k codewords for some integer k. *p167*

6 The parity check matrix can be used to check and correct received messages. *p172*

7 A linear code of length n with 2^k codewords is **generated** by $n-k$ linear equations. When these equations are written in matrix form their matrix is the **parity check matrix** of the code. p175

Test yourself

What to review

1 A firm's employee numbers consist of five digits in which the last digit is a check digit: — *Sections 4.3 and 4.4*

abcde

e is chosen so that $6a + 5b + 4c + 3d + 2e$ is divisible by 7.

(a) What is the check digit of:

1256x?

(b) There is one error in the number:

14311

What is the largest number it could be?

---

2 Decode 1000001 in the Huffman code illustrated: — *Section 4.3*

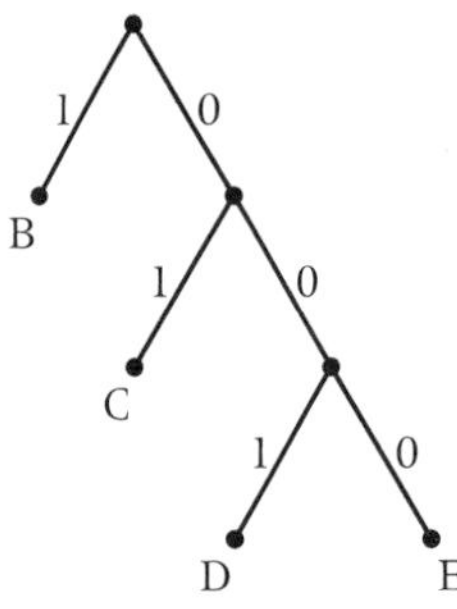

---

3 A code has codewords:

11011
00100
00000
11111

(a) Is it linear? — *Section 4.6*

(b) What is its length? — *Section 4.5*

(c) What is its Hamming distance? — *Section 4.5*

(d) Can it detect errors? — *Section 4.5*

(e) Give three equations which generate the code. — *Section 4.6*

(f) Give a parity check matrix of the code. — *Section 4.7*

Test yourself (continued) | What to review

4 A parity check matrix: *Section 4.7*

$$\begin{pmatrix} 1 & 1 & 1 & 0 & 0 \\ 0 & 1 & 0 & 1 & 1 \\ 0 & 0 & 1 & 0 & 1 \end{pmatrix}$$

can be used for a given code. Use it to correct the message 11110.

Test yourself ANSWERS

1 **(a)** 1, **(b)** 94311.

2 BED.

3 **(a)** Yes,

(b) 5,

(c) 1,

(d) No,

(e) $x_1 + x_2 = 0,\ x_1 + x_4 = 0,\ x_1 + x_5 = 0.$

(f) $\begin{pmatrix} 1 & 1 & 0 & 0 & 0 \\ 1 & 0 & 0 & 1 & 0 \\ 1 & 0 & 0 & 0 & 1 \end{pmatrix}$

[There are alternative answers to **(e)** and **(f)**: they must ensure that $x_1 = x_2 = x_4 = x_5$.]

4 11010.

Exam style practice paper

Time allowed 1 hour 45 minutes

Maximum marks: 80

Answer all questions

1 Find the minimum cut of the network given below: *(3 marks)*

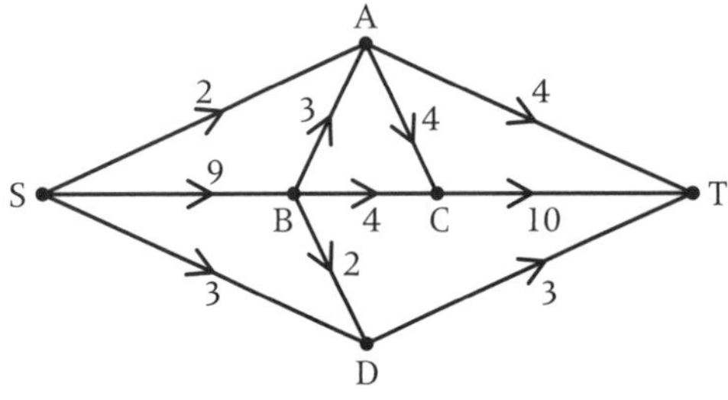

Find a flow equal in value to the capacity of the minimum cut. How do you know that this is a maximum flow? *(4 marks)*

2 Find the general solution of the recurrence relation

$$u_n = 4u_{n-1} - 4u_{n-2} + 3^n. \qquad (7\ marks)$$

3 In the given **Huffman code** the word DEAN encodes as 101101000:

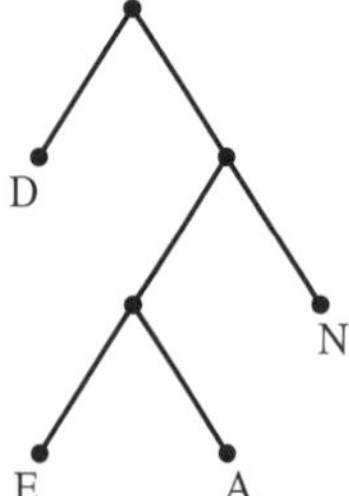

(a) Draw a tree for a Huffman code of just the four letters D, E, A, N so that DEAN encodes as 000101001 *(4 marks)*

(b) Show that there is no tree for a Huffman code of just the four letters D, E, A, N so that NEED encodes as 00010011. *(3 marks)*

4 The network below shows the distances between five towns. A North-East tourist board official wants to start at Middlesborough, visit each town once and return to Middlesborough.

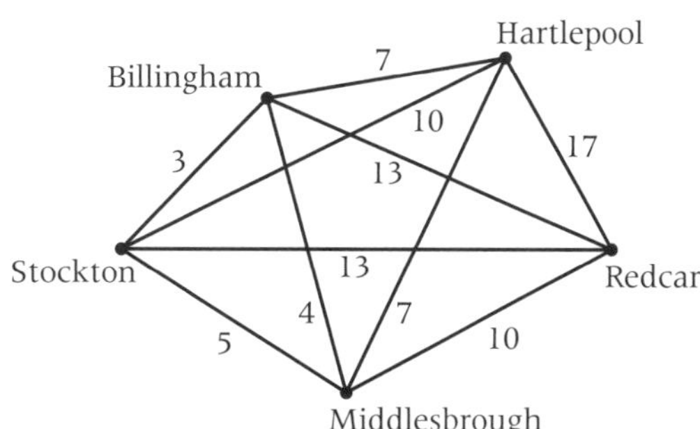

(a) Apply the nearest neighbour algorithm to find a route for the official. *(4 marks)*

(b) Is the route you found in **(a)** the shortest? Give reasons for your answer. *(2 marks)*

5 The table gives the lengths (in 100s of metres) of telegraph wire (where it exists) between the six points A–F.

	A	**B**	**C**	**D**	**E**	**F**
A	–	4	–	5	3	10
B	4	–	3	–	10	7
C	–	3	–	10	–	2
D	5	–	10	–	4	–
E	3	10	–	4	–	–
F	10	7	2	–	–	–

(a) Draw a network to represent this information. *(2 marks)*

(b) A BT technician wishes to inspect the wire, ending the tour of inspection back at the starting point. Apply an appropriate pairing algorithm to find the minimum distance the technician must travel. *(5 marks)*

(c) The previous year there had not been a telegraph wire from A to B. If you had applied the algorithm to that earlier network, how many pairings of vertices would you have to consider? (Do **not** carry out the algorithm in this case.) *(2 marks)*

6 The following patterns are made up of matches:

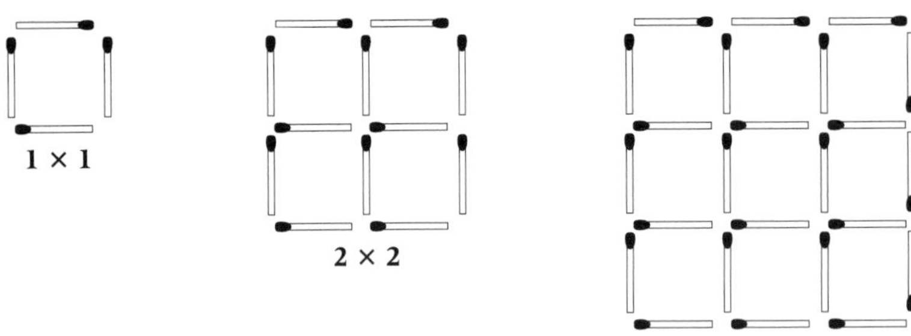

(a) How many matches are used in the 1-by-1 case? *(1 mark)*

(b) How many **extra** matches are needed in going from the 3-by-3 case to the 4-by-4 case? *(2 marks)*

(c) How many **extra** matches are needed in going from the $(n-1)$-by-$(n-1)$ case to the n-by-n case? *(2 marks)*

(d) Let u_n be the number of matches needed in the n-by-n case. Write down a first order recurrence relation in u_n including an initial condition. *(2 marks)*

(e) Iterate with your recurrence relation to prove that:

$$u_n = 2n(n+1)$$ *(5 marks)*

7 A linear code has 8 codewords. Six of them are:

0000111
0011100
0011011
1110000
1101100
1110111

(a) State the other two codewords. *(3 marks)*

(b) State the Hamming distance of the code. *(3 marks)*

(c) Given that the codewords $x_1 x_2 x_3 x_4 x_5 x_6 x_7$ satisfy:

$$x_1 + x_2 = 0$$
$$x_2 + x_3 + x_4 = 0$$
and $x_4 + x_5 + x_6 = 0,$

find one other equation involving x_7 and one other x which they all satisfy. *(2 marks)*

(d) Write down a parity check matrix for this code and use it to correct the message

000101111010101110110 *(6 marks)*

8 Consider the linear programming problem:

Maximise	$P = x + 2y$
subject to	$x + y \leqslant 20$
	$3x + y \leqslant 30$
	$y \leqslant 16$
	$x \geqslant 0$
	$y \geqslant 0$

(a) Introduce three slack variables and rewrite the problem involving equations together with five non-negativity conditions. *(2 marks)*

(b) Construct a simplex tableau representing this problem. *(3 marks)*

(c) By first **increasing** y apply two iterations of the simplex method to your tableau. *(7 marks)*

(d) What conclusions can you draw from the final tableau? *(2 marks)*

(e) Illustrate the feasible region and the route taken by the simplex method. *(4 marks)*

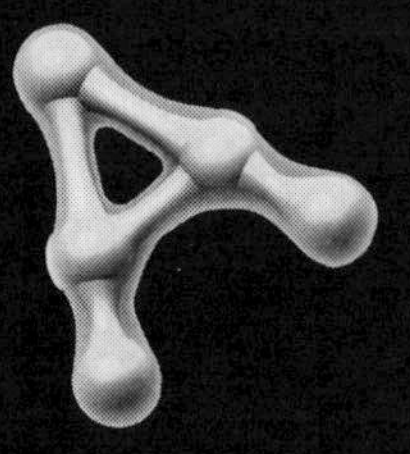

Answers

1 Networks

EXERCISE 1A

1 ABCEDA.

2 Minimum connector = 33 + 44 + 45 + 66 + 81 + 105 +132 = 506;
506 + 51 + 124 = 681; SEPAbTIFGAyS; 918.

3 **(a)** Off BADC Off, **(b)** e.g. try beating 29 with one per row.

4 **(a)** A : 15 + 11 B : 14 + 12 C : 18 + 7 D : 20 + 5 E : 16 + 9 F : 18 + 6
(b) $\geqslant$ all of those in **(a)**.

5 ABCEHFGDA; no, ABCEHFDGA better.

6 e.g.

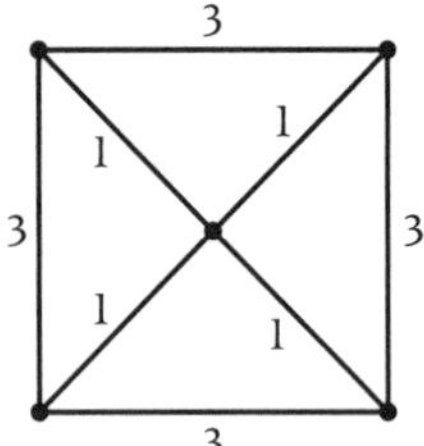

7 **(a)** e.g. 54 by nearest neighbour from A
(b) e.g. 52 removing A or D
(c) $52 \leqslant L \leqslant 54$
(d) ABEFCDA; 53.

8 **(a)** AD, DC, CB, BE; 29
(b) e.g. ADCBEA; 41
(c) 39, 40, 40, 39, 40
(d) **(a)** + EA = 41 and is a cycle.

EXERCISE 1B

1 + edge of 2 for Eulerian trail; already Eulerian; +3 + 3.

2 + 45 for Eulerian trail = 257.

3 + AD + BC; e.g. ADABDCBCA = 250.

4 + IH + EC + CD = 34 in total; e.g. DCBAIHGFECIHECD.

5 + BE (= 60) to be repeated; e.g. HEBACFGDCBDEBEGH.

6 + PS + ST + TU; e.g. PSTUQRTSQPSVUTVP = £9.82.

7 (a)

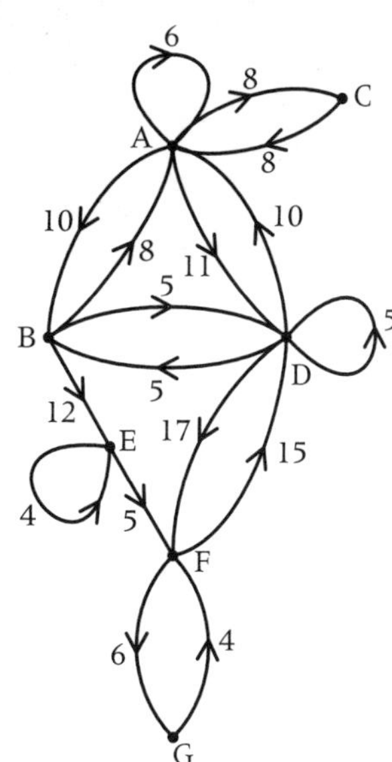

(b) odd ≡ number in ≠ number out
∴ need route **from** F **to** B
∴ + FD + DB
e.g. AACADDABDBEEFGFDFDBA

8 (a) A, C, F, G odd. **(b)** + AF + CG; e.g. AEFGCGDCBDFBAFA = 48.

EXERCISE 1C

1 26, 16, 53(AB + DC + DT + ET).

2 75

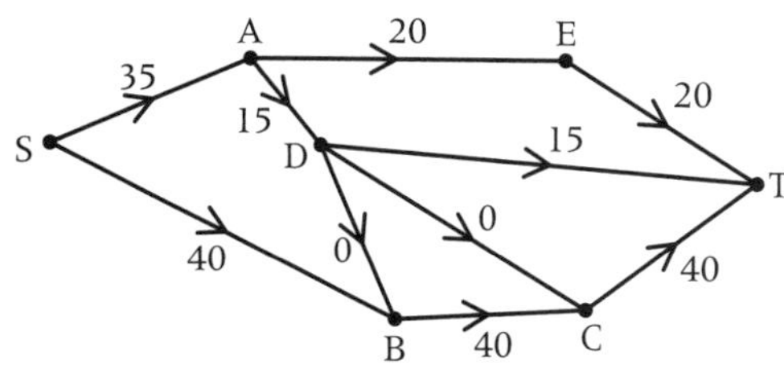

3 28 (e.g. 12 SCT + 4 SCBT + 12 SABT),
23 (e.g. 5 SADBT + 6 SABT + 12 SCDT),
111 (e.g. 35 SAT + 20 SBT + 10 SBAT + 2 SCBAT + 30 SCT + 14 SCDT).

4 16; increase the right-hand 4 by 3; the incoming 6, 8, 5 will then be saturated.

5 (a) B, F **(b)** 12 + 13 + 18 = 43, **(c)** e.g. BCHGF by 4,
(d) BCHGEF by 1 to make 43 = maximum, **(e)** = a cut.

6 (b) e.g.

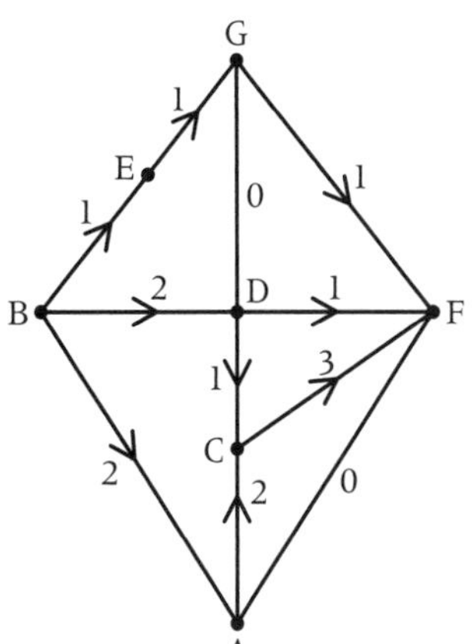

max flow = 5 (= cut BA, DC, DF, GF).

7 (b) e.g.

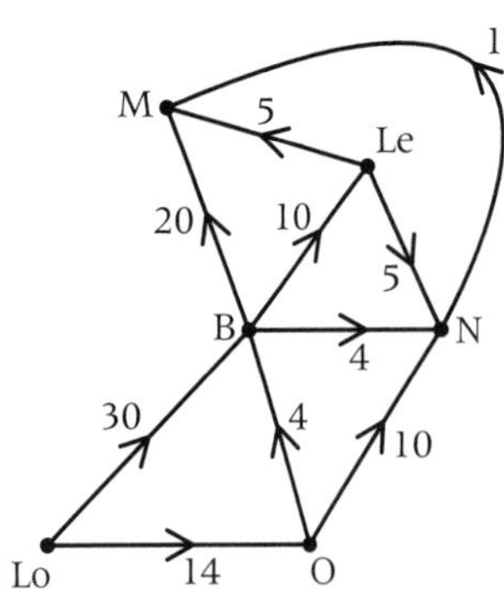

max flow = 44(00) reduces to 25(00)

(c) e.g.

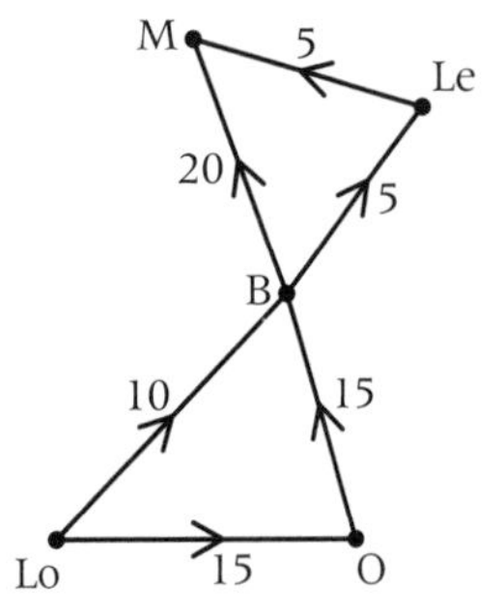

8 (a) e.g.

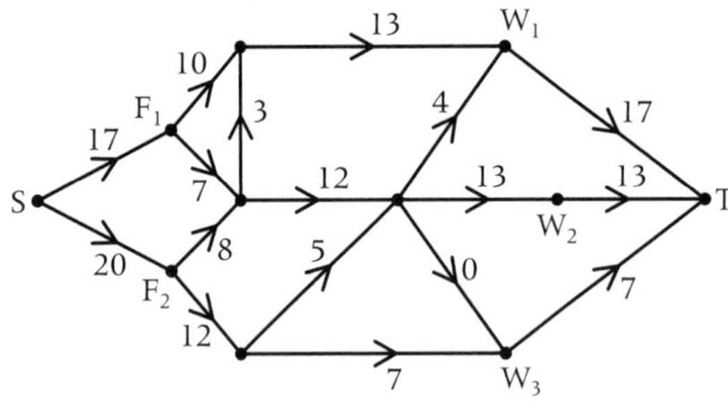

(b) 17 leave F_1, 20 leave F_2, e.g. 17 reach W_1, 13 reach W_2, 7 reach W_3.

MIXED EXERCISES

1 18, 57, 38.

2 22 (e.g. 10 SABT + 6 SACT + 6 SDT),
35 (e.g. 15 SBET + 5 SBECDT + 10 SACDT + 5 SADT).

3 For Eulerian trail + AB + CD; e.g. ABCDEACDBA = 405 metres.

4 (a) total degrees = 2 × number of edges = even,

(b) 15, 105,

(c) 1.3.5.7. … $(2n - 1)$ (see Exercise 3B, Question 4).

5 + FG = 830 in total.

6 42.

7 + 4 + 9 (or + 8 + 5) = 91 in total.

8 **(a)** e.g. Br T Bat So Sw Bas O G Br = 381,

(b) TBat, Bar Sw, Sw G, Sw O, O Bas, Bas So = 214,

(c) upper 381; lower 214 + 13 + 35 = 262.

9 max 20(00); e.g.

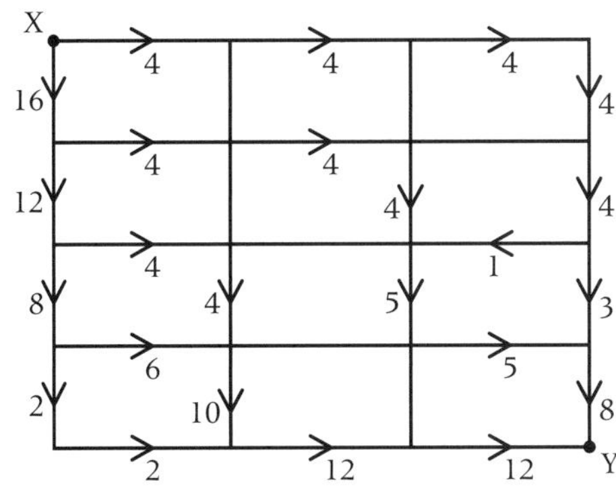

10 **(a)** AEBDCA = 42,

(b) EB, BD, DC = 26,

(c) upper bound 42, lower bound 26 + 3 + 7 = 36.

11 **(a)** FE, ED, DC, CB = 39;
lower bound = 39 + 11 + 14 + 64,

(b) AFEDCBA = 64.

12

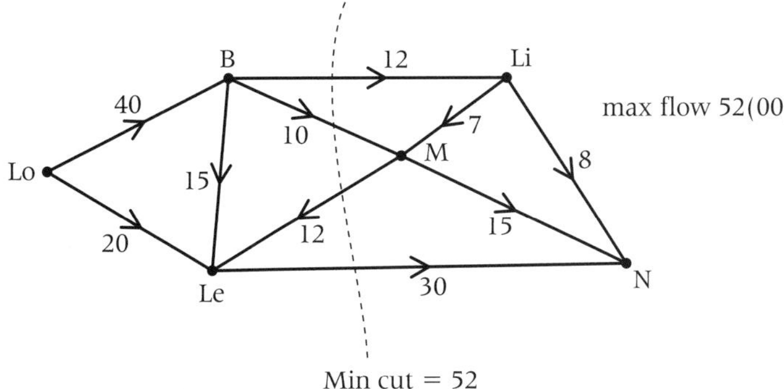

when Liverpool is removed, max flow = 40(00).

13 **(a)**

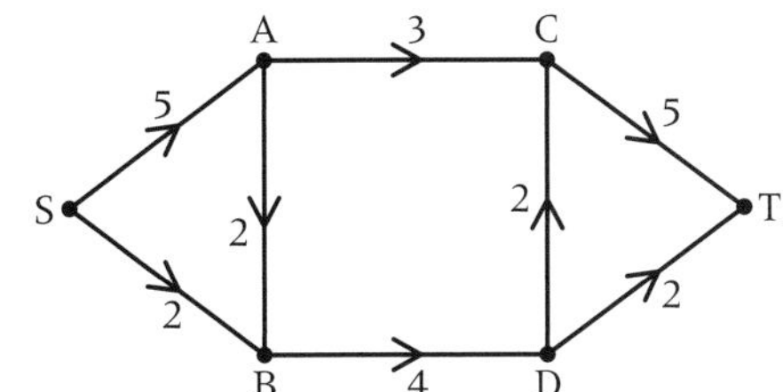

(b) AC, DC, DT

(c) 7 (all flows ⩽ all cuts)

14 Both = 9.

15 (c)

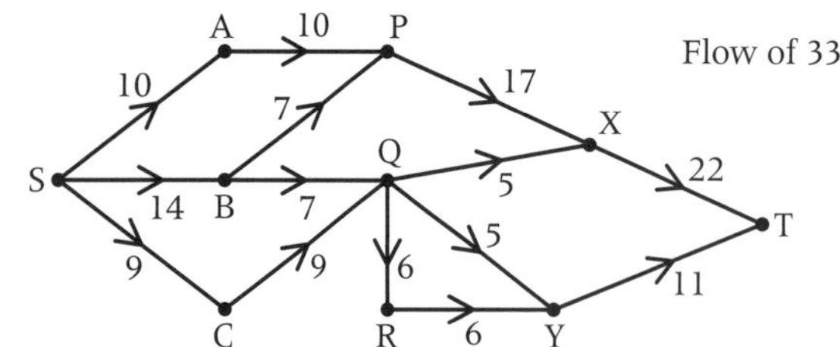

Flow of 33

(d) SA, BP, QX, QY, RY = cut of 33,

(e) Shows supply of 33 is made up of 10 from A, 14 from B, etc.

(f) SCQPXT + 3 = 36 new maximum.

16 (a) $k = 9$ cut = SA, BA, BT, CT

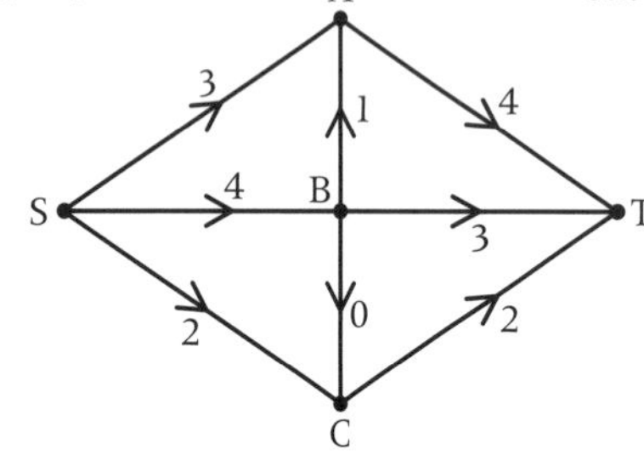

(b) all flows $\leqslant$ all cuts

17 (a) + ABC + FI = 2620 in total;

B : 3 C : 2 D : 2 E : 2 F : 3 G : 2 H : 2 I : 2

(b) all edges used twice; Eulerian; $2 \times 2300 = 4600$,

(c) replace each edge by two edges, one directed each way.

18 (a) 750; BT = 300, CT = 350, DT = 100,

(b) 550,

(c) DT by at least 70.

19 (a) CH 9 4 1 3 8 5 2 7 6 CH = 1850,

(b) 13, 14, 25, 27, 38, 49, 58, 67 = 1000,

(c) upper bound 1850, lower bound = 1000 + 50 + 100 = 1150.

20 (a) TGEDCBHAFT = 850
e.g. TGEDCBHFAT = 840,

(b) AH, BC, BH, CD, DF, DG, EG = 360,
lower bound = 360 + 70 + 100 = 530.

2 Linear programming

EXERCISE 2A

1

Maximise	$75x + 120y$
subject to	$x + 2y \leqslant 40$
	$3x + 4y \leqslant 100$
	$x \geqslant 0$
	$y \geqslant 0$

2

Maximise	$x + y$
subject to	$x + 2y \leqslant 24$
	$4x + y \leqslant 44$
	$2x + y \leqslant 24$
	$x \geqslant 0$
	$y \geqslant 0$

3

Maximise	$40w + 35x + 32y + 30z$
subject to	$4w + 3x + 2y + z \leqslant 84$
	$5w + 4x + 5y + 6z \leqslant 120$
	$7w + 6x + 8y + 4z \leqslant 168$
	$w \geqslant 0, x \geqslant 0, y \geqslant 0, z \geqslant 0$

4

Maximise	$x_1 + x_2 + x_3$ (or $x_6 + x_7$)	
subject to	$x_1 \leqslant 5$	$x_1 \geqslant 0$
	$x_2 \leqslant 7$	$x_2 \geqslant 0$
	$x_3 \leqslant 6$	$x_3 \geqslant 0$
	$x_4 \leqslant 2$	$x_4 \geqslant 0$
	$x_5 \leqslant 3$	$x_5 \geqslant 0$
	$x_6 \leqslant 6$	$x_6 \geqslant 0$
	$x_7 \leqslant 10$	$x_7 \geqslant 0$
	$x_1 + x_4 - x_6 = 0$	
	$x_2 - x_4 - x_5 = 0$	
	$x_5 + x_6 - x_7 = 0$	

EXERCISE 2B

1

Maximise	$P = 250x + 200y + 150z$
subject to	$4x + 6y + 9z + s = 36$
	$3x + 2y + 9z + t = 18$
	$12x + 9y + 2z + u = 36$
	$8x + 9y + 6z + v = 72$
	$x \geqslant 0, y \geqslant 0, s \geqslant 0, t \geqslant 0, u \geqslant 0, v \geqslant 0$

2 (a) $x + y + s = 24$, $y + t = 10$, $x + 4y + u = 42$,

(b) (i) $x = 14$, $y = 10$, $u < 0$, $P = 78$,

(ii) $x = 18$, $y = 6$, $t \geqslant 0$, $P = 66$,

(iii) $x = 2$, $y = 10$, $s \geqslant 0$, $P = 54$.

(c) $P = 2x + 5y = (x + y) + (x + 4y) = (24 - s) + (42 - u) = 66 - s - u$
$\therefore P \leqslant 66$ and equals 66 only when $s = u = 0$; i.e. at (18, 6).

3 (a)

Maximise	$P = x + y$
subject to	$2x + y + s = 48$
	$x + 2y + t = 60$
	$x + 4y + u = 116$
	$x \geqslant 0, y \geqslant 0, s \geqslant 0, t \geqslant 0, u \geqslant 0$

(b) $P = 36 - \frac{1}{3}s - \frac{1}{3}t$,

(c) Maximum 36 at (12, 24).

4 (a) add/subtract the given equations,

(b) $P = 35 - 1\frac{1}{2}s - \frac{1}{2}t$,

(c) Maximum 35 at (15, 5).

EXERCISE 2C

1 Maximum 570 at (15, 8).

2 Maximum 48 at (6, 12).

3 Maximum 24 at (4, 2, 0).

EXERCISE 2D

1 (a) (5, 0),

(b) 25,

(c) $s = 0, t = 6$.

2 (e.g. with x first)

P	x	y	s	t		
1	−1	−2	0	0	0	(0, 0)
0	4	1	1	0	18	$P = 0$
0	1	3	0	1	21	$s = 18$
						$t = 21$

P	x	y	s	t		
1	0	$-1\frac{3}{4}$	$\frac{1}{4}$	0	$4\frac{1}{2}$	$(4\frac{1}{2}, 0)$
0	1	$\frac{1}{4}$	$\frac{1}{4}$	0	$4\frac{1}{2}$	$P = 4\frac{1}{2}$
0	0	$2\frac{3}{4}$	$-\frac{1}{4}$	1	$16\frac{1}{2}$	$s = 0$
						$t = 16\frac{1}{2}$

P	x	y	s	t		
1	0	0	$\frac{1}{11}$	$\frac{7}{11}$	15	(3, 6)
0	1	0	$\frac{3}{11}$	$-\frac{1}{11}$	3	$P = 15$ (max)
0	0	1	$-\frac{1}{11}$	$\frac{4}{11}$	6	$s = 0$
						$t = 0$

3 (a) Maximum 27 at (3, 6).

(b)

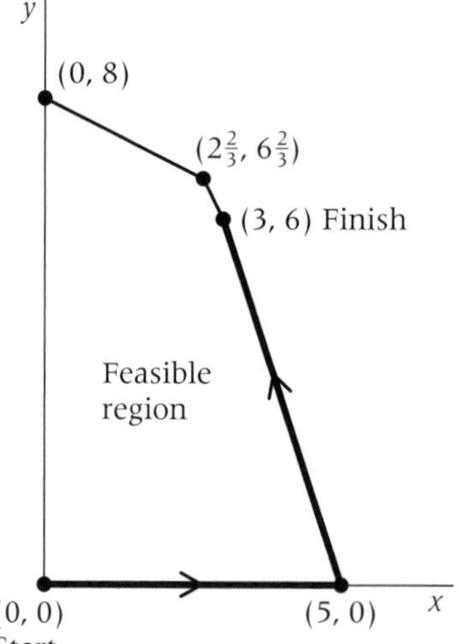

(c) clockwise route, three iterations.

EXERCISE 2E

1 $X = x - 5$

Maximise	$2X + y + 10$
subject to	$X + 5y \leqslant 75$
	$X + y \leqslant 19$
	$3X + y \leqslant 49$
	$X \geqslant 0$
	$y \geqslant 0$

Maximum 44 at $X = 15$ $(x = 20)$, $y = 4$.

2 **(a)** Minimum 11 at (3, 5).

(b) Maximum 11 at $(\frac{1}{4}, \frac{1}{4}, 0)$.

(c)

nos	x	y
	2	1
36	7	3
8	1	1
30	3	5

nos	x	y	z
	36	8	30
2	7	1	3
1	3	1	5

3 x = no of lengths of A
y = no of lengths of B

Maximise	$P = 12x + 15y$
subject to	$4x + y \leqslant 56$
	$5x + 3y \leqslant 105$
	$x + 2y \leqslant 56$
	$x \geqslant 0$
	$y \geqslant 0$

Maximum £447 at (6, 25).

MIXED EXERCISES

1 **(a)** Maximum 26 at (6, 4), **(b)** Maximum 10 at (0, 2),
(c) Maximum $3\frac{1}{2}$ at $(2, 1\frac{1}{2})$.

2 **(a)** **(b)** Maximum $47\frac{1}{2}$ at $(0, 6\frac{1}{2})$.

(c)

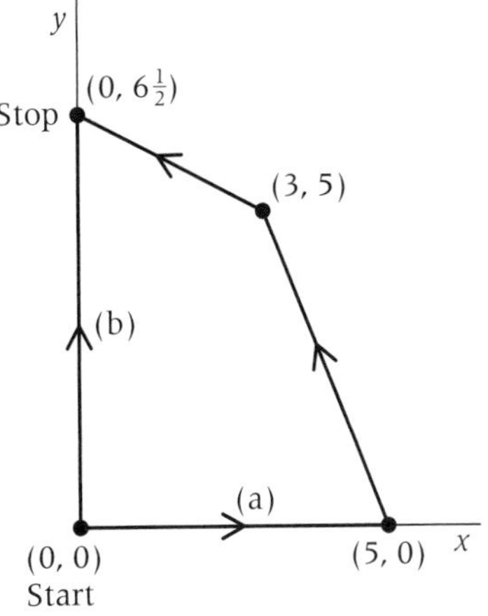

3 **(a)** Maximum 45 at $x = 0, y = 2\frac{1}{2}, z = 1\frac{7}{8}$.
Maximum $2\frac{2}{5}$ at $x = \frac{2}{5}, y = \frac{1}{5}, z = 0$.

(b) Duals:

Minimise	$5x + 15y$
subject to	$2x + 5y \geqslant 10$
	$2x + 3y \geqslant 12$
	$y \geqslant 2$

Minimum 45 at (3, 2)

Minimise	$2x + y$
subject to	$3x + y \leqslant 3$
	$4x + 3y \geqslant 6$
	$x + y \geqslant 1$

Minimum $2\frac{2}{5}$ at $(\frac{3}{5}, 1\frac{1}{5})$.

4 (a) Maximum 38 at (3, 5).

(b) (4, 3); $P = 36 - 6u + 2v$; v can increase,

(c)

P	x	y	s	t	u	v	
1	0	0	0	2	2	0	38
0	0	0	1	-3	1	0	1
0	0	0	0	1	-2	1	1
0	0	1	0	2	-1	0	5
0	1	0	0	-1	1	0	3

5 (a) $P = 20x + 30y$; $3x + 5y \leqslant 225$, $2x + y \leqslant 80$,

(b) £1400; $x = 25$, $y = 30$

(c) £1350; $x = 0$, $y = 45$.

6

Maximise	$P = 100x + 40y + 10z$
subject to	$x + 4y + 2z \leqslant 100$
	$2x + 8z \leqslant 40$
	$x \geqslant 0, y \geqslant 0, z \geqslant 0$

Maximum 2800; $x = 20$, $y = 20$, $z = 0$
No; tables need chairs.

7 (e.g. increasing x first)
(0, 0); $P = 0$, $s = 30$, $t = 30$
$\rightarrow$ (15, 0); $P = 15$, $s = 0$, $t = 15$
$\rightarrow$ (12, 6); $P = 24$, $s = 0$, $t = 0$ (max)

8 (a) (b) Maximum 20 at (10, 0)

(c)

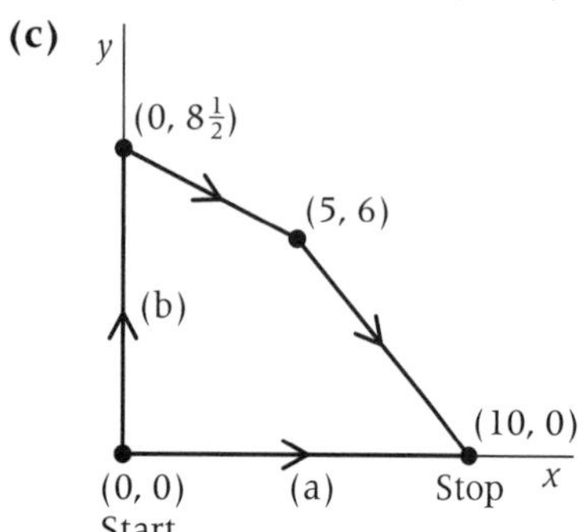

(d) $s = 0$, $t = 7$.

3 Recurrence relations

EXERCISE 3A

1 (a) $u_1 = 1,\ \ u_n = u_{n-1} + 3\ (n > 1)$,

(b) $u_1 = 2,\ \ u_n = u_{n-1} + 3 \times 2^{n-2}\ (n > 1)$,

(c) $u_1 = 0,\ \ u_2 = 1, u_n = 2(u_{n-1} + u_{n-2})\ (n > 2)$,

(d) $u_1 = 0,\ \ u_2 = 1, u_n = 2u_{n-1} + u_{n-2}\ (n > 2)$,

(e) $u_1 = 16, u_2 = 0, u_n = \frac{1}{2}(u_{n-1} + u_{n-2})\ (n > 2)$.

2 $u_0 = 1000$, $u_n = 1.04u_{n-1} + 100\ (n \geqslant 1)$

3 $t_1 = 1$, $t_n = t_{n-1} + n\ (n > 1)$

EXERCISE 3B

1 **(a)** $u_n = 4n + 1,$ **(b)** $u_n = 2^{n+1} - 3,$ **(c)** $u_n = 20\left(1 - \frac{1}{2^{n-1}}\right),$

(d) $u_n = 4n + 2,$ **(e)** $u_n = 1.$

2 $u_0 = 1000,\ u_n = 1.05u_{n-1} + 200\ (n \geqslant 1)$
$u_n = 5000(1.05)^n - 4000;\ n = 13.$

3 **(a)** $p_0 = 100,\ p_n = 0.9p_{n-1} + 20\ (n \geqslant 1);\ p_n = 200 - 100(0.9)^n,$

(b) settles down to 200 pairs,

(c) $p_0 = 100,\ p_n = 1.05p_{n-1} + 20\ (n \geqslant 1);\ p_n = 500(1.05)^n - 400;\ p_{10} \approx 414.$

5 First part uses $t_0 = 1$. Then
$$t_0 + t_1 + \dots t_{98} = \binom{98}{0} + \binom{98}{1}99 + \binom{98}{2}99^2 + \dots + \binom{98}{98}99^{98} = (1 + 99)^{98} = 100^{98}.$$

EXERCISE 3C

1 **(a)** $u_n = 2^n + 3,$ **(b)** $u_n = (n - 1)4^n,$
(c) $u_n = 2^{n-1} + (-2)^{n-1},$ **(d)** $u_n = 4.$

2 $u_n = 2^n + 2(-1)^n$

3 $r_1 = 50,\ r_2 = 80,\ r_n = 2r_{n-1} - r_{n-2}\ (n > 2)$
$r_n = 20 + 30n;\ n = 33$

4 **(b)** $u_n = \frac{1}{\sqrt{5}}\left(\frac{1 + \sqrt{5}}{2}\right)^{n+2} - \frac{1}{\sqrt{5}}\left(\frac{1 - \sqrt{5}}{2}\right)^{n+2}$ (or equivalent)

$n = 4$ gives $u_4 = 8.$

5 **(b)** $u_n = \frac{1}{2}(1 + \sqrt{2})^{n+1} + \frac{1}{2}(1 - \sqrt{2})^{n+1}$ (or equivalent)

$n = 4$ gives $u_4 = 41.$

EXERCISE 3D

1 **(a)** $u_n = 2^{n+1} + (-3)^n - 3,$

(b) $u_n = 4^n + 2^n + 1,$

(c) $u_n = (2 + n)(3^n + 1).$

2 **(b)** $u_n = \text{A}.6^n + \text{B}(-2)^n - 2,$ **(c)** $u_n = 6^n + (-2)^n - 2.$

3 $p_n = \frac{3 + n}{2^n} + 4n^2 + 16;\ n = 11.$

MIXED EXERCISES

1 $u_n = 2 - \frac{1}{2^{n-1}}.$

2 $u_n = \frac{1}{2}n(n + 1).$

3 $u_n = 2 - \frac{1}{2^n} \to 2.$

4 $t_1 = 1,\ t_n = 3t_{n-1} + 2;\ t_n = 2 \times 3^{n-1} - 1.$

5 $u_n = \frac{4}{5} \times 3^n + \frac{1}{5}(-2)^n.$

6 $u_n = (n - 1)3^n.$

7 $u_n = u_{n-1} + 2u_{n-2};\ u_n = \text{A} \times 2^n + \text{B}(-1)^n;\ u_n = \frac{2^n}{3} - \frac{(-1)^n}{3}.$

8 $r_n = \frac{3^n}{2} + \frac{(-1)^n}{2}.$

9 $u_n = \frac{4^{n-1}}{2} + 3 \times 2^{n-2};\ n = 9.$

10 $p_n = 4 + 2 \times (-\frac{1}{2})^n \to 4$.

11 $u_n = \left(a + \dfrac{k}{1-\alpha}\right)(1+\alpha)^n - \dfrac{k.2^n}{1-\alpha}$

(a) $n = 4$, **(b)** **(ii)** dies out, **(iii)** $n = 7$.

12 $u_n = u_{n-1} + 2u_{n-2} + 10$; $u_n = \frac{10}{3} \times 2^n + \frac{5}{3}(-1)^n - 5$; $n = 9$.

13 $u_1 = 3$, $u_2 = 8$ and $u_n = 2u_{n-1} + 2u_{n-2}$; $u_n = \dfrac{2+\sqrt{3}}{2\sqrt{3}}(1+\sqrt{3})^n - \dfrac{2-\sqrt{3}}{2\sqrt{3}}(1-\sqrt{3})^n$.

14 **(a)** $u_n = A \times 2^n + B \times 5^n$,
(b) $u_n = n2^n$,
(c) $u_n = (1+n)2^n + 5^{n+1}$,

15 $u_n = (1+n)5^n + n$.

16 Use $\binom{m}{k} = \binom{m-1}{k} + \binom{m-1}{k-1}$. It is the Fibonacci sequence.

17 Fibonacci numbers.

18 $u_n = 1 + 3(-1)^n + 2^n$.

4 Codes

EXERCISE 4A

1 **(a)** 10, **(b)** 6, **(c)** e.g. different flags in each hand.

2 5 (or 6 to be safe).

3 127; e.g. several look like 1; e.g. have extra lights.

4 **(a)** –• → – – **(b)** KJ = NKM.

EXERCISE 4B

1 **(a)** No, **(b)** No, **(c)** Yes; e.g. 3A → 5B.

2 One error causes misread; pauses needed to avoid ambiguity.

3 32 − 26 = 6 unused.

4 e.g.

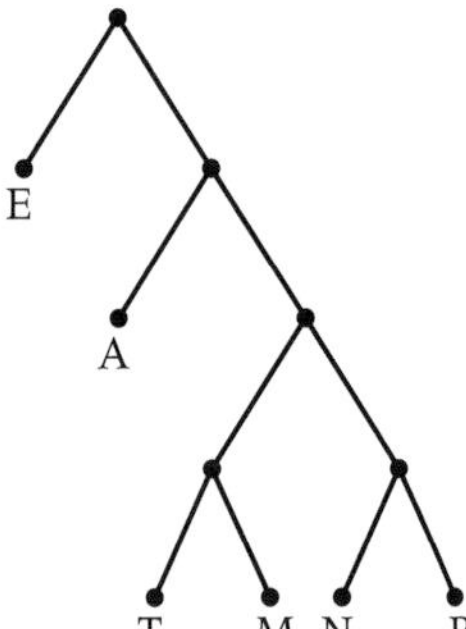

5 (a)

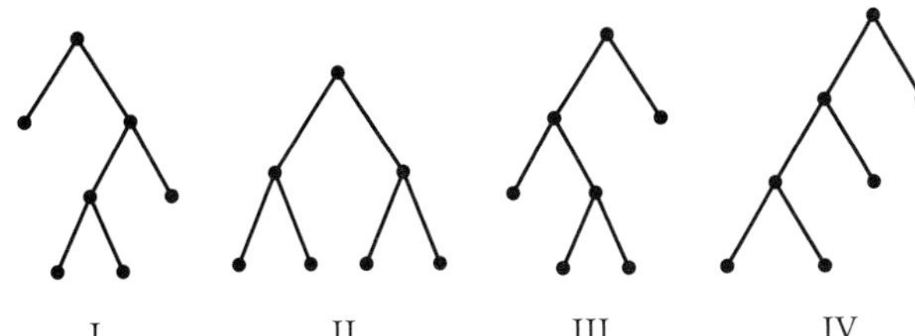

(b)

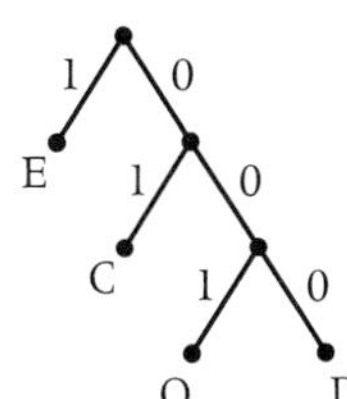

(c) I → CC, II → 8 bits, III → COO, IV → COC.

6 (a) n, **(b)** 1, **(c)** $m - n - 1$,
(e) $n + 2 + 3(m - n - 1) = 2(m - 1) \Rightarrow m = 2n - 1$.

EXERCISE 4C

1 (a) 2, **(b)** 4, **(c)** 6.

2 (a) 0876001231, **(b)** 3876001234, **(c)** 8076001234.

3 (a) 34012581, **(b)** 34012529,
(c) 43012589/34021589/34012598.

EXERCISE 4D

1 (a) 11000, 10100, 10010, 10001, 01100
01010, 01001, 00110, 00101, 00011
(b) 10 codewords,
(c) 2, **(d)** 1.

2 (a) 4, **(b)** $< \delta$ **(c)** 1.

3 length 7, $\delta = 4$, detect 3, correct 1.

EXERCISE 4E

1 Check all pairs added together.

2 00000, 00001, 11010, 11011, 10100, 10101, 01110, 01111; $\delta = 1$.

3 (a) 2^n, **(b)** $\frac{1}{2}$, **(c)** m equations $\Rightarrow 2^{n-m}$ codewords.

4 (a) 101000, **(b)** e.g. $x_1 + x_3 = 0$, $x_2 + x_4 = 0$, $x_5 + x_6 = 0$.

EXERCISE 4F

1 1110, 1011, 0101, 0000; $\delta = 2$.

2 (a) 4, **(b)** detect 3, correct 1, **(c)** 1101100.

3 (a) 4, **(b)** **(i)** 1, **(ii)** 3, **(c)** 1100101.

4 $\begin{pmatrix} 1 & 0 & 0 & 1 & 1 & 0 \\ 0 & 1 & 1 & 1 & 1 & 0 \\ 0 & 1 & 0 & 0 & 1 & 1 \end{pmatrix}$, 011110.

MIXED EXERCISES

1 e.g. add extra • or — to make each number of • even.

2 (a) 110000, 100100, 100110, 100010, 110100,
(b) $\delta = 1$,
(c) a 'check dot' making each letter use an even number.

3 (a) 3 and 9,
(b) 10431182/10435102/80435182/18435182/10475182/10435192/10435184,
(c) 10453182.

4 (a) 0000110011, (b) DEED, (c) 4 each.

5 (a) A7 B7 C8,
(b) A3 B3 C4,
(c) detect: A2 B2 C3, correct: A1 B1 C1,
(d) A
(e) C 01101001, 10010110.

6 (a) 3,
(b) e.g.

$$\begin{pmatrix} 1 & 1 & 0 & 0 & 0 & 0 \\ 1 & 0 & 1 & 0 & 0 & 0 \\ 0 & 0 & 0 & 1 & 1 & 0 \\ 0 & 0 & 0 & 1 & 0 & 1 \end{pmatrix}$$

000111111111000111.

7 e.g.

$$\begin{pmatrix} 0 & 1 & 1 & 0 & 0 & 0 & 0 & 0 & 0 & 0 \\ 0 & 1 & 0 & 0 & 1 & 0 & 0 & 0 & 0 & 0 \\ 0 & 1 & 0 & 0 & 0 & 1 & 0 & 0 & 0 & 0 \\ 0 & 1 & 0 & 0 & 0 & 0 & 0 & 0 & 1 & 0 \\ 1 & 0 & 0 & 1 & 0 & 0 & 0 & 0 & 0 & 0 \\ 1 & 0 & 0 & 0 & 0 & 0 & 1 & 0 & 0 & 0 \\ 1 & 0 & 0 & 0 & 0 & 0 & 0 & 1 & 0 & 0 \\ 1 & 0 & 0 & 0 & 0 & 0 & 0 & 0 & 0 & 1 \end{pmatrix}$$

100100110101101100l0.

8 (a) 7,
(b) 16,
(c) 0000000, 1011010, 1110000, 0001111, 0100101, ...,
(d) 0111100.

9 (a) 2, (b) 1111111111, (c) Yes.

10 (a) 1001110, 0011101, 0111010, 1110100, 1101001, 1010011, 0100111,
(b) 4,
(c) 1,
(d) zero word not included, adding it makes it linear,
(e) 01001111101000011101.

11 (a) 5, 2, (b) 0010010111.

12 (a) 000000, 111000,

(b) 3,

(c) $x_2 + x_3 + x_4 = 0,$
$x_4 + x_5 + x_6 = 0,$
e.g. $x_1 + x_3 + x_5 = 0,$

(d) e.g. $\begin{pmatrix} 0 & 1 & 1 & 1 & 0 & 0 \\ 0 & 0 & 0 & 1 & 1 & 1 \\ 1 & 0 & 1 & 0 & 1 & 0 \end{pmatrix}$

101101011011001110.

Exam style practice paper

1 SA, BA, BC, DT = minimum cut of 12

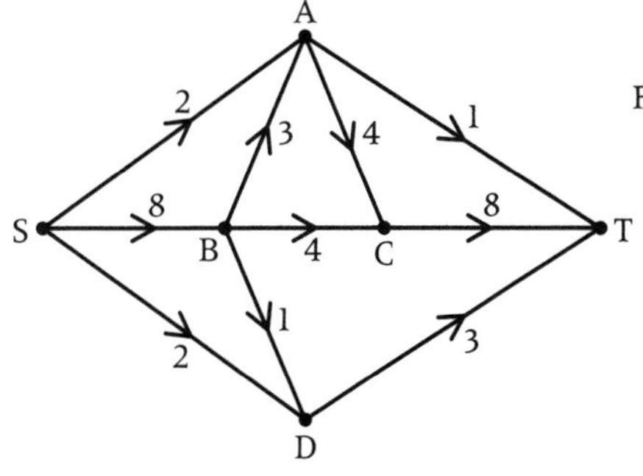

Flow of 12

maximum because all flows ≤ all cuts.

2 $u_n = (A + Bn)2^n + 3^{n+2}$.

3 (a)

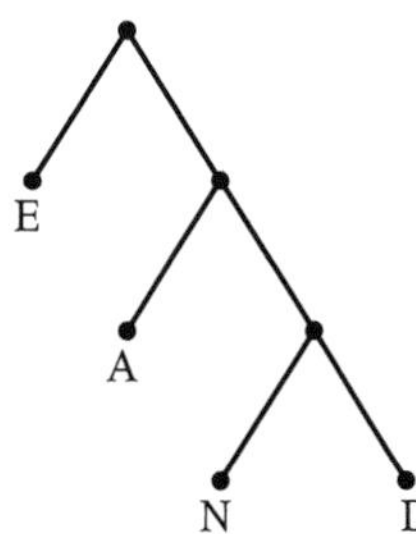

(b) only repeat = 001 ⇒ N = 0, E = 001 which is impossible.

4 (a) MBSHRM = 44

(b) No; MSBHRM = 42.

5 (a)

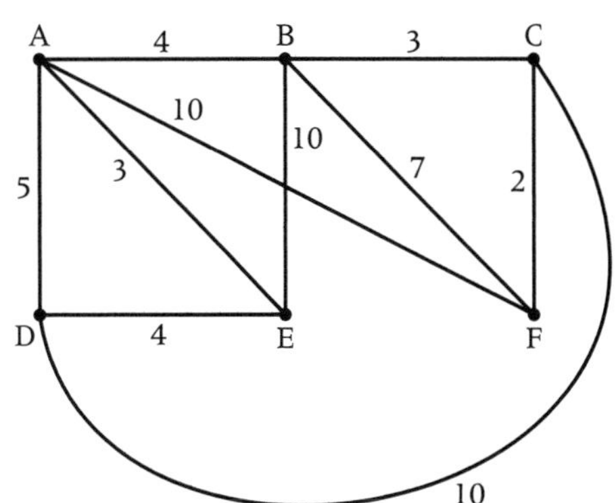

(b) repeat DE and CF to give total distance 6400 metres,

(c) 6 odd vertices ⇒ 15 pairings.

6 **(a)** 4.

(b) 16,

(c) $4n$,

(d) $u_1 = 4$, $u_n = u_{n-1} + 4n$,

(e) $u_n = 4n + 4(n-1) + \ldots + 4 = 2n(n+1)$.

7 **(a)** 0000000, 1101011,

(b) 3,

(c) $x_6 + x_7 = 0$,

(d) $$\begin{pmatrix} 1 & 1 & 0 & 0 & 0 & 0 & 0 \\ 0 & 1 & 1 & 1 & 0 & 0 & 0 \\ 0 & 0 & 0 & 1 & 1 & 1 & 0 \\ 0 & 0 & 0 & 0 & 0 & 1 & 1 \end{pmatrix}$$

0011011110101111110111.

8 **(a)** $x + y + s = 20$; $3x + y + t = 30$; $y + u = 16$; $x, y, s, t, u \geqslant 0$,

(b)

P	x	y	s	t	u	
1	−1	−2	0	0	0	0
0	1	1	1	0	0	20
0	3	1	0	1	0	30
0	0	1	0	0	1	16

(c)

P	x	y	s	t	u	
1	0	0	1	0	1	36
0	1	0	1	0	−1	4
0	0	0	−3	1	2	12
0	0	1	0	0	1	16

(d) Maximum of 36 at (4, 16).

(e)

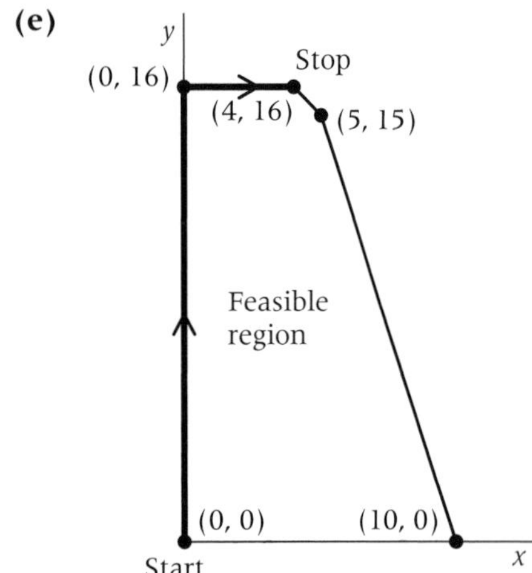

Further reading

The following books, written largely for use in higher education, expand much of the material in this book.

A First Course in Coding Theory, *R. Hill*, 1986 (OUP) 0 198 53804 9.

A First Course in Combinational Mathematics (2nd ed), *Ian Anderson*, 1986 (OUP) 0 198 59674 X.

An Introduction to Linear Programming (2nd ed), *G. R. Walsh*, 1990 (Wiley) 0 471 90719 7.

Aspects of Combinations, *Victor Bryant*, 1993 (OUP) 0 521 41974 3.

Decision Making, Models and Algorithms, *Saul I. Gass*, 1985 (John Wiley & Sons) 0 471 80963 2.

Discrete Mathematics, *Norman L. Biggs*, 1989 (OUP) 0 198 53252 0.

Discrete Mathematics for New Technology, *R. Garnier* and *J. Taylor*, 1992 (Adam Hilger) 0 7503 0136 8.

Essential Discrete Mathematics, *R. Johnsonbaugh*, 1986 (Macmillan) 0 02 360630 4.

Graphs, Networks and Design, Open University Course booklets, 1999.

Introduction to Graph Theory, *R. J. Wilson*, 1996 (Longman) 0 582 24993 7.